PLAYTIME

Peter Mortimer is a poet, playwright, editor, and traveller who has lived in the North-East of England since 1970. More than twenty of his adult stage plays have been produced and he is the founder and artistic director of Cloud Nine Theatre Productions. In 1973 he founded IRON Press, a respected independent literary publisher of new fiction, poetry and drama, and he remains editor to this day. In addition to three poetry collections, he has published various 'extreme' books, including *Broke Through Britain*, his account of a penniless 500-mile journey from Plymouth to Edinburgh, *Cool for Qat*, about his travels through remote parts of Yemen to research a play, *The Last of the Hunters*, six months working as a fisherman in the North Sea, and recently *Camp Shatila*, describing the two months he spent living in a Palestinian refugee camp in Beirut.

website: www.petermortimer.co.uk

PLAYTIME

Peter Mortimer

Eight Plays For and With Young People

FlambardPress

First published in Great Britain in 2011 by Flambard Press
Holy Jesus Hospital, City Road, Newcastle upon Tyne NE1 2AS
www.flambardpress.co.uk

Typeset by BookType
Cover Design by GDA
Cover photographs by David Turnbull (front) and Vicky Riley (back)
Printed in Great Britain by Bell & Bain, Glasgow

A CIP catalogue record for this book is available from the British Library.

ISBN: 9781906601270

Flambard Press wishes to thank Arts Council England
for its financial support.

Flambard Press is a member of Inpress.

The paper used for this book is FSC accredited.

Contents

In memory of the life and work
of the playwright C.P. Taylor

'We do not stop playing because we grow old.
We grow old because we stop playing.'

George Bernard Shaw

Introduction

I remember a small but significant incident from my time working with Allendale Middle School in rural Northumberland, a project which led to the creation and performance of the play *Whiter than Wight* at The Queen's Hall, Hexham in July 1996. I was lucky enough to spend one day a week over a full term with a class of thirty eleven-year-olds, plus their teacher Anne Brown. The entire class was involved in the play: some children were natural actors, some less so; some wanted speaking parts, others not. Living in rural Northumberland, many of the children had little experience of live theatre. I noticed one boy, Jamie Eales, who always hovered at the periphery and kept silent. 'He's terribly, terribly shy,' said Anne, 'we'll find him some job to do, backstage, but not acting. He would absolutely hate that.' I agreed. The project was not about inflicting torture.

As each week's writing workshop came and went, the play began to take shape, fed to a large extent on the children's own ideas. Anne and I encouraged Jamie as much as possible, but he spoke not a word. Eventually we had put together a full two-act play of our very own to which everyone had contributed. We were all rightly proud. We felt the play was funny, topical, and ambitious.

Competition was keen at auditions, especially for the main roles (thirty parts in all, with some of the smaller ones doubling up). One minor character was the bailiff, who walked on, read out a property repossession order, fixed it to a door, then was chased off.

'Anyone want to audition for the bailiff?' I asked.

A few seconds silence, then a small voice said, 'I would

like to audition for the bailiff.' It was Jamie Eales. Anne and I picked our jaws up off the floor. Jamie stared at us through his glasses. 'I would like to, yes.'

He auditioned, got the part, and made it his own. In all my theatre work with children, this stands as one of the most satisfactory moments, knowing the silent though seismic journey Jamie went through to give him the confidence to volunteer for that part.

It symbolised for me how important theatre can be for young developing minds; any theatre, of course, but particularly if children help to create and then perform that theatre piece. To be involved with a professional writer in the full evolution of a play, not only interpreting the character on stage but also creating him or her in the first place, can be something special. Projects such as Allendale, and the other six in this book, can be disruptive to the education system. This is part of their value. They don't fit over-comfortably into the educational framework, the pupils are not marked, the activity leads to no specific qualifications, there are no examinations – none of those convenient pigeonholes. They also go against the doctrine that sees a schoolteacher arriving with a suitcase full of knowledge which he or she then hands over to pupils who duly reproduce it as required. This may be a dull necessity in some technical/scientific subjects, but not in creating theatre. I often learnt as much as the youngsters themselves.

The radical ideas of drama specialist Dorothy Heathcote had a profound effect on schools in the North-East of England for many years. From her position in the Faculty of Education in the University of Newcastle from 1951 to 1986 she was able to bring about a new approach to the use of drama in the classroom. Her own background, starting as a weaver in a woollen mill at the age of fourteen, with only a short spell in the Northern Theatre School in Bradford and no academic qualifications, shows how unusual her abilities were. Instead of presenting a play for children to learn she worked with the pupils to explore their own ideas and concerns. From this a unique drama would emerge. It was a new and unorthodox approach, which caused controversy at first, but then became profoundly influential throughout the UK and beyond. Dorothy Heathcote showed teachers how to use drama as a creative, holistic experience that widened the framework of the curriculum. The difference between Dorothy Heathcote and myself is that she is an academic while I am a playwright.

When I started to work with young people in schools in the 1980s this was the atmosphere I inherited, although I never worked with her directly. Theatre in Education was active around this time too. This brought companies into schools to perform drama pieces that embraced part of the syllabus. It was an interesting concept, but the end product was often more worthy than exhilarating, and the philosophy that theatre had to be put to use in this way was always a bit suspect. I saw some pretty bad TIE plays. One dramatist who did stimulating work with youngsters in the region was the late C.P. Taylor, who died in 1981. He became a great personal friend and also a big influence, even from beyond the grave, and many actors and writers from the North are hugely indebted to him.

Every school drama project I have worked on has been different. Each has depended as much on the group of children (and teacher) as myself. When I walk into that classroom for the first session, I don't have the slightest idea what will happen. At such moments I am always terrified, but know this 'blank slate' is necessary if the experience is to be genuine. Some children (and teachers) suspect I arrive with a play idea up my sleeve just in case, but this is not so. And whatever play finally appears is unique to that particular combination. Take away myself, or the children, or the teacher, and that piece of theatre would never have come into being. So that specific creative dynamic created in that specific classroom is vital to the whole project. Which means starting on square one.

Some writers work in schools with a series of 'devices' or set methods. They produce postcards or objects, to which the children can respond. They ask the children to imagine themselves as something inanimate, or to put down as many words associated with 'red' as they can. All these devices are interesting and I don't want to run them down in helping unlock creativity, but (as far as I know) no professional writer uses them as starting blocks, so why ask others to do so?

There is also a fashion to 'train' writers to work in schools. This is another attempt to compartmentalise authors and fit them into the system. As such it is a loss of nerve and vision, and a denial of the individual qualities creative artists can bring to young minds. Training writers is no doubt safer and on some levels more efficient (though I'm not sure who 'trains' them), but is much more likely to produce conformity – the very thing creativity should challenge.

The creative process is not always neat and tidy. It cannot easily be formulated. It leads us down paths we never knew existed. Some of these paths become dead-ends. In one play project, on day three after we all sat silent and seemingly defeated for several moments, I tore up everything we had done so far. It wasn't working, nor was it likely to. Initially the children were aghast. Did this mean it was all wasted? I told them nothing was wasted, and we had now learnt what *not* to do. They then became almost giddy with delight that we were allowed to fail. After which we got on. As W. B. Yeats put it, 'By logic and reason we die hourly. By imagination we live.' A bit extreme perhaps, and some daily drudge is part of life's painful necessity, but it's still true that we shamefully under-develop the capacity and potential of young minds.

Not all children respond in the same way, whatever the process. God forbid that we should make good writers or actors of everyone, no more than we can make good footballers, composers, long-distance runners or astrophysicists of everyone, whichever methods we use. *Vive la différence!* But we can stretch them. We can take them to areas they have never been or are ever likely to go in the normal school syllabus. By helping to create other people, who they then act out on stage, they find out a great deal about themselves. By making up and acting out stories, their own reality takes on extra meaning.

All the plays in this book sprang from long-term drama projects which allowed a gradual evolution of the writer's creative relationship with the youngsters. Such projects are an increasingly rare luxury in an education system strait-jacketed by functional and inflexible syllabuses. Time after time I came across good and imaginative teachers frustrated by endless 'initiatives' handed down from on high, which seemed to understand nothing about young people's curiosity for knowledge, but to be in thrall to form-filling. And many good teachers have become disillusioned with a system that seems less to do with developing young minds and spirits, and more with churning out units to ensure the growth of the GNP, which itself is increasingly seen as an ineffective measure of human fulfilment and happiness.

All these teachers sincerely believed in the benefits of less structured, more creative parts of the syllabus. Few had a chance to practise them. And I appreciate that for all the schools featured in this book, accommodating the long-term drama project was not easy and required a good deal of admin tweaking and rearranging. I hope they all found it eventually worthwhile. Teaching is the most valuable, most challenging and most difficult profession. It shapes our future world unlike anything else. We might throw all the bankers, estate agents, PR people and consultants into the sea. But we must keep and nurture the teachers.

Yet our present system leaves many education practitioners too harassed, too stressed to take stock and ask themselves exactly what is that education *for*? It's worth remembering that the word 'education' comes from the Latin meaning 'to lead out', which is more than pushing people through exams. Not that I am envisioning some quasi-hippy school society endlessly producing plays, paintings, music and sculpture, while the crops rot in the fields, and factories and offices lie silent. Life is a mix of the functional and the aesthetic and earning a crust comes pretty high on most people's list of priorities, even if that crust-earning does not fill them with creative delight. Artists, who are only really happy when working, tend to forget that many other people are only really happy when they are not.

Or maybe 'work' is the wrong word. Creating theatre should not feel like 'work' but 'play'. This makes it no less difficult, no less demanding. I am much more exhausted through 'play' then I ever was through 'work', and it can drive me to distraction. But I am more fulfilled too. Ironically, though it has no specific function, writing seems to have more purpose than when I was employed in functionality. I called this book *Playtime* specifically for that reason. That some of that sense of 'purpose', that sense of how vital 'play' is, might rub off. Which is not to say society doesn't need 'work' too. Few of the many children whose names feature in this book will have gone on to become professional actors or writers (though it does occasionally happen). This is not the main point.

Creating and performing a play shows them an alternative to the norm, it stimulates them, invigorates them, frightens them, challenges them, provokes them, maddens them. I noticed how writing workshops, where the play is created, can slowly suck in some (though not all) of those pupils whose normal inclination is to do as little as possible, to make skiving an art form. As the different nature of the experience dawns on them, they often get more interested. Later, they realise some things in life depend on both individuality and teamwork. Acting is about individuality, a chance to show off, be the centre of attention, or make a fool of yourself in public. But it is also teamwork; unless you are aware of those around you, and how much interdependence there is, you have learnt nothing. Miss your entrance cue through some distraction, and the scene is ruined.

Nor is this theatre potential limited to young people. I'm artistic director of Cloud Nine Theatre Productions, whose community wing, The Sixties Group, works on the same principle, but with people aged sixty and over. They also work with a professional writer to create then perform their own theatre pieces. It is the whole ritual of theatre that's central to this, and something increasingly lost as we sit alone in front of our computer screens: that sense of people coming together to watch and hear stories performed by other people. This ritual began with people gathering round campfires and it continues in both village halls and in the auditoria of the RSC. But here, for the performers, there is an extra dimension. They have helped create the theatre piece themselves. I accept it's unlikely such projects will produce another *King Lear* or *Death of a Salesman*. Dramatic master-pieces are born via a single, often pained, vision. But even the greatest plays change in rehearsal. The input of actors and a director can bring a metamorphosis that makes theatre unlike other art forms. Painters sculptors, poets – none is exposed to such treatment. And the process that produced the plays in this book is merely an extension of that pattern.

Young people love an end product, something to aim for. They also love being challenged, scared and excited by knowing that on a certain specified date their play has to be written and ready for performance. Pointing to that date is one of the first things I do with any group. 'No matter what,' I say, 'on that day we shall be performing the play, even though none of us at the moment has a clue what that play will be.' It is a moment when you can feel a sense of disbelief or even mild panic run through the room. Much of it is my own.

My own starting point has always been as someone outside the education system. I am a working playwright, not a teacher, and do not wish to be embraced by the whole set-up, nor be seen as mainly an aid to passing exams. In all these projects I've relied greatly on a supportive member of staff, one in sympathy with the fairly unpredictable methods sometimes used. Any teachers who slowly suck in their breath, shake their heads and murmur 'that's not how we do it here', may not be the ideal candidates.

Finally, a few random points gleaned from more than twenty years working on drama projects in schools. These are not rules, more guidelines. As I said, every experience, every group of children, every school, is unique.

1. Throw around as many ideas, characters, plots, and locations as possible early on, and dismiss none out of hand. In some of those early stages, as writer, teacher and children get to know one another, anything might happen, not all of it to do with creating a play. With one group it suddenly seemed the natural thing to go out for a two-mile walk, so we did.

2. Write it all down. Big sheets of paper Blu-Tacked to the walls look quite dramatic and remind you how much you've done, even if most of what you've written is never used.

3. Remember most of what the children 'learn' at school will rapidly be forgotten. They should never forget being involved in this drama project.

4. Keep everyone involved all the way through. After each workshop session, I take away what we've come up with and type it up into play form. At the next session the children read it out and discuss it (it's at this stage some children begin to identify with individual characters in the play). I always listen carefully to any suggested changes. Young minds can come up with brilliant ideas

which your own mind may not even consider. But do not be afraid of giving them the benefit of your own experience as a working writer. You know things they don't and, as always, it's a two-way process. Then move on to the next session.

5. Don't be content with just 'process'. Some teachers are happy that the children have undergone the experience and are not overworried if the play itself is a shambles. The children, they will say, 'did their best'. This is patronising and must be resisted. I tell young actors that professionalism is not a matter of being paid but a state of mind, and though the project should be fun, it will also push them hard. To stand up and repeat lines is not enough. They need to learn to use their bodies, their voices, the stage space; they need to cast off inhibitions and 'become' the characters they portray, to rid themselves of self-consciousness, so they command the stage when they walk on. Casting off these inhibitions can be difficult, and the writer must be prepared to work hard with the young actors, taking them through that self-conscious 'barrier'. Once they have passed through they will never go back. They will become young actors rather than a crowd of children huddled on a stage sporting cheesy grins. And they will undergo a revelation.

6. Don't use prompters, to my mind the most debilitating of 'supports' any actor can have. I'm a strong believer that, channelled properly, nerves and fear can be a positive stimulus in the creative arts, whereas one of the worst feelings is complacency, in this case the knowledge that any time you forget a line it will be spoon-fed to you from the wings. Fear can concentrate the mind, can push actors to another level. Prompt them in early rehearsals when needed, but in the later stages, in the dress rehearsals and when on that public stage, actors should

know they are in charge whatever age they may be. And whatever happens they should use their talent to deal with it. Many young actors have initially been aghast to learn from me that there will be no prompter. Later, they're proud to have managed without.

Should any schools out there wish to perform any of the eight plays published here, they are more than welcome to do so at no charge. Please advise the publishers of any such plans. If I'm around, I'll come and see the production. The cast lists of the original productions are included as an appendix to this book.

Peter Mortimer
Summer 2011

Dorothy Daydream
&
The Invasion of the Dirties

*Ashley Road Junior & Infants School, South Shields,
June 1991*

I was lucky enough in my first real venture in school drama to have a teacher who was sympathetic, imaginative, and commanded the respect of the youngsters. Jen Scott loved drama almost as much as I did, and the idea of having a drama project was her own brainchild, which means this whole sequence of plays may never have come into being without her initial input. Jen's love of theatre transferred itself to the children, who at eight and nine are still the youngest I have worked with in creating drama. And for reasons that the passing years have now blurred, we ended up writing not one but two short plays.

The youngsters were involved not only in creating the plays but also in designing the posters, programmes, props and set. We performed at The Library Theatre, South Shields in June 1991, but the brace of plays went down so well that we were invited to reprise the production at South Tyneside Flower Show two months later. Dreams of a world tour began to take shape, but somehow never quite happened.

Ashley Road was a stimulating school to work in. The head teacher, Phil Grice, had stayed in touch with the real requirements of nurturing young minds. This is not always so. Teaching is similar to my own previous occupation, journalism, in that promotion can eventually remove you from the activity that drew you into the work in the first place. Editors rarely get to write, heads rarely get to teach, and this can distance them from the real heartbeats of schools. Phil Grice was in close contact and had a rapport with his pupils, and managed not to disappear behind a paper mountain of bewildering and nonsensical new initiatives from the Min. of Ed.

The children at Ashley Road felt an immediate owner-ship of the plays and gave the name *The Cool Dudes* to their actors' group. This was displayed on the poster and programme publicity, and also on the badges they designed, printed and handed out. The first play, *Dorothy Daydream*, is the tale of a young girl whose drifting off in class is both a distraction from her studies and something that leads to adventure. The second play, *The Invasion of the Dirties*, features an industrialist called Mr Bossyboots who is secretly in league with an alien race. Together, they plan to pollute the earth to a level which would make it safe for the aliens to invade. Both plays had a serious undercurrent but were also a lot of fun. We invented characters such as Slimeball and Bonkers, and in *The Invasion of the Dirties* one young-ster played a feather duster, which may be a dramatic first.

Character List

Dorothy Daydream

Sally

Teacher

Michael Machine

Bonkers

Mr Tenpercent

Bodyguard

Rodney

DOROTHY DAYDREAM

Scene One

[*The scene is the classroom. Dorothy and her best friend Sally are sat at their desks while the Teacher is talking. Dorothy is obviously daydreaming.*]

Teacher: And if we add all the angles in a triangle they will make 180 degrees. How many, Dorothy?

Dorothy: Er – what, miss?

Sally: [*Whispering to her.*] 180 degrees, Dorothy, in a triangle.

Dorothy: Erm . . . erm . . . 180 degrees, miss?

Teacher: You are listening to your teacher aren't you, Dorothy?

Dorothy: Yes, miss.

Teacher: You wouldn't be daydreaming again now, would you?

Dorothy: Oooh, no, miss.

Teacher: Because daydreams won't get you anywhere, you know that, don't you?

Dorothy: Yes, miss.

Teacher: Very well, now I'm going to put some figures on the board and I want you all to copy them down. [*Starts writing on the board. Dorothy is still daydreaming.*]

Sally: Dorothy – you've got to write those down.

Dorothy: Oh, silly old figures. I wish I were somewhere

else, Sally. Somewhere exciting.

Sally: Where?

Dorothy: Oh, anywhere. In a big house, on a desert island, riding in a great big car. With you as well, Sally, because you're my best friend.

Sally: You'd better write these figures down, Dorothy, or you'll be in trouble.

Dorothy: Just look out that window, Sally. Imagine you could fly up there in the sky. [*Teacher possibly walks about miming teaching.*]

Sally: You are funny, Dorothy. And I do like you.

Teacher: [*Catches them unawares.*] And so what would the answer be, Dorothy?

Dorothy: Oh, hmm – er –

Teacher: The equation. What is the equation?

Dorothy: [*Looks for help from Sally but she's been caught unawares too.*] Oh, it's – [*seems to drift away*] Mickey Mouse plus Pluto equals Goofy –

Teacher: It's what?

Dorothy: Oh, that is . . . oh . . . I thought I was in Disneyland. Er . . .

Teacher: Dorothy, I've had quite enough of all this day-dreaming.

Sally: Oooh, she looks angry, Dorothy!

Teacher: You've paid no attention to the maths lesson at all. And for the English storytelling lesson you can go and stand in the corridor, and if the head teacher comes along, you must tell her you've been a naughty girl, you understand?

Dorothy: Oh, but, miss. I didn't do anything.

Teacher: That's right, Dorothy, you didn't do anything – except sit around and daydream. Now off you go. [*Dorothy gets up and goes. She squeezes Sally's hand.*]

Sally: I'm sorry, Dorothy.

Dorothy: That's alright. [*Goes into corridor and we see her standing there looking sorry for herself for a few minutes. But then she seems to go into a daydream and we see her animating some of it. Eventually, Michael Machine arrives from the other side. He has obviously been sent out of another classroom and now stands alongside her. Slowly they become aware of each other, although at first they are cautious.*]

Michael: Huh. Been sent out have you?

Dorothy: Well hark whose talking!

Michael: Yeah, well, it's not fair.

Dorothy: It's not fair with me either.

Michael: Why's it not fair with you then?

Dorothy: 'Cos it's not.

Michael: Yeah, well it's not fair with me either. [*They stand in silence for a few minutes.*] What did you do anyway?

Dorothy: Nothing.

Michael: Yeah, I did nothing as well. [*Again, stand in silence.*] Well, nearly nothing.

Dorothy: What's that mean? [*During these exchanges a teacher walks past regularly and each time they freeze while he/she inspects them.*]

Michael: [*Starts to get excited.*] I was just building this machine see, in history lesson. That's what I like, building machines, and that's what I'm called: Michael Machine. And it's more interesting than rotten old history.

Dorothy: Well, I was just daydreaming, because that's more interesting than maths, and I was thinking of all the people I could be, and all the places I could go if I wasn't sat in that rotten classroom. That's what I'm called, Dorothy Daydream.

Michael: I can make a machine to do anything, make things three times as big, turn porridge into lavatory seats, make things change colour.

Dorothy: Like being a pop star, or dead rich, or being in Disneyland or . . . what did you say?

Michael: I said I can make a machine that can do anything.

Dorothy: Could you make a dream machine then?

Michael: How do you mean?

Dorothy: You know, put me into my daydreams. Make them real.

Michael: Well, I suppose I could.

Dorothy: Honestly? Honestly?

Michael: Don't see why not. Just need some extra sproggles and glimglums and needlewops.

Dorothy: So where do you make all these magic machines?

Michael: In me garden shed. Why don't you come round tonight?

Dorothy: Right, I will!

Scene Two

[*Scene is Dorothy and Michael approaching garden shed.*]

Michael: You have to go in there.

Dorothy: In here?

Michael: It'll be alright when you get inside. You'll see. [*They both go through the tiny entrance. It's a squeeze. The shed is much bigger inside than out.*]

Dorothy: But this is twice as big inside!

Michael: Course it is. I've got a machine to make it. Here's some machines, look. [*We have various machines made up of various moving parts which can be synchronised to move in an automatic way.*]

Dorothy: Do you make these by yourself?

Michael: Me and Bonkers here. Bonkers is my assistant. [*Enter Bonkers, a loveable nincompoop.*]

Bonkers: Hi . . . hi . . . hi. [*Starts oiling machine. It dribbles down him.*]

Michael: So, what would you like to be, in this dream of yours?

Dorothy: I could be . . . a famous film star. [*Goes into film star daydream. Reporters cluster around her writing in note books etc.*] No comment, boys, no comment. See my agent. Yes, I'll be signing for another picture tomorrow, yes with Mel Gibson or Tom Cruise, but no more comment, boys, please . . .

Michael: Film star? We could do that. OK, Bonkers?

Bonkers: Yep, yep, yep . . .

Dorothy: Or – I could travel in space! [*Whooshes round as if in space rocket. Speaks like a commander.*] This is Captain Dorothy. Captain Dorothy, five zillion miles from Earth in the Galaxy Fudge, travelling at fifteen times the speed of sound . . .

Michael: Space travel. What do you think, Bonkers?

Bonkers: Yep, yep, yep . . .

Dorothy: Or I could be the richest girl in the world. Just imagine! [*Struts about the stage as if wearing expensive clothes.*] I think I'll go for a swim in my private pool, then maybe a drive in one of my Rolls-Royces, then off to the Bahamas for the weekend, and . . .

Michael: What do you think, Bonkers?

Bonkers: Yep, yep, yep . . .

Michael: So, what's it to be, Dorothy? Film star, desert island, space captain, or the richest girl in the world?

Dorothy: [*Takes time before deciding, maybe even gets the audience to make suggestions.*] I want . . . I want . . . I want . . . to be the richest girl in the world!

Michael: OK, me and Bonkers better build the machine.

Dorothy: How long will it take?

Michael: Oh, Bonkers takes lots of tea-breaks, so maybe if you come round tomorrow. We'll have to work all night.

Dorothy: That's brill! [*Exits.*]

Michael: OK, Bonkers, let's build this machine. [*This is a choreographed routine, slowly building up the machine with human bodies, maybe a large clock to show passing time. Bonkers keeps getting things wrong. Possible sound effects. Eventually the machine is built.*]

Michael: OK, Dorothy Daydream, we've built the machine, and it's captured your daydream. All you've got to do is get in it. [*Enter Dorothy with Sally.*]

Dorothy: Look, Sally, it's ready for me.

Sally: Careful, Dorothy, it could be dangerous.

Dorothy: You could come with me.

Michael: Uh, uh. Only one allowed in this daydream. Stand here.

Sally: But how will you get back?

Michael: Bonkers here has built a special return switch, isn't that right, Bonkers?

Bonkers: Yep, yep . . .

Sally: But I'm worried about you!

Dorothy: Don't be worried. Everything I dreamed of is about to come true. It's wonderful.

Michael: Here we go, Dorothy, hang on tight! [*He presses the switch. Maybe she revolves or some such, the others back off stage, and when she is still, she is on her own, if possible wearing something rich.*]

Dorothy: I'm here, look. [*Admires herself, looks around, is delighted.*] It's me, Dorothy Daydream, and I'm in my own daydream. I'm the richest girl in the world – yeah! [*Enter Mr Tenpercent, her investment expert, with a box full of money, which he plonks down in front of her. He has a mobile phone, flip-charts etc.*] Oooh, look at that money, and who are you?

Mr Tenpercent: Why, your investment expert, of course. [*She goes to pick up the money.*] Don't touch that money!

Dorothy: But it's mine, isn't it?

Mr Tenpercent: That's going to earn 15 per cent, per annum, over 36 years, compound interest, deposit account. [*Phone rings. He answers it.*] What? Yes, buy. Yes, sell. Yeah, buy.

Dorothy: What are you doing?

Mr Tenpercent: Buying and selling your shares.

Dorothy: Can't I touch this money?

Mr Tenpercent: Course not. This money's got to earn more money. [*Takes it away. Does flip charts.*]

Dorothy: Oh, well. Maybe I'll go and find my private swimming pool. [*Enter bodyguards with dogs, who can be actors.*] Who are you?

Bodyguard: Bodyguards. We can't allow you to walk around unprotected.

Dorothy: You mean you're going to be here all the time?

Bodyguard: Too valuable an investment. [*She walks around and the bodyguard follows her faithfully. Goes over to Mr Tenpercent again and his phone rings. She tries to talk to him but he's busy.*]

Mr Tenpercent: Yes, buy. Buy, buy, sell. Yes, yes, yes.

Dorothy: Look, Mr . . . er . . . investment expert, can I just have a bit of this money to buy an extra big ice-cream.

Mr Tenpercent: Money is not to be spent.

Dorothy: But what's the use of it then?

Mr Tenpercent: To make more money, of course. That's what the rich do. [*Walks round the stage. Bodyguard follows her, shifting this way and that. The dogs are particularly aggressive.*]

Dorothy: How come there's a huge big fence round my lovely garden?

Bodyguard: Security.

Dorothy: You mean I can't just walk around, like normal people?

Bodyguard: Security. You're the richest girl in the world.

Dorothy: But what about my friends? Girlfriends, boy-friends? [*Enter Rodney, the chinless wonder.*]

Rodney: Hello, old fruit. Ha, ha, ha, ha. Spot of polo, what?

Dorothy: Who's that?

Bodyguard: Rodney Ffflewyllyn-Smithington-Smythe. Your fiancée.

Rodney: Drop of champers on the yacht, old gel. Pop in to see mater, toodle-pip and all that, what?

Dorothy: But he's just stupid.

Bodygurad: Yes, but he's very rich, you see. Can't have the rich mixing with the non-rich.

Rodney: Frighteningly good pheasant for lunch, what? Bagged the blighter meself, this morning.

Mr Tenpercent: That's right. Sell and buy, buy and sell. Buy and buy, sell and sell. That's right. [*Dogs are barking. Bodyguard is looking this way and that. Rodney is prancing about. Sally appears at the side of the stage.*]

Sally: Dorothy! Dorothy, are you in there?

Dorothy: Sally! Come and help me!

Sally: I can't, Dorothy. I can't get into your daydream. [*There is an invisible wall between them, which they mime pressing against.*]

Dorothy: But nobody's my friend in here. I want to come out!

Sally: But it's your daydream, Dorothy. It's where you always wanted to be.

Dorothy: I want to be with my friends now. Help me out. [*Enter Michael Machine at Sally's side.*]

Michael: Something's gone wrong with the switch. This is a job for Bonkers! [*Enter Bonkers, who makes a big thing of getting the switch right. There's a build up until he finds it.*]

Michael: Get ready, Dorothy Daydream. Bonkers is going to pull the switch! [*Bonkers does so. Dorothy comes out of* *the dream. Everyone dissolves.*]

Scene Three

[*Dorothy is back in the classroom with Sally and the Teacher. Dorothy looks around, dazed, and grabs Sally.*]

Dorothy: Sally, I got out of it.

Sally: Out of what?

Dorothy: The dream machine, with Mike and Bonkers, and the guards and . . .

Sally: You been daydreaming again, Dorothy? You'd better pay attention, it's the English story lesson.

Dorothy: That's just it you see – daydreams. They're not what you think and . . .

Teacher: Dorothy, any suggestions?

Dorothy: What, miss?

Teacher: Have you been listening, Dorothy? I told all the class to think up a good short story for this lesson. Now, don't tell me you've been daydreaming again and haven't come up with one.

Sally: You'll be for it this time, Dorothy!

Dorothy: Er, well . . .

Teacher: I'm waiting, Dorothy.

Dorothy: I've got a story, miss. It's called The Dream Machine, and it's about a young girl who was so in love with her daydreams that she wanted to live in them. And one day someone built her a special dream machine to make this possible. But then, everything went wrong, and when she came back, the girl had learnt quite a lot.

Teacher: That's a splendid story, Dorothy. Go to the top of the class!

END OF PLAY

Character List

Jackie Kleene

Feather Duster

Bossyboots

Slimeball

King Dirt

King Dirt's Army

THE INVASION OF THE DIRTIES

Scene One

[*Enter Jackie Kleene, armed with her cleaning materials. As she speaks she cleans everything in sight.*]

Jackie Kleene: Hello! I'm Jackie Kleene, and I make sure everything round here is sparkling and bright. I clean the floor, I clean the windows, I clean the chairs, I clean the kitchen. In fact I clean everything! And this is the house of the famous businessman, Mr Bossyboots, who's so rich he can afford to pay me to keep his house clean for him. I'm off to the supermarket to buy some new cleaning things. Want to come? [*She goes off to the supermarket, and walks round the shelves with her basket, maybe selecting a few items such as Flash, Vim, toilet cleaner etc. Finally she comes up to where the feather duster is lying on a shelf.*] Now let's see, I need a feather duster – ooh! What's that? [*The feather duster comes alive.*]

Feather Duster: I'm a feather duster, what do you think I am?

Jackie Kleene: But you can talk?

Feather Duster: Well, so can you. But you can't do this. [*Twirls and swirls in a duster sort of way.*] Realise how long I've been waiting on that shelf?

Jackie Kleene: Waiting – what for?

Feather Duster: For someone right to come along, of course. Someone who can clean things up a bit. Any idea how filthy this world is? Muck, oil, pollution, acid rain.

Jackie Kleene: Oh, I clean all the time. Polish, wipe, scrub.

Feather Duster: Well you'll do then. Where to start, that's the thing . . .

Jackie Kleene: I work for Mr Bossyboots, the famous businessman.

Feather Duster: Mr Bossyboots!

Jackie Kleene: Yes, he's got a great big house and goldfish in the pond and –

Feather Duster: But his factories produce more filth and pollution than anyone. Bossyboots Industries are making this whole world a dustbin!

Jackie Kleene: I never knew that, I mean –

Feather Duster: He's got factories in fifty countries, and they're all filthy.

Jackie Kleene: Well nobody told me –

Feather Duster: So there you are, polishing his brass doorknobs, while he's polluting the world.

Jackie Kleene: Blimey – we'll have to do something!

Feather Duster: Good job I'm a magic duster, isn't it? [*Does some magic here, possibly making something instantaneously clean.*]

Jackie Kleene: But this is terrible.

Feather Duster: Bossyboots never listens to anyone. Just keeps churning out all that filth and dirt.

Jackie Kleene: But why?

Feather Duster: That's what we've got to find out. Then we've got to stop him. While there's still time.

Jackie Kleene: You come with me Magic Duster. I'm not having this!

[*Exit both.*]

Scene Two

[*Scene is Bossyboots mansions. Bossyboots is with his assistant Slimeball who is making entries into a book. They stand stage right. Possible 'revolve' here.*]

Bossyboots: Alright, Slimeball, tell me the latest figures.

Slimeball: Certainly, your filthiness. Last week our factories polluted fifty rivers, leaked oil and toxic waste over three continents. We've wiped out fifteen kinds of birds, and helped eat away another few feet of the ozone layer.

Bossyboots: It's not good enough, you blundering fool! [*They freeze and Jackie and the duster enter stage left.*]

Jackie Kleene: This is it then, Bossyboots Mansions.

Feather Duster: Just as I thought. Lovely and clean while the world's all filthy.

Jackie Kleene: Now to find Bossyboots, and see what's going on.

Feather Duster: I can do that. I've got a special pollutant seeker. [*Goes into his pollutant seeking act.*] There – in that room!

Jackie Kleene: Oh – he can't be in that room, Duster. That's the room that's always locked. No one's ever allowed in *that* room!

Feather Duster: Look, when I say he's in there, he's in there!

Jackie Kleene: But why on earth would Mr Bossyboots be locked up in that secret room? [*They freeze. Action back on stage right.*]

Bossyboots: You've been slacking again, Slimeball, taking tea breaks.

Slimeball: No, Your Great Effluence, I –

Bossyboots: I've told you, if we don't pollute this planet at the right speed, there'll be no bags of money at the end for me – or you.

Slimeball: I'm doing my best, Your Sludgefulness.

Bossyboots: Well your best isn't good enough, Slimeball. [*They freeze again.*]

Jackie Kleene: We'll never get in there, Duster. Let's put our ear to the keyhole.

Feather Duster: I haven't got an ear.

Jackie Kleene: Well, I'll put mine, and tell you what's going on. [*She does so and they freeze.*]

Bossyboots: Slimeball, we only have three days left to pollute the world for the Dirties to invade. They can't survive unless the whole place is filthy and polluted.

Slimeball: Yes, Your Sewageness.

Bossyboots: And you realise Bossyboots Industries has been chosen to make it filthy enough so the race of Dirties can come up from the centre of the world, to take over?

Slimeball: Of course, Your Huge Filthiness.

Bossyboots: And they'll pay us a great deal of money, Slimeball. And they've promised to leave Bossyboots Mansions as the only clean place on earth, so we'll be alright, won't we?

Slimeball: Yes, Your Disgusting Muckiness.

Bossyboots: Why do you think we keep this locked room in a filthy state? It's so that King Dirt and his cronies can visit us in safety while we prepare for the invasion. In fact, they're due for their next visit any minute. Is the room dirty enough?

Slimeball: I'll just make sure, Your Illegal Dischargefulness. [*Starts scattering rubbish. Then they freeze.*]

Jackie Kleene: Blimey, Duster! They're doing it deliberately, for money! And in a few days we're all going to be invaded by a race called the Dirties who live at the centre of the Earth. Then we'll be finished, the whole world!

Feather Duster: I knew it! I knew it! I said it would be a bad day when I woke up!

Jackie Kleene: Keep your fluff on, Duster. I'll listen some more. [*Does so. Back to Bossyboots.*]

Bossyboots: Come on, Slimeball, dirty yourself up there a bit. Got to look your worst for King Dirt. Here they come now. [*Special effects here for the entrance of King Dirt and his army of dirt followers.*]

[*King Dirt enters with his gang. They are all disgustingly filthy in habit and appearance, picking noses, chucking litter, scratching etc, habits they keep up throughout the visit. They stand in a line and their movements are carefully staged.*]

Bossyboots: [*Who now becomes the humble one.*] Greeting, oh Great King Dirt!

King Dirt: Is the plan going well, Bossyboots? [*Hands over part of the money.*]

Bossyboots: Oh, absolutely, Great King. Filth, dirt, slime, pollution, acid rain, we're making huge amounts of them, all the time. Isn't that right, Slimeball?

Slimeball: Well er – [*King stands on his toe to prompt him.*] Yes, of course, absolutely to plan. Trees are dying, birds are dying, fish are dying . . .

King Dirt: You realise we have been working the last twenty years to prepare the surface of the planet for us, hiring important businessmen such as yourself?

Bossyboots: Course we do. Eh? You get what you pay for!

King Dirt: And soon, our plan will be complete. A totally filthy polluted planet where only we, the Dirties, can survive.

Bossyboots: And – er – Bossyboots Mansions of course, Your Majesty.

King Dirt: What? Oh – oh yes. You see my people here? If they were exposed to the surface of the earth before it was ready, they would die.

Bossyboots: I understand. And yourself as well. Which is why we keep this room so beautifully filthy.

King Dirt: I am their King. In our underground world, if the King dies, everyone dies.

Slimeball: That sounds a bit rough. [*Bossyboots shushes him.*]

King Dirt: I shall return to this room tomorrow at 6 a.m. Make sure it is securely locked and totally filthy. [*Freeze.*]

Jackie Kleene: This is terrible, Duster! A couple of days and the world will be taken over by millions of Dirties, and we'll all be wiped out.

Feather Duster: I'm good at wiping out.

Jackie Kleene: Me and you – we've got to do something.

Feather Duster: Course we have.

Jackie Kleene: Let's listen again. [*Freeze.*]

King Dirt: Dirt people! Prepare to return to our under-ground home in the centre of this planet. In two days, we shall at last take over the planet surface. Our plans will be complete! Do not fail me, Bossyboots!

Bossyboots: Absolutely not. [*King and his dirt followers* *make their way off and down back to the centre of the Earth with some dirty ceremony.*] We must hurry, Slimeball. We must increase our pollutant speed. Do you have the key to get us out of this room?

Slimeball: I do, your Smelliness. [*Produces monstrous key.*]

Bossyboots: This room is so secure even an army couldn't break down that door. Nice and filthy for King Dirt's next visit. Come along, Slimeball, there's a lot of work to be done before we get our money! [*Prepare to go. Jackie and Duster jump back.*]

Jackie Kleene: Hide, Duster – they're coming out! [*They hide, the two unlock the door, emerge then relock it. Maybe rather ornate actions here. Both exit.*] Blimey! Look at that door, Duster.

Feather Duster: We've got to stop them somehow or else –

Jackie Kleene: Or else the whole planet's finished.

Feather Duster: Even my magic couldn't keep the whole planet clean, not with them lot on it.

Jackie Kleene: Not the whole planet, Duster, but –

Feather Duster: But what?

Jackie Kleene: I've got it. How small can you scrunch yourself up?

Feather Duster: Me? Oh, I can get as thin as a pencil if I want, I can get all sorts of shapes. [*Twists around a bit.*]

Jackie Kleene: What about the keyhole, could you get through there?

Feather Duster: Well, I suppose I –

Jackie Kleene: If you could get in there, Duster, do your magic cleaning before that horrible King comes back tomorrow.

Feather Duster: You mean?

Jackie Kleene: Yes – he can't survive unless it's filthy, and if he dies, the entire race of Dirties die.

Feather Duster: I could try. I should think it's pretty dirty in there.

Jackie Kleene: I never thought I'd betray Mr Bossyboots. But now we've got to. Come on, Duster! [*Duster now manages to fit through the keyhole and into the room.*]

Feather Duster: Blimey, you seen it in here? I've never ever seen so much filth in all my life. Yuk!

Jackie Kleene: [*Through keyhole.*] You can do it, Duster. I'll buy you an extra large tin of wax polish if you do. You've got until six o'clock tomorrow! [*If possible the dirt room now disappears and Jackie comes down stage.*] I had to leave the magic duster there, and get on with my own work. I couldn't make Mr Bossyboots suspicious. I just got on with my own little bits of cleaning, wondering if the world would still exist in a couple of days' time. [*Goes into cleaning routine. Bossyboots comes out.*]

Bossyboots: Ah – getting a nice shine on those surfaces, eh Jackie?

Jackie Kleene: Yes, Your Smelliness – I mean Mr Bossy-boots.

Bossyboots: Nothing like a nice clean house, Jackie, is there, sweet smelling, well polished, no germs eh?

Jackie Kleene: Of course, Mr Bossyboots, I keep it as clean as I can.

Bossyboots: Course you do, course you do – there's a good girl. [*Exits.*]

Jackie Kleene: So I just got on with my work, and went to bed that night thinking of the Magic Duster and wondering whether it would be able to clean that room in time. [*Small prop such as cut-out pillow to show her bed. Then alarm rings.*] And the next morning, I woke up early, because I knew King Dirt was coming back to that room at 6 a.m.! So I rushed to the room and shouted through the keyhole. [*Does this; we don't yet see the room.*] Duster! [*No reply.*] You in there, Duster! [*Sound of snoring.*] Wake up, Duster!

Feather Duster: [*Voice only.*] What? Oh – erm – yes, oh, I –

Jackie Kleene: Oh, Duster – you haven't been asleep all the time, have you?

Duster: Me? No, no, I've got to have a kip now and then haven't I?

Bossyboots: [*Off stage.*] Come along Slimeball, time to meet King Dirt again.

Jackie Kleene: They're coming, Duster, quick, get out of there, quick! [*Duster gets out and they hide before the other two enter.*]

Jackie Kleene: Did you do it, Duster? Did you do it? [*No time to answer before they have to hide when Bossyboots and Slimeball enter.*]

Bossyboots: Open the door of our one hundred per cent impregnable room, Slimeball!

Slimeball: I will, Your Rottingness.

Bossyboots: King Dirt will be here any moment. We must ensure the reception is as filthy as it should be. [*Slimeball goes through ceremony of opening the door. The room is revealed in a state of absolute cleanliness.*]

Jackie Kleene: [*Voice at one side.*] Duster – you did it!

Bossyboots: Slimeball – look at this, it's – disgusting – it's clean!

Slimeball: Yuk!

Bossyboots: But this is terrible, Slimeball. What have you done?

Slimeball: Me? Nothing, I –

Bossyboots: I left you in charge of this room, I told you to dirty it up, now look at it. You stupid fool. [*Begins thwacking him.*]

Slimeball: It wasn't me, I never – I mean –

Bossyboots: Wrecking everything – a million pounds – everything. [*Still grappling with him when we hear the noise of King Dirt approaching.*] Oh no! It's King Dirt and his Dirt followers! Go back King! Don't come yet, go back! [*Too late. Enter the King and his army.*]

King Dirt: I come once again from my underground kingdom, I come – aaagh! [*Begins to shrink, as does his army.*] No! No! Cleanliness.

Bossyboots: Quick, Slimeball, muck, muck! [*They start throwing around what much they can but it's not enough. Looks as if the King is dying but instead he and his army lose all their dirt, and recover in a state of cleanliness.*]

King Dirt: What? What's this? [*Inspects himself. Gets used to it.*] But who is responsible for all this? [*Enter Jackie Kleene.*]

Jackie Kleene: We are, me and the Magic Duster here.

Bossyboots: You! [*Goes to grab her but the Duster makes it impossible, dances between them.*]

Jackie Kleene: You should be ashamed of yourself, a grown man, playing with all that dirt. Well, it's finished, so you can just get those factories of yours cleaned up, or we'll make sure they're closed down, won't we, Duster?

Feather Duster: We sure will, yeah . . .

King Dirt: But where is all my filth and dirt?

Jackie Kleene: Maybe you don't need it like you thought. Maybe once you get away from it, you can be just clean and natural.

King Dirt: To live – without filth and dirt?

Jackie Kleene: That's right. Tell you what, you and your army could come up on the surface and help clean it all up. Like Mr Bossyboots is going to do, aren't you?

Bossyboots: Well, I –

Slimeball: We may as well – Your Cleanliness.

Bossyboots: Your? – Oh, very well. I hereby appoint every member of the former Dirt Army to the position of a factory cleanliness inspector, and you shall be cleanliness director.

Feather Duster: I cleaned it up good, eh Jackie?

Jackie Kleene: You did brilliantly, Duster. And you've made a friend for life.

King Dirt: Men – prepare for your new duties. We have left the Kingdom of Dirt, forever!

Bossyboots: Right. Let's get on with it. Slimeball, what are you hanging about for. Get this place cleaned up! [*All set to, for a few moments.*]

END OF PLAY

The Magic Shell

Christ Church C of E Primary School, Shieldfield, Newcastle, December 1994

This was the only play staged 'in the round', as it were, being performed in the unique but little-visited All Saints Church just above Newcastle Quayside, a circular building which recent developments have left stranded and difficult to access. *The Magic Shell* was part of a project called *Fahrenheit 451*, the brainchild of the novelist and the then Northern Arts Literature Development Officer, Kitty Fitzgerald. It was funded by Northern Arts, Waterstone's Bookshop Newcastle, the Tyneside Cinema, and the Leisure Department of Newcastle City Council. The project allowed children across the North-East region to explore the relationship between books and films, which I suppose our play did in some way, but I've forgotten quite how. We all had a good time, though.

Eleven writers took part in *Fahrenheit 451*, the kind of big-scale cultural schools venture that now rarely happens. The North-East-based Bay Press published a book called *Burning Books* about the various activities involved (readers will know *Fahrenheit 451* as the Ray Bradbury sci-fi novel set in a bookless future, the title referring to the temperature at which paper burns). Actually, it's all coming back to me now; we chose to write a play with 'filmic' possibilities. Thus we have five locations: a hotel, a Brazilian beach, an airport, on board an aircraft, and a tropical island. It also includes a plane crash. At the time of writing, we still await the offer of a production deal from Stephen Spielberg.

We called our temporary theatre company *The Christ Church Combustibles*. Once again we chose to centre the play on a North-East family (children are more interested in families than they might let on). While holidaying in Brazil the family's children discover half of a magic shell which, if united with its other half, will give the owner untold powers. Needless to say various people are quite keen to lay their hands on it, and an adventure ensues.

Every play in this book evolved in its own distinctive way. *The Magic Shell* uses a lot of knockabout humour, and the two villains had great fun perfecting their comic timing in the hapless *Chuckle Brother*-style parts. Recently I bumped into Judith Bremner, now retired, who was the energetic head of Christ Church, and we reminisced unashamedly about the experience. Judith, teacher Miles Clarke and I were the core of the production team, and I remember much laughter as the piece evolved and was finally performed. Laughter is an essential part of any creative venture, and has to be taken seriously.

Character List

Boy

Girl

Friend

Dad

Mum

Villain One

Villain Two

Shell

Pilot

Announcer

Co-Pilot

Passenger One

Passenger Two

Security Person

Stewardess

King

Queen

Bodyguard

THE MAGIC SHELL

Scene One

[*A hotel bedroom in a Brazilian holiday resort. Mum and Dad are getting ready to leave at the end of the holiday. Mum is packing the case while Dad is hunting round looking for many of his things. Mum is centre stage with a case. Dad criss-crosses throughout the scene.*]

Mum: Oooh, George, what a lovely holiday we've had here in Brazil.

Dad: I just can't seem to find my swimming trunks anywhere.

Mum: [*Holds them up for him to see. He walks up and takes them as she speaks.*] I don't think I'll ever forget you doing that samba in the bar that afternoon. Quite carried away you were.

Dad: I knew I put my razor down here somewhere.

Mum: [*Again holds up his razor; Dad comes and takes it off her. She just continues without acknowledging.*] Fancy, having to return to Shieldfield this afternoon. I bet there's fog and snow and ice and slush there when we get back. Just think.

Dad: Now what on earth can I have done with my sunglasses?

Mum: [*Holds them up. He takes them. Same routine.*] And I know the kids have had a lovely time here. And they've made a nice new friend. That's nice. Have you seen them anywhere, by the way, dear?

Scene Two

[*The Brazilian beach. The sea is a large cloth (blue) which comes in and out like the tide above the head of various actors. There are holes cut in it to allow the effect of swimmers with snorkles. These swimmers occasionally surface and wave to the audience. This continues for a few seconds then the boy runs on. He stops centre stage and turns back to the way he's run just in time to catch a beach ball thrown by the girl, his sister.*]

Girl: I hope we can come back here again some time. Just imagine living here!

Boy: I'd never get to see United, man. [*Goes into song.*] Andy Cole, Andy Cole, Andy, Andy, Andy, Andy Cole . . .

Girl: You and your football. Anyway, Brazil are World Champions.

Boy: Yeah, but they haven't got Peter Beardsley. [*Into song again.*] One Peter Beardsley, there's only one Peter Beardsley.

[*Each of them speaks the lines when they have the ball, then throws it to the other.*]

Girl: I'm going to miss it all, you know. And especially I'm going to miss our new friend. I wonder where she got to? [*Throws the ball and Friend walks on to catch it before it reaches the boy.*]

Friend: I'm here!

Girl: Why don't you come back to Tyneside with us? Go on.

Boy: She can't, man. The spare room's full of Dad's lawn-mower parts.

Friend: This is my home. But I will always remember my Geordie friends. I wish there was something I could give you, a souvenir to remember Brazil by.

Girl: Maybe we could find something on the beach?

Boy: Yeah, sand!

Friend: The beach has many treasures. Let's look. [*They start to look, and each in turn finds something which the others dismiss.*]

Girl: [*Finds a stone.*] How about this? [*Gather round, look at it. Shake their heads. They look on.*]

Friend: This? [*They gather round. It is a starfish. Shake their heads. Look on.*]

Boy: Got it! [*They gather round, he holds up a very nasty-looking crab. They scream and jump back. Boy laughs. As he's laughing we have music effect and a hand rises out of the sea holding a large illuminated shell.*]

Girl: Just look at that!

Friend: The hand from the sea!

Boy: Is it an advert for petrol? Shell, gettit, petrol . . . ? [*The others get it, but aren't impressed.*]

Girl: I think it is offering the shell to us.

Friend: Then we must take it!

Boy: Right, I'll get it. [*Gets ready to go into the sea; arms stretch, knees bend, exercises etc. Makes a meal of it, then plunges in. Takes the shell, hand disappears into the waves. Boy comes ashore. Spits out water. Removes a goldfish from his pockets (a piece of carrot) looks at it and eats it. They all gather round and stare at the shell which gives off a strange glow.*]

Friend: Never have I seen a shell like that on the beach.

Girl: It seems to have a strange sort of – I don't know . . .

[As they are looking at the shell, Villains One and Two enter stage right, react to seeing the shell.]

Villain One: Curses! Those blasted children have found the all-powerful shell. How long have we been searching for it?

Villain Two: Twenty minutes?

Villain One: *[Clips him round the ear.]* Ten years, you blithering fool! Day in day out, for ten years. To have that shell and all it means!

Friend: Let this shell always remind you of Brazil and our friendship, whatever it might be.

Boy: It'll look nice on the mantelpiece. Next to that bull from Majorca.

Villain One: We must have it

Girl: By this time tomorrow, this shell will be in Newcastle.

Villain One: Newcastle? Curses!

Villain Two: Doesn't Peter Beardsley play for Newcastle? *[Villain One pokes him in the eye.]*

Boy: Better get it packed then. Plane leaves in four hours.

Friend: I will wave you off from the airport.

Villain One: *[Evil laugh.]* You will not be the only one going to the airport, dear!

Villain Two: You know someone else do you?

Villain One: *[Biffs him.]* Us, you fool! *[Kids make their way off stage.]* Don't let those blasted kids out of your sight!

Scene Three

[*The busy airport. Security Person is using a detector on the passengers as they pass through the barrier.*]

Security: This way, please. Flight 506 to Tyneside: all passengers this way, please. [*Enter passengers including the family, with friend.*]

[*As each one goes through the detector we have a bit of business. On Dad, something is discovered, but it's just the razor he couldn't find before. Mum is tickled by the detector. Boy is a bit scared of it and reacts. When Girl goes through with the shell it makes a very strange noise and is examined but is let through after the official can find nothing wrong with it. Villains enter the back of the passenger queue as this is going on.*]

Villain One: I have a brilliant plan!

Villain Two: I'd love a hot dog!

Villain One: [*Hits him.*] Not now, you fool! Watch me get us on that plane. [*He approaches the last two passengers in the queue.*] Excuse me, sir and madam. Airport security. We have to check the tickets of all passengers on this flight, if you don't mind.

Passenger One: Oh, well, if you say so, yes [*Produces tickets and hands them over.*]

Villain One: This won't take a moment, if you'd just like to wait in that room.

Passenger Two: That room there? Do we have to, I mean –

Villain One: It is in your own interest, sir, and it won't take a moment.

Villain Two: Are you stealing their tickets? [*Villain One kicks him in the shins, ushers the passengers off stage and returns in triumph.*]

Villain One: Got them! Follow me. [*They go through security showing their tickets. Detector picks something up on Villain Two. It is a Big Mac. He starts eating it to the disgust of the official. Villain One pulls him through. We hear Announcer.*]

Announcer: Please note, flight 506 to Tyneside will very shortly be taking off. [*Friend comes down stage to wave to the plane, indicating it is now in the sky. As she does so the two other passengers emerge and look up.*]

Passenger One: But – but – that's our plane!

Passenger Two: We've been tricked!

Scene Four

[*The plane is now in flight. We have family plus villains, plus other passengers arranged in rows. The Stewardess is walking down the aisle handing out packs of peanuts. At the front is the Pilot and the Co-Pilot.*]

Pilot: Ladies and gentlemen, welcome to Flight 506 to Newcastle. This is Captain Rhubarb speaking. We shall be flying at 36,000 feet and our flight time will be eleven hours. If you'd care to look to your left you will see the River Amazon. [*All passengers and crew lean over slowly to the left, look then come back upright again.*] And if you look to your right [*Do the same but the other way.*] you will clearly make out the mountains rising from the deep impenetrable forest.

Mum: Give a final wave to Brazil dear.

Dad: You know, I do think I've left a blue sock there somewhere.

Girl: I feel so sad. But at least we have this beautiful shell.

[*Stewardess moves down the plane. She gives nuts to Villain One, and offers them to Villain Two.*]

Villain Two: Got a cheeseburger instead? [*Moves on.*]

Boy: I quite liked Brazil. I miss *Byker Grove* though.

Villain One: We shall wait for the right moment. Then the shell will be ours.

Girl: I can feel something. With the shell. It's vibrating.

Co-Pilot: Skipper, I think there's something wrong with the plane. It's not responding.

Pilot: Give it more throttle.

Co-Pilot: It's not responding.

Pilot: [*On address system.*] Would the stewardess come to the flight deck please? Meantime if you would all like to fasten your seatbelts as we are at present experiencing some slight difficulty. [*Enter Stewardess.*] We have engine failure. Keep the passengers calm. [*Stewardess goes to passengers.*]

Stewardess: As a precaution only, ladies and gentlemen, please ensure you are well strapped in and – [*Plane begins to go into a dive. Sound effects, and everyone leans backwards.*]

Girl: It's the shell! The shell's doing this! [*Gets steeper. Louder.*]

Dad: Good heavens, what's happening?

Villain One: We're going to crash!

Villain Two: This is a short flight, boss.

Stewardess: Ladies and gentlemen, please prepare for a crash landing! [*Plane crashes, people are thrown everywhere.*]

[*After the plane crash people slowly stand up and stagger about. Some are dazed. We have tweeting bird effects. Mum and Dad come forward. Dad is clearly not himself.*]

Dad: Are we home, dear? A bacon sandwich did you say?

Mum: I'm afraid the plane's crashed, dear. We're in the middle of the jungle.

Dad: The central heating again? Good heavens, I'll have to get the man in.

Mum: That's right, dear, everything will be all right in a minute.

[*Boy and Girl come forward. Girl has shell.*]

Boy: We survived, man! Maybe we'll be on that 999 programme!

Girl: It's the shell – I think it protected us. Like it knew where it was going.

Boy: But it's just a shell, man!

Girl: No I think it's more than that.

[*Villains come forward.*]

Villain One: The next time I take a taxi

Villain Two: This Newcastle airport, boss? There's no burger bar.

Villain One: [*Biffs him.*] Does it LOOK like Newcastle airport, you buffoon? Look, they've still got the shell.

Villain Two: I'll ask them for it. [*Goes to, but Villain One pulls him back.*]

Villain One: Not yet, you blithering idiot. Our moment

will come.

[*We now hear the faint sound of drums. This slowly increases and as it does so the movement of the crashed passengers gradually increases from being dazed to catching the drums' rhythm. One by one they begin dancing so that by the time we have the entrance of the King the entire crew and passengers are dancing. Enter the Bodyguard sweeping all before him.*]

Bodyguard: Make way for the Great Deliciousnesses, their most Highlyfuls the King and Queen of all Rainbow Island.

King: [*Who is holding another shell and is mighty fierce.*] Who dares set foot on the sacred soil of Rainbow Island?

Queen: It looks like a package tour from Turista to me, me love.

King: [*Addressing passengers.*] What is the purpose of your visit?

Queen: I should think it was the sunshine.

King: The wrath of Rainbow Island will descend on all infidels!

Queen: Oh, he's on about that again. [*This to passengers.*]

Bodyguard: Remember, Oh Great Monarch, it was prophesied that one day those of pale skin would fall from the skies, and that we should beware. [*He now goes into a dance with the shell holding it above his head etc.*]

Villain One: There it is! The second shell. You realise what this means?

Villain Two: Well I do, boss, but they don't. [*Indicates audience.*]

Villain One: Whoever brings these two shells together controls the minds and thoughts, the very dreams of other human beings. The power that men have sought for centuries.

Villain Two: How's that again?

Villain One: If we both have shells, people think what we tell them to think. Control the minds and you control the world!

[*Bodyguard dances on. Suddenly he sees the other shell in Girl's hand. Indicates to King and Queen.*]

Bodyguard: The second shell – it is here!

King: Then the prophecy is true – and I shall be all powerful.

Dad: All powerful, what's that all about then?

Mum: I think it's those two shells, dear. As far as I can tell, whoever has them when they come together controls the minds of everyone else.

Dad: You mean – everyone's mind?

Mum: As far as I can tell, yes. [*Dad gets a crazed look.*]

Boy: I don't like the look of Dad!

Girl: There's something pulling on this shell – like a magnet. [*Shells are now slowly pulled together.*]

Boy: So what do we do?

Girl: We have to stop them coming together!

Villain One: Any minute now, the shells will be united, and the power will be ours for the taking!

King: All infidels will bow down and be slaves to the Great King of Rainbow Island. They will submit to his power!

Dad: Control the minds . . . ? Well I might just do something a bit different. I might just tell everyone I don't like, to jump off a cliff. Like traffic wardens. I might get that next-door neighbour of ours to – to sit in a bowl of custard for a week and say he's enjoying it.

Girl: They're all going crackers! And I can't hold this shell for much longer. Help me! [*Boy tries to drag her back but she is pulled towards the other shell which is held by the bodyguard.*]

Girl: Oh no! I can't hold on to it any longer! [*The shells now unite if possible to loud noise – plus light effects. The new united shell is in a prominent place and the adults move round it chanting.*]

Adults: The shells! The shells! The shells! The shells!

Girl: We're in big trouble!

Boy: Those shells – they've sent them all bonkers!

Girl: But what can we do?

[*Villain One comes forward and holds up shell.*]

Villain One: Ha! Ha! [*King comes forward and takes it off him, holds it up.*]

King: Ha! Ha! [*Dad does same and holds it up.*]

Dad: Ha! Ha! [*Pilot ditto.*]

Pilot: Ha! Ha!

[*Voice of their Friend in Brazil is heard.*]

Friend: Divide the shells – before they are sealed for-ever!

Girl: It's our holiday friend, Abbye! Come on! [*They grab the shells and manage to tear them apart.*]

Friend: Now cast one shell away.

Girl: But where?

Friend: Look – for the hand! [*They look, the same hand *appears. They offer it one of the shells, and it takes it and disappears. Everyone watches it. King now takes the single shell. Looks at it. Passes it on to Dad who looks at it. Passes it on to Villain One who looks at it then biffs Villain Two on the head with it.*]

Villain One: You fool – it's all your fault! [*Villain Two protests.*]

King: The power – it is gone!

Queen: Probably for the best, Kingy. All that bowing and scraping, well, I mean . . .

Dad: For one minute there, I thought I could control people's minds.

Mum: I think one mind's probably enough to control, dear. Even that's a bit much for you sometimes.

Girl: Thanks – Abbye!

Dad: Who?

Girl: I bet that hand was glad to get that shell back.

Boy: Yeah, but what we gonna do here? Stuck on some remote island and the Toon play Leeds in three days' time. [*Pilot comes forward.*]

Pilot: I think you'll find this might help.

Dad: What's that then?

Pilot: A homing device in event of a crash landing. I expect a rescue plane will be here any time now. Mind you, I think some of our so-called passengers might have a bit of explaining to do. [*Looks at Villains.*]

Villain Two: [*Starts crying.*] It wasn't my fault. He made me do it. He said there'd be hot dogs if I didn't, he . . . [*Sound of plane overhead.*]

Boy: There it is! [*All point, and wave. The drum beat starts up again and everyone is involved in a final celebratory dance during which the whole cast take their bows.*]

END OF PLAY

Whiter than Wight

Allendale Middle School,
July 1996

This was not a typical writer-in-schools venture. It was back-to-front for a start. I had been doing some work with BBC Radio 4, and the producer Julia Shaw was keen to put up new ideas for forty-five-minute documentaries. We stuck in a proposal for a programme following through a long-term school drama project, beginning with the first meetings between myself and the children, tracking how the ideas, characters and plot for the play were formed and took shape, showing the piece's gradual creation, including the casting, rehearsals, broadcasts, and extracts from the eventual public performance. There could be interviews with teachers, children, myself, and the audience. The BBC were keen on the idea, and gave it the green light. One small problem. At that stage I had no play, no school, no funding. Only the idea.

Looking back from these stringent and straitened times, it seems remarkable that the BBC showed such faith in what was little more than a glimmer in the eye, and that no stern functionary asked the questions: 'And *when* exactly, and *which* school exactly, and paid for by *whom* exactly?' Luckily they didn't, and the support of the BBC meant several schools showed an interest, plus which Northern Arts – as then was – agreed to fund the project (ah – nostalgia!). As did Northumberland County Council, whose arts officer, Pauline Moger, led me on a royal tour of various interested county schools. I was in the rare but pleasant situation of being able to choose, and I finally plumped for Allendale Middle School, the only establishment I visited where staff brought in homemade cake and biscuits on a daily basis – what more evidence did I need?

Allendale is a beautiful, remote village in West North-umberland, home of the famous New Year's Eve tar-barrel ceremony when village males carry blazing barrels of tar on their heads, in a ritual said to go back to pagan times. Drop your barrel and you're in disgrace. Being a natural urbanite, I was curious to discover what interested the thirty rural youngsters, many from farming stock who daily travelled down from the hills. We spent the first two sessions scribbling down thoughts and ideas on large pieces of paper which we pinned up around the classroom. Three topics gradu-ally emerged as holding their interest: the National Lottery (which obviously they all dreamed of winning); new-age travellers, some of whom had recently been encamped just outside the village; and nuclear-waste dumping, which had been in the North-East news of late. Just combine all three into a play then? Which is what we did.

The story involved the Wight family from the Leam Lane Council Estate on Tyneside. When their dream of winning the Lottery came true they bought a big posh house in a big posh private estate, only to find the transition from poverty to riches was not that simple. Furthermore some of the family began to act peculiarly when eating locally grown produce, as did other members of the community. A highly unpopular group of new-age travellers camped close by included the one-time nuclear scientist and drop-out Wisdom, who realised the land had been bought cheaply by the developers from a nuclear-power company that had used it for nuclear-waste dumping. Now the toxins were creeping through the soil. This plot gave us a lot to go on in our two-act social comedy.

On the poster we used the National Lottery logo, but with the smile inverted into a grimace and the caption changed to: *Watch out – It Could be You!* This was highly illegal and caused some nervousness in the village since it had other Lottery bids in elsewhere. The play was performed for two nights at The Queen's Hall Arts Centre, Hexham, and the forty-five-minute Radio 4 documentary was broadcast later that year. The project led to the formation of the Allendale Youth Theatre, created with members of the cast by co-producer George Welton. The children's teacher, Anne Brown, was producer, and her enthusiasm was a big part of the success. Anne recently contacted me to say she planned to stage a new production with her local WI. Another version of the play was done by Marden Bridge Middle School, Whitley Bay in the late 1990s.

Character List

Pluto	Film Director
Workmen	Bank Manager
Billy (Dad)	Shipping Magnate
Priscilla	Businesswoman
Steve	Car Salesman
Andrew	Jewellery Assistant
Jessica	Farah
Gran (Nelly)	Marie
Voice	Carstairs
Creepers	Zoot
Flunky One	Wisdom
Flunky Two	Freya
Flunky Three	Baliff
Maid	Police Officer

Action of the play:
Takes place on Tyneside, Utopia Estate
and in a new-age travellers' camp.

WHITER THAN WIGHT

VISUAL PROLOGUE

[*Suggested background music: Mussorgsky, 'Pictures from an Exhibition'.*]

Centre Stage – Self-supporting large flat possibly with play title on the front.

Flat is opened by two figures in protective anti-radiation gear to reveal **Pluto**.

Inside of flat is painted with a giant radiation/radioactivity symbol.

Pluto summons the lowering of a hoist from the roof. This is an open-frame structure on which is a pile of material, which begins to glow.

Pluto instructs radiation workers to shovel the material from the structure. One is hesitant, but is given a large wad of money to do so, and to encourage the others.

The activity is repeated, more money handed over, but the hesitant worker finally refuses. He removes his protective mask. He is **Wisdom**. **Pluto** dismisses him, and he exits stage right.

Pluto orders the hoist to be lifted again, and exits stage right with the other radiation workers, who take with them the unfolded flat.

Behind the flat, asleep on a settee is **Billy Wight**. He wakes and comes down stage.

Act One

Billy: [*Bottle of beer in his hand.*] Just imagine it, winning the Lottery, down the boozer every night, salt-and-vinegar crisps with every pint – and a big colour telly! [*He goes and sits down. An old black-and-white telly is brought on and he stares at it.*]

Voice: [*Off stage.*] And tonight's winning Lottery numbers are . . . !

[*Roll of drums etc. Billy goes through motions of some excitement, but mainly disappointment. Enter Priscilla.*]

Priscilla: I should have been a star, big mansion, swimming pool, world premieres in Leicester Square. I should have been – Cilla Black. [*Imitates her.*] And maybe, if we win the Lottery . . . [*She takes her place next to Billy. Both stare at the telly.*]

Voice: [*Off stage.*] And tonight's winning Lottery numbers are . . . [*Again they go through the motions, eventual disappointment. Enter Steve.*]

Steve: Me? I'm Steve, Mr Fixit. When it goes wrong, I'm your man. And here I am, working on clapped-out Ford Fiestas, busted lawn mowers. I should be fixing Rolls Royces, Concorde, the QE2 – and when this family wins the Lottery . . . [*Joins the other two in front of the telly.*]

Voice: [*Off stage.*] And tonight's winning Lottery numbers are . . . [*The three simulate the reactions. Again disappointment. Enter Jessica, reading a book.*]

Jessica: I've never bought a Lottery ticket in my life. I prefer reading Wordsworth. [*She sits in front of the telly but continues to read.*]

Voice: [*Off stage.*] And tonight's winning Lottery numbers are . . . [*The process is repeated. Enter Andrew.*]

Andrew: Look at this place. My family lives in a tip. It's a dump. And when I take a girl out, I want to bring her back somewhere special. I want to impress her. I want – to win the Lottery! [*Takes his place.*]

Voice: [*Off stage.*] And tonight's winning Lottery numbers are . . . [*Same process. Only Jessica remains unmoved by it all. Enter Gran.*]

Gran: We used to play Lottery in my day. Or was that lotto? Or is that a dog food? Or am I thinking of Rin Tin Tin? Or is that a rock band? I remember the song. [*Breaking into Vera Lynn.*] 'We'll meet again . . .'

Billy: Get yourself over here, you silly old fool – the Lottery's on! [*Gran takes her place.*]

Voice: [*Off stage.*] And tonight's winning numbers are . . . [*Same process. Gran is not bothered. Eventual disappointment. Billy jumps up and switches telly off. Chorus ends.*]

Billy: We're never going to win it.

Priscilla: But we've got to!

Andrew: I'm not carrying on like this!

Steve: That Fiesta's clapped out. I'm sick of it!

Jessica: [*Reading from her book.*] 'My heart leaps up when I behold/A rainbow in the sky.' [*They are all up and on their feet again at this stage.*]

Billy: The Lottery would solve everything.

Priscilla: Everything.

Steve: Everything.

Andrew: Everything.

Jessica: 'It is a beauteous evening, calm and free.'

Gran: I've not seen a whip and top in years.

Billy: Why isn't it next Saturday night?

Andrew: It is.

Billy: Right – let's get that telly on! [*They all sit down again.*]

Billy: This is the one, I know it.

Priscilla: I mean, my name's Priscilla Wight, that's what she was called at first. But you can't be famous and poor, can you? I mean if you're famous, you've got to be rich as well. [*Sound of the telly. It is the start of the Lottery programme.*]

Voice: [*Off stage.*] And welcome to the *National Lottery* – [*Voice goes off, we get fuzzy sound to suggest reception has gone off.*]

Billy: It's gone off! [*Frantic.*]

Andrew: Get it fixed! [*Frantic.*]

Priscilla: This is a tragedy! [*Frantic. Billy leaps up and begins banging and kicking the telly, increasingly desperately.*] Blast it! Curse it! [*Steve stands up calmly and produces a screwdriver, which he holds up to show the audience.*]

Steve: This looks like a job for . . . Mr Fixit. [*Moves his desperate dad Billy to one side, and within seconds the telly is OK again.*] No problem. [*Sits down. Pleased with himself. Everyone else calms down.*]

Billy: It's on the wrong side now – where's the remote control? [*Gran produces her walking stick and presses the buttons without getting up. It brings the programmes back.*]

Priscilla: You see – Gran does have her uses.

Billy: I told you – the silly old bat should be in a home. Where's that bottle opener? [*Opens another bottle of beer.*] I've got a feeling this week, in me bones.

Andrew: Like this is the week. Like all our prayers will be answered.

Steve: Just go out tomorrow – buy my own Rolls.

Priscilla: Maybe I'll invite Elton John round for dinner first. Or Rod Stewart.

Jessica: Look at them all. [*Carries on with her book.*]

Gran: Nice to have a family get-together. [*Jessica stands to go off, trips over cable, and pulls plug out. Others react in extremis.*]

Billy: The telly's off!

Priscilla: We're missing it!

Steve: Stay Calm. [*Rises.*]

Andrew: The numbers! [*Steve replaces the plug, telly comes back on. Everybody calms down.*]

Voice: [*Off stage.*] And now, ladies and gentlemen, this week's Lottery draw made by our celebrity guest, superstar and pin-up idol, Clarence Pickle. And the first Lottery number is . . . fifteen – making its twenty-second appearance in the Lottery.

Billy: Fifteen? That's one of ours! [*The four of them begin to get interested.*]

Voice: . . . and the second number is forty-two, making its fifteenth appearance.

Priscilla: That's us – look, that's us too!

Steve: Yeah – it is. [*Bit more interested.*]

Voice: And the third lucky number tonight ladies and gentlemen is – thirty-six, the twelfth time that has appeared.

Andrew: Thirty-six! We've got it! We've got it! [*Now they start to get very agitated. Priscilla has long false nails, which she begins to chew down. Dad shakes his beer bottle etc.*]

Voice: And the fourth number tonight is – number eight. That's one that hasn't been seen that often, only ten times.

Billy: It's us! That's us as well! [*Now they are really getting excited, except for Jessica who carries on reading, and Gran, who seems uninvolved.*]

Gran: Can I just see a bit of *Blind Date?* [*Presses the button with her stick. Channel changes. Everyone leaps up in horror.*]

Billy: No! [*Changes it back.*]

Voice: . . . the fifth number tonight, which is . . . [*This is delayed slightly to show their eager anticipation.*] . . . number twenty.

Priscilla: I don't believe it . . .

Billy: Me heart! [*Slumps down and pats his heart.*] It won't stand it . . .

Andrew: Number twenty – but that's ours too!

Steve: Yes. [*With this number the reaction is numbed to disbelief, to contrast with the coming announcement of the sixth.*]

Voice: And so ladies and gentlemen, the vital sixth number tonight, which Clarence Pickle will pick . . .

Voice: . . . and it is . . .

Billy: [*Mouthing it.*] Twenty-three.

Priscilla: [*Same.*] Twenty-three.

Andrew: [*Same.*] Twenty-three.

Steve: [*Same.*] Twenty-three.

Voice: . . . number twenty-three! [*There is a small silence as everyone stares at the screen in disbelief. A silent count of three and then . . .*]

All: Yeeeeees!

[*Ecstatic scenes. Everyone explodes. Music and dance here to suggest their new-found wealth. They pose and their Velcro clothes are pulled off in turn to reveal much more expensive clothes underneath. When this happens to Gran she is exactly the same underneath. A giant £20 million cheque is paraded, and the trappings of their simple home are removed to be replaced with some sumptuous fittings. A table is brought on by flunkies and Billy orders them around, enjoying his new status. When it is set they sit down and examine the posh cutlery etc. Each now in turn comes out of the scene – Gran and Jessica apart – to show they deal with their own wealth.*]

Billy: More caviar anyone?

Priscilla: I couldn't drink another drop of it.

Andrew: I liked that burnt salmon.

Steve: Smoked salmon, you berk.

Priscilla: And what are you doing today, dear?

Billy: I'm doing – what rich people do. [*Takes out golf tee, produces club and golf hat, and mimics driving off. Holds out club. Enter caddie with golf bag. Billy now walks over to hole the ball with a putt. He marks his card.*]

Billy: Thirty-two over par. I'm improving. I'll celebrate. Champagne! The drinks are on Billy Wight! [*He's surrounded. Drinks rapidly and slowly falls back into his chair.*]

Priscilla: Steven, eat up your greens. Even rich people get spots.

Steve: That snotty-nosed git in the car saleroom. Well, now I'll show him. [*Stands and goes into salesroom scene. Enter humble Car Salesman.*]

Steve: And that one – how much?

Car Salesman: [*Holds up a cut-out of car.*] A very exclusive model, sir, and retailing at £28,000.

Steve: A bit poky. How about that one?

Car Salesman: Even more exclusive, with fitted cocktail cabinet and trouser press. £35,000.

Steve: Hmm. I don't like the colour. And what about – this? [*Holds up a monstrous stretch limo.*]

Car Salesman: Oh, sir, top of the range: for royalty, sheikhs and presidents. Fitted satellite, tropical fish tank, sauna and Olympic-sized swimming pool. I'm afraid it runs out at £56,000.

Steve: Any discount for cash? [*Laughs at his own joke and produces wads of money which he chucks at the Car Salesman who scrabbles and grovels for them. Is still laughing when he sits down again. They carry on eating for a few seconds.*]

Priscilla: I've written to Elton John.

Andrew: What?

Priscilla: And Rod Stewart. I've invited them over.

Billy: Will they bring a bottle?

Priscilla: Noel Edmonds, Richard Branson, Chris Evans, Sue Lawley, Madonna, Mick Jagger, Princess Di and, of course, Cilla.

Billy: I'll play them at golf – I'll beat them all!

Priscilla: I might buy myself something. Nothing too showy, you understand, for when they come. [*Goes into* *jewellery-shop scene. Jewellery Assistant is showing her a range of items, necklaces, bracelets, brooches etc.*] That's nice – and that – ooh, I like that – yes, that one I think – oh and that – yes. [*Jewellery Assistant can scarcely keep up, keeps adding more jewellery to Priscilla who is soon drenched in it.*]

Priscilla: [*To Jewellery Assistant.*] What do you think? Does it suit me?

Jewellery Assistant: Madame looks – unique.

Priscilla: You never know who might turn up. [*Mimes curtseying for royalty, and engaging in small talk with them.*]

Billy: Oi! [*Snaps her out of it.*] Your salmon salad's getting cold. [*Priscilla returns to the table. They carry on eating. Gran looks across at Andrew.*]

Gran: Save those bread crusts, young Andrew.

Andrew: What?

Gran: I'll make a bread-and-butter pudding later.

Andrew: A bread-and-butter pudding? [*Andrew, Billy, Priscilla and Steve roar with laughter, silently count to five then stop.*] She's a dreamboat, she's classy, she speaks posh, she wears dead animals round her neck, and she fancies me – because I'm rich. I'll bring her back to this place – no sweat. And it's her birthday tomorrow. [*Goes out, crooks his arm anticipating her.*] So what's it to be, eh? Come on! [*Enter Farah, crooks his arm.*]

Farah: Gosh, Andrew, you mean I can have – anything?

Andrew: You name it.

Farah: Well, I'd like . . . [*Secretly gets out her calculator and does some sums as she's looking at various things.*] There again maybe . . . [*More calculations.*] Well, if I really could just . . .

Andrew: Only the best with Andrew Wight.

Farah: I only want one.

Andrew: Well?

Farah: You'll probably think I'm silly.

Andrew: Just say it.

Farah: I feel rather daft.

Andrew: Don't feel daft. Feel rich.

Farah: Very well. Could I please have a – a . . .

Andrew: Yeah?

Farah: A Concorde? [*Both freeze on this.*]

Priscilla: Well do you want any of this *sole meuniere* or don't you, Andrew? And look at you Jessica, you haven't touched your pheasant on toast.

Jessica: I don't want it.

Priscilla: Don't want it – best pheasant?

Billy: We used to live on chicken lips!

Jessica: I'm not sure winning the Lottery is very good for you.

All: WHAT?! [*Followed by riotous laughter. They clear away the table while they are still laughing. Exit all except Billy who is still laughing as he arranges a line of drinks, which he drinks one by one as he talks.*]

Billy: This is the life all right. Drinking all day. No work. No pressures. Beer, whisky, gin, rum, more beer, more whisky, more gin, more rum. Yes, this is the life all right. Cheers! [*This to nobody.*] Down the hatch! Bottoms up! Here's to mud in your eye! Yes, this is the life all right. Nothing to do. Nothing to do . . . [*His mood changes* *slightly at this final phrase. Enter Priscilla who is sorting through the morning's mail. Billy exits when the focus goes on her.*]

Priscilla: Now let me see what's in today's mail. There must be an answer from someone . . . Anthea Turner, Chris Evans, Rod Stewart . . . [*Sorts through.*] Gas bill . . . circulars . . . book club . . . It's two weeks since I wrote to them all . . . postcard from Skegness . . . special carpet offer . . . I just can't understand it at all . . . I suppose it must be the delivery service. They'll all arrive tomorrow!

[*Enter Steve with a shiny new tool kit, obviously delighted. Priscilla exits as he takes the focus.*]

Steve: Now that's what I call a tool kit! What do you think, Creepers? [*Enter Creepers the butler.*]

Creepers: It is admirable, sir.

Steve: Now I can really start fixing things. Where's the Rolls Royce? Let me under that bonnet!

Creepers: The Rolls is serviced by the official agents, sir.

Steve: Is it? Right – that big expensive lawnmower must need attention.

Creepers: Under strict warranty sir.

Steve: Warranty? Right – I'll just take a look at the central-heating system – must need checking.

Creepers: The guarantee is for six monthly inspections, sir. We are not allowed to touch it.

Steve: No? OK, I'll take a look at the motor-driven golf car. [*Moves to go off.*]

Creepers: No sir! [*This stops him.*] It is all arranged.

Steve: Very well. The swimming-pool heating system. [*Again.*]

Creepers: No sir! [*Stops him again.*] The manufacturer's agreement.

Steve: Oh, I see. [*Enter Gran. Steve talks to her.*] Seems like everything here is already sorted out, Gran. Wonderful isn't it? [*Exits with tool kit.*]

[*Gran has an old-style wind-up gramophone, and a pile of records, which she begins to sort through – 78s if possible.*]

Gran: Oooh, I remember that one, Brighton Pier in 1947: the wind blew right up me skirt. Oh, and that one, that naughty man from Rotherham in 1954 who ruined me lipstick. And this one, I was listening to this one when a bomb flew right past me left ear hole and ended up in Mrs Jenkins casserole unexploded. The bomb that is, not the casserole. [*Picks one.*] Now that's my favourite! [*Enter Maid who begins dusting. Gran puts record on and plays it. 'White Cliffs of Dover'. She begins to dance. Maid looks on.*] Come, my dear, dance with an old lady! [*Invites her but the maid shakes her head.*]

Maid: Non, non, it is not allowed. The servants to dance with the employers.

Gran: Fiddlesticks and dirty bottoms! There's nothing like a good dance. [*Invites her again.*]

Maid: I will get into trouble.

Gran: They really are white, you know, those cliffs. Come on. [*Dances with her. Gran sings. Maid begins to relax. They enjoy it. Enter Andrew with Marie.*]

Andrew: Gran! What are you doing?

Gran: I'm dancing. [*Maid breaks away in embarrassment, exits. Gran carries on dancing.*] Everyone should dance. Every day. [*Gran dances off stage slowly on her own. Andrew is embarrassed.*]

Andrew: She's – er – my Gran. You know, a bit . . . [*Marie *looks bored – bored little rich girl.*] I've got this surprise for you Marie. A round-the-world trip. What do you say?

Marie: I went last week.

Andrew: Oh. I know, this will knock you out. Fly to Paris for a slap-up French meal, and home in time for tea!

Marie: Garlic brings me out in spots.

Andrew: It does? Oh, I see. Like the house, do you?

Marie: The swimming pool's a bit small.

Andrew: Yeah, well, you know, get a new one soon, just temporary. Hey, being out with a classy rich girl like you, that's really something, know what I mean? [*No response.*] Ever been to the opera? Them ashtrays, binoculars, we could go tonight.

Marie: I can't understand a word they talk about.

Andrew: Yeah, I know what you mean. Maybe not. So . . . [*They begin to walk off.*] I wonder what we *could* do? [*Exit. Enter Jessica reading her book. She sits centre stage and one by one the family members approach her. Enter Billy swinging his golf club.*]

Billy: I guess those other members of the golf club must be too frightened to play me. I'm getting too good! [*Sees Jessica.*] Jessica, come and play a few holes of golf with your dad!

Jessica: I'm reading, Dad.

Billy: Just a few holes maybe.

Jessica: I'm happy just here, Dad.

Billy: Anyway, what do you mean, reading? You're rich now, you don't have to read.

Jessica: I enjoy it.

Billy: Enjoy it? What do you know about enjoy? You've

hardly spent a damn thing since we moved here!

Jessica: I'm OK here, Dad. [*Exit Billy swinging his golf club. Enter Steve. Comes up and examines Jessica's wrist.*]

Steve: Is it bust?

Jessica: What?

Steve: Your wristwatch – is it bust? I could mend it.

Jessica: It's not bust.

Steve: Oh – so it doesn't need fixing then?

Jess: The watch is fine.

Steve: Maybe – something else?

Jessica: What?

Steve: Needs fixing. Maybe you've got something else?

Jessica: No.

Steve: Right then. [*Exits looking slightly lost. Meets Priscilla on the way.*]

Priscilla: You did post all those letters, Jessica, didn't you?

Jessica: Course I did, Mum.

Priscilla: I mean, the stamps were stuck on properly and everything?

Jessica: I stuck them on myself.

Priscilla: And the postcodes. You did check the postcodes?

Jessica: They all had postcodes on.

Priscilla: I mean, imagine sending a letter to Terry Wogan without a postcode! Or Selina Scott!

Jessica: Mum, all the letters were stamped, sealed, with postcodes, and they all went into the letterbox. I took them myself, even though the servants didn't want to let me.

Priscilla: [*Exiting.*] Well, I just don't understand it . . .
[*Enter Andrew staring at his airline tickets.*]

Andrew: Don't suppose you want to go with me then?

Jessica: Go where?

Andrew: Oh, you know – round the world.

Jessica: Where's – Marie, is it?

Andrew: Oh – yes, well, she couldn't make it.

Jessica: There must be loads of people would go round the world with you.

Andrew: Oh yes, course, yeah . . .

Jessica: There you are then.

Andrew: Yeah, right. [*Exits flapping tickets. Enter Gran still dancing. She dances around on her own for a little time, then Jessica gets up and dances with her. 'The White Cliffs of Dover' plays quietly in the background. One by one the members of the family come to stand in a line behind them to look at them, and to sing the following words to the same tune. Arrangement to be decided upon.*]

Family:

All our fears are over
And we're in clover
Now we've won the Lottery.
No more debt or worry
No more work or hurry
We're all as happy as can be.

If we want to try it
We go and buy it
Anything, any time, anywhere.
The Lottery's saved us
We've got rich neighbours
Our lives don't have a single care.

[*Gran and Jessica continue to dance round the stage. Family continue to stare forward, tune can still be heard but softly.*]

Billy: Where are our neighbours, by the way?

Priscilla: I don't think I've seen any yet.

Andrew: All these lovely big houses.

Steve: Maybe they've all been busy since we moved in.

Billy: Yes, that's it. Busy.

Priscilla: But it would be nice to meet them. Other rich people.

Andrew: Just think. When we were poor. All those bothersome neighbours.

Priscilla: Yes, just think.

Billy: I know what.

Steve: What?

Billy: We'll throw a posh garden party – and invite all our rich neighbours!

[*Music ends. Enter Film Director, Businesswoman, Bank Manager and Shipping Magnate holding garden-party drinks and food. The family also break rank and become part of it. Family and guests circulate in garden-party fashion. They talk in pairs and in turn drift towards the front of the stage where they engage in short snatches of dialogue then drift back into the general throng. First Priscilla and the Film Director, who has a megaphone which he/she occasionally talks through.*]

Priscilla: A real live film director – I don't believe it. You must know a lot of famous people.

Film Director: Like I said to Mel Gibson yesterday, have a peanut.

Priscilla: Mel Gibson? Gosh! How about – Kermit the

Frog? Julia Roberts? ET?

Film Director: One by one, they all come to work with me. I guess I must have something. Talent, looks, modesty . . .

Priscilla: I always thought I could make it you know, in show business.

Film Director: I mean, so they tell me. Arny, Sly, the others –

Priscilla: I once sang in a country pub. And at Butlins' talent night!

Film Director: Do you know Barry Norman?

Priscilla: What? Oh, I –

Film Director: Time he had me on his show again. You tell him that.

Priscilla: Maybe if I sang, you know, a Cilla Black number.

Film Director: What?

Priscilla: 'You're my world, you're everything I own' – [*Film Director looks distracted, starts checking Filofax or something.*]

Priscilla: Well?

Film Director: Yeah, yeah, terrific. I'll ring you. [*Sharp exit. Priscilla follows him in hope. Andrew and the Bank Manager come forward.*]

Andrew: I've never met a real-life bank manager.

Bank Manager: Liquidity ratio, collateral, variable rates of interest, deposit-account transfers, indemnity bonds –

Andrew: Yeah, that's right! I bet it's dead exciting. All that money.

Bank Manager: Standing orders, direct debit, preference shares.

Andrew: I might want to invest the odd million. Any advice?

Bank Manager: Invest? Why, Nasty Plutonium Ltd. They pay rich dividends.

Andrew: Nasty Plutonium?

Bank Manager: Carstairs is your man. A senior executive. [*Points out Carstairs, the Businessman. We isolate Carstairs for a few seconds. Others fall back to emphasise and the scene freezes.*]

Andrew: All that radioactive stuff – is that what they make?

Bank Manager: A four-fold increase in profits last year. If only others could follow their example. [*Moves away. Andrew follows him. Shipping Magnate comes forward, talking to Steve.*]

Steve: What do you mean, boats – like on a boating lake?

Shipping Magnate: My fleet is among the largest in the world. Ten luxury liners, twenty oil tankers, cross channel ferries –

Steve: Do they ever break down?

Shipping Magnate: Break down?

Steve: Need fixing, you know, I'm good at that.

Shipping Magnate: You would find my boats in the North Sea, the Red Sea, the Black Sea, the White Sea, the Dead Sea.

Steve: I see.

Shipping Magnate: And very soon, I hope the entire fleet will be fuelled by nuclear power.

Steve: Nuclear power?

Shipping Magnate: My good friend Carstairs, of Nasty Plutonum Ltd. I offered him and his wife a little cruise, to clinch the deal. [*Points to him. We again isolate him and freeze for a few seconds. Businesswoman walks past with Billy in tow. Billy has had a few drinks.*]

Billy: Did you say athletics?

Businesswoman: Cosmetics. My company has fifty factories in a dozen countries producing our health products. You must know the brand name. Skin Deep.

Billy: Sheep dip?

Businesswoman: Our mascara and lipsticks are especially popular.

Billy: I've never seen a sheep in mascara.

Businesswoman: I beg your pardon?

Billy: Can they put their own lipstick on?

Businesswoman: Who?

Billy: Sheep.

Businesswoman: Sheep?

Billy: They're cleverer than I thought.

Businesswoman: Where exactly did you say you lived before you moved here?

Billy: Gateshead

Businesswoman: Yes, I see . . .

Billy: Sheep putting their own lipstick on – it makes you think, I mean. [*Businesswoman walks away during this.*] Hey, where are you going? I wanted to ask you about pigs, and nail varnish! She's gone! How about you? [*Catches hold of Carstairs, who stares at him and moves off to talk to Jessica, who is not mixing.*]

Carstairs: You'll know who I am of course.

Jessica: I haven't a clue.

Carstairs: How quaint. Alphonse Carstairs. Senior Manager, Nasty Plutonium Fuels Ltd. [*Holds out his hand. Jessica stares at it.*]

Jessica: You make all that radioactive stuff?

Carstairs: Press hysteria, my dear. We are the future.

Jessica: Maybe I don't like the future.

Carstairs: A pretty girl like you could have an interesting career. Public relations. We're always on the look-out. Take the public round our day-centre. Free lemonade for the kiddies.

Jessica: Where do you bury it all – the toxic stuff?

Carstairs: Now don't you worry your pretty little head about such things. Dangerous? They said that about the bubonic plague! [*As he says the following words, Jessica notices Zoot skulking round the apple trees suspiciously. He is also encouraging his dog to come through the fence but it won't. Jessica is intrigued and eventually goes off, leaving Carstairs spouting to himself. Someone comes up and leads him off eventually, after which dialogue between Jessica and Zoot starts.*] Leave it to us. We know what we are doing. We're the experts. No cause for alarm. It's a profitable industry. Waste products? Don't worry your pretty little head, like I said. Out of sight, out of mind eh? It's a competitive world. No room for flabby idealism, sentimentality . . .

Jessica: [*To Zoot.*] Who are you? [*He reacts in a startled way.*] What are you doing here? How did you get in? What have you got? [*She realises he has got apples in his jumper, goes up and looks. They spill out.*] You stealing our apples?

Zoot: You've got thousands of apples.

Jessica: You're one of those new-age travellers, aren't you?

[*Zoot makes a run for it, trips on one of the apples and falls heavily. He holds his ankle and groans. Jessica helps him.*]

Jessica: You've probably sprained it. Here. [*Helps him, takes him to a seat. Examines it.*] It's swollen.

Zoot: So? [*Tries to get up. Can't.*]

Jessica: It needs a new bandage. Wait. [*Exit. Return with bandage. Zoot meantime tries again unsuccessfully.*] Have you stolen anything else? [*They exchange a look. Slowly he takes a succession of things from his pocket and lays them out.*] You shouldn't steal.

Zoot: You've got plenty.

Jessica: That doesn't make it right.

Zoot: What does then?

Jessica: We used to be poor.

Zoot: Oh yeah?

Jessica: Then we won the Lottery. Twenty million.

Zoot: Twenty million – stolen from other people. And you're worried about a few apples.

Jessica: What's your name?

Zoot: Zoot.

Jessica: I'm Jessica. Why do you live on the road, in cara-vans?

Zoot: Why do most people live in prison?

Jessica: You think we're in prison?

Zoot: Maybe not you. Most of them.

Jessica: 'We talked with open heart and tongue/Affec-tionate and true.'

Zoot: 'We lay beneath a spreading oak/Beside a mossy seat.'

Jessica: Not many people know Wordsworth. They'll throw you out, you know. They don't like you.

Zoot: We'll go somewhere else. Only trees are planted. Is there something funny about this place?

Jessica: Funny?

Zoot: My dog. She wouldn't come through the fence.

Jessica: Have an apple. [*Zoot eats one but spits it out.*] What's the matter?

Zoot: These apples. Must be something in the soil. They're –

Jessica: What? [*Enter Billy. Spots Zoot.*]

Billy: Hey! You! What do you think you're doing here! Police! Thief! Intruder! Police! [*Runs over to get him. Zoot manages to get up and flee.*]

Jessica: No – Don't!

Zoot: We'll meet again soon.

Jessica: How?

Zoot: Soon. You'll see. [*Makes off limping. Billy is coming over, a bit tipsy.*]

Billy: Scotland Yard! The Flying Squad! Get him! Surround him! Seal off the area . . . Jessica, are you all right?

Jessica: Yes

Billy: He could have – oh anything, ruffians, scroungers –

[*Zoot has made his exit. As he does so he bumps into the Bank Manager, who is carrying a bunch of flowers. The two stare at one another, then the Bank Manager very deliberately starts eating the flowers.*]

Zoot: Something – not right – about this place. [*Exits.*]

INTERVAL

[*During the interval the guests at the garden party mingle with the audience. The guests are acting very strangely to reinforce Zoot's suspicions. Each can be given a few lines to keep repeating. Ask each actor to choose his/her lines.*]

Act Two

[*The scene is the new-age travellers' camp. On stage are Wisdom, Freya and extras. Music and movement to start it. Zoot brings on in turn various vegetables and fruit which he hands over to Wisdom who holds them up, examines them and shakes his head, placing them in a line in front of him until he has a collection.*]

Wisdom: Apples, carrots, onions, cabbage, pears – all the same.

Zoot: And all from the gardens at Utopia Estate.

Freya: Why are we wasting our time on a few lousy vegetables? Why not steal something worth having?

Wisdom: They are all contaminated.

Freya: So? It serves those filthy-rich parasites right.

Wisdom: Do you know who owns Utopia Estate? Who built those luxury houses?

Freya: Who cares?

Wisdom: A subsidiary of Nasty Plutonium Fuels Ltd.

Zoot: You mean the people who –

Wisdom: Were once my employers yes. Till I gave it all up. Because they were poisoning the world.

Zoot: What's this got to do with vegetables?

Wisdom: Utopia Estate was built just at the time the company was trying to get rid of some particularly horrible radioactive waste. Of course, no one would have it. They were stuck with it.

Zoot: Unless of course –

Wisdom: Unless they can dig a huge hole in the ground with no one noticing, right under everyone's noses, and bury it there.

Zoot: And stick a luxury housing estate on top!

Wisdom: And just hope it never leaks out.

Zoot: But it looks like –

Wisdom: It's started. [*They pick up the fruit and vegetables and look at them.*]

Zoot: But what will be the effects?

Wisdom: Unpredictable. We must do something. To save them.

Freya: Save them? That load of wealthy toads? They've been trying to get rid of us for weeks.

Wisdom: Nevertheless –

Freya: Never mind nevertheless. I say let them get contaminated. Let them die for all I care. [*Enter Jessica.*]

Jessica: Does that include my family?

Freya: No one asked you to come to this place.

Jessica: I could say the same about all of us. [*Goes to Zoot who puts his arm round her. They are obviously in love.*]

Zoot: Jessica is one of us now.

Freya: She's one of them – always will be.

Wisdom: Us – them – why do we always have to talk like that?

Freya: Because that's the way it is, Wisdom. Or hadn't you noticed? And we travellers have to survive.

Zoot: Maybe if we just talked to them – [*Enter a Bailiff with a notice which he reads out.*]

Bailiff: 'It is hereby announced that persons residing outside the North-East perimeter of Utopia Estate without lawful permission and of a temporary nature do move all articles, possessions and persons from aforesaid land not later than 4 p.m. on Friday, 12th July –'

Zoot: But that's only two days' time!

Bailiff: – 'and failure to do so will necessitate forced removal of said persons and possessions and legal action for violation of the law . . .' [*Looks a bit nervous.*] Er – I have to – er – stick this up . . .

Wisdom: So stick it up. [*Bailiff moves nervously into camp and nails notice to a post. Exits nervously.*]

Freya: That's it then. We haven't got time to worry about that lot and their vegetables. I say we bust a few of their houses tonight and flit.

Wisdom: Freya, where is your spirit?

Freya: They have more than they need. We have less than we need. It's that simple.

Wisdom: And who decides exactly how much everyone needs?

Jessica: Look, there's no point any of you trying to talk to them.

Zoot: They fear us. Mistrust us.

Jessica: And there's no point telling the police.

Wisdom: A few new-age travellers accusing a huge multi-national corporation? We'd have no chance.

Freya: So there you are. It's decided.

Jessica: *I* have to do something.

Zoot: But they've disowned you. Your family are ashamed of you.

Jessica: Not all of them.

Wisdom: What?

Jessica: I think there is one who will still have faith in me.

[Enter Gran who again is dancing with herself to the tune of 'We'll Meet Again'. During this dance and her speech, the new-age travellers exit, and the scene is set once again in the Wight household.]

Gran: 'We'll Meet Again' . . . well, I'll never meet Jack again. Dead and buried these five years. I loved dancing with him down the Palais, that silver ball covering us in bright spots, and he'd buy me a drink with a little umbrella poking out. His shoes were so well polished I could see the hairs inside his nostrils. No Jack to dance with. No Jessica either. And they won't let me dance with the servants. Say it's beneath me. Only the carpet's beneath me. *[Dances on. Enter Priscilla.]*

Priscilla: Oh the silly, silly, silly girl. Those nasty smelly gypsies with their dog dirt and straggly hair. Am I happy? Yes, of course I am. I'm happy everyone. *[This to no one.]* I said I'm happy. *[Enter Billy.]* Are you drunk again, Billy?

Billy: Have you seen the size of the wine cellar? Where's my sons? At least they haven't walked out of the family. Steven! *[Enter Steven.]* What you doing?

Steven: Nothing.

Billy: What do you mean, nothing?

Steven: There's nothing to do. Every day I get up, walk about, eat. Nobody lets me do anything. Watch this. Creepers! [*Enter Creepers.*]

Creepers: Yes sir?

Steven: I'd like a bath, Creepers.

Creepers: Certainly, sir. You there! [*Summons a minor servant.*] Go and have a bath for Mr Steven.

Steven: See what I mean? I can't do anything. [*Enter Andrew.*]

Andrew: Gold diggers – that's all they are. [*Looking in wallet.*] She spent two thousand pounds of my money, then she was off like a shot.

Creepers: Dinner is served [*They all sit. Food is brought in.*]

Billy: Have you made any peas pudding, Priscilla?

Priscilla: I'm not allowed in the kitchens, I told you.

Creepers: It's *salmon en croute*, sir.

Billy: I could murder some peas pudding. Salmon what?

Creepers: *En croute*, sir.

Billy: *Croute?* What's a *croute*? Anyone know what a *croute* is? Anyone ever met a *croute*?

Priscilla: You're making a scene. I don't want a scene when my famous guests arrive.

Steve: There aren't any famous guests.

Andrew: The only guests are people after our money.

Billy: Our money? [*Produces pocket calculator.*] We've only got nineteen million, seven hundred thousand, two hundred and sixty-eight pounds and twenty-three pence left!

Priscilla: You don't have to work it out every day.

[*Gran dances past the table.*]

Priscilla: She should really be in a home, you know.

Billy: I could have one built for her. That would be something to do tomorrow.

Steve: Aren't you playing golf tomorrow, Dad?

Billy: I'm fed up with golf. Where's Jessica?

Priscilla: Gone – with that rabble.

Billy: There's gratitude for you. Pass me an apple. [*Eats it.*] I feel funny.

Priscilla: We're too rich to feel funny.

Billy: I feel – [*Produces shaving brush foam and razor and proceeds to shave himself.*]

Andrew: Doesn't he normally do that in the bathroom?

Priscilla: Billy? Oh – I say. [*Eats an apple, leaps up and holds out her hand, greeting imaginary guests.*] Why, Michael Jackson, so glad you could make it – and Mr Mel Gibson – quite delightful. Do sit there, right next to Madonna, that's right. Dinner will be served quite soon, just waiting for Paul McCartney, yes . . .

Steve: What's up with these two?

Andrew: Search me. [*Bites an apple. Starts laughing.*] Yes, go on search me, that's right, search me. And everyone else. [*Laughs more.*] And the octopus. And the First Lord of the Admiralty. All got to be searched! Oh yes!

Steve: Gran – they've all gone funny.

Gran: They've been funny since we left Gateshead.

Steve: It can't be these apples can it? [*Bites into one.*] Just an apple. [*Now starts repeating this rapidly, sitting and* *standing rapidly while he does it.*] Just an apple . . . Just an apple.

Gran: [*Watches him and produces a Netto bag from which she takes an apple and starts eating. Watches the others. Enter Jessica.*]

Jessica: Oh no – it's started, it's got to them. Gran, are you all right?

Gran: They don't think so, my dear. But how are you?

Jessica: I'm fine. But the family, they're being – poisoned.

Gran: I know that dear.

Jessica: You know? About the buried radioactive waste and –

Gran: I know they're being poisoned, Jessica.

Jessica: But you can't – I mean –

Gran: What would you like me to do, Jessica?

Jessica: Help me warn them. Before it's too late.

Gran: We'll try. [*Shouts to them all.*] Wake up! You're being poisoned! [*They all snap out of it.*]

Billy: Poisoned?

Priscilla: Did someone say – poisoned?

Andrew: It's Jessica!

Priscilla: Our daughter – the bare-faced cheek!

Steven: She's come back!

Jessica: Listen, you're all in great danger.

Billy: Danger? With more than eighteen million pounds in the bank?

Priscilla: Danger? Just listen to her.

Jessica: This estate was secretly built on a load of

radioactive waste, which is now leaking out and getting into the fruit and vegetables. That's what's affecting you.

Billy: What?

Priscilla: What nonsense is she spouting now?

Billy: Trying to weedle her way back in I suppose.

Gran: She's right, you know. You should listen.

Priscilla: Oh yes, she's got you on her side, has she?

Billy: I said you should be put away in a home, your age. Half senile.

Steven: Maybe we should hear what she says dad.

Billy: You be quiet!

Priscilla: Show a bit of respect for your father, after all he's done.

Gran: I'm just a silly old lady. But I know when things aren't right.

Billy: That's right. A silly old lady. And you should have stayed in Gateshead. You're not cut out for this high life. Like what we are.

Jessica: Look, Dad. This is your daughter and your mother. And we're appealing to you. [*They stare at each other for a few moments.*]

Priscilla: See what's happened to her, Billy? Mixing with that rubbish. Now trying to stir up trouble here.

Jessica: Why do you think you act funny sometimes?

Billy: Who acts funny?

Jessica: It's no use, Gran . . .

Billy: That's right, girl, it's no use.

Priscilla: Not until you apologise for your terrible

behaviour. In front of all our important neighbours too.

Billy: I suggest you get back to Mr Bojangles and his mates.

Priscilla: We don't want their sort round here. And if you're one of them, we don't want you either. So clear off! [*Jessica runs off. She runs into Zoot, who has entered to witness these last words.*]

Zoot: She tried to warn you. Why won't you listen?

Billy: I told you to stay off our property! Get out before I call the police!

Zoot: The richer you are, the blinder you are. [*Exits with Jessica. Family are left to look at one another, trying not to show their unease.*]

Gran: [*Producing Netto bag again.*] A Netto's apple anyone?

[*Scene is new-age camp. Soon afterwards. Possibly we see some hovering police officers in this scene, emphasising that the travellers are being shortly forced off. Freya is stirring up the emotions of the travellers.*]

Freya: We try to warn them – they spit at us! They reject their own! They reject us! Do we go quietly? Well? [*Murmurs of dissent.*] Do we slink off, like cowardly dogs? Or do we resist. [*More murmurs.*]

Wisdom: [*Rising.*] We must expose the treachery, the danger on that estate.

Freya: [*Points to Jessica.*] She has tried. And failed. And why should we? So they can herd us off again like cattle? You are too old, Wisdom. Get out your slippers, and your pipe. I say we teach Utopia Estate a lesson before we leave. Who's with me? [*Cries of support.*]

Wisdom: Freya, your energy is borne from bitterness.

Freya: And all your energy has gone old man. Follow Freya! [*Leads them off stage. Carstairs and Pluto are on the phone, wheeled on if possible and divided by the comic-book style zig-zag line.*]

Carstairs: Carstairs here. Mr Pluto, sir, senior manager North-East, weekly report. Small problem I think.

Pluto: Problem?

Carstairs: Rumours. About buried nuclear waste. Under Utopia Estate. Where I live. Bad for the corporate image.

Pluto: Then see to it. You are in charge there.

Carstairs: Yes, Mr Pluto. Thank you, Mr Pluto. Appreciate the big house, the big salary, the big office, the big secretary, Mr Pluto.

Pluto: Good. What are a few rumours?

Carstairs: Of course, Mr Pluto. Except people on the estate are beginning to act strangely. My marrows taste odd, and yesterday my neighbour stood on his head in the road and whistled the national anthem.

Pluto: Yes?

Carstairs: I think the new-age travellers might cause problems.

Pluto: A bunch of smelly hippies?

Carstairs: But you see, Mr Pluto, one of those smelly hippies just happens to be – Wisdom. [*At this, Pluto reaches through and grabs Carstairs by the neck.*]

Pluto: Did you, by the teeniest remote chance, say Wisdom?

Carstairs: Yes, Mr Pluto. I mean, there's *not* any nuclear waste under the estate, is there, Mr Pluto? I mean, you wouldn't have given me, a loyal company manager, a free house there if there was, would you, Mr Pluto? Mr Pluto? [*Pluto releases him.*]

Pluto: I think it's time for the chairman of Nasty Plutonium Ltd to pay a personal visit to the North-East . . .

[*Scene is the Wight household. Billy is quite drunk and slumped in a chair trying to build up a pile of beer cans, which keeps falling over. Creepers rebuilds them when this happens, but Billy always waves him away. Priscilla is pacing the floor.*]

Priscilla: What sort of life are we leading? My husband is drinking his way through twenty million, my daughter has run off with a layabout, one son sits twiddling his expensive spanners all day, the other son lets endless silly young women rob him blind. And me? I'm alone. I remember Billy Wight when you used to tickle my ear with your tongue. [*Tries to get affectionate with him. He is too sozzled.*]

Billy: Hic! [*Knocks over cans again.*]

Priscilla: We are rich, Billy. Why are we not happy? [*Enter Gran.*] Well, what do you have to say?

Gran: I just spend what I have. In my little box. [*Shows it.*]

Priscilla: What's wrong with this place?

Gran: Nobody ever dances. [*Twirls around the stage.*]

Priscilla: I don't feel very well. [*Enter Andrew, also not well.*]

Andrew: Mother – that feeling again. Funny . . . money? . . . funny . . . funny . . . money . . . funny money funny money . . . [*Goes into strange routine.*]

Priscilla: Billy – your son. Look at him! Don't you care?

Billy: Hic! [*Again tries to build up the beer cans.*]

Priscilla: Steven. Come and help.

Steven: [*Enters.*] Yes. Yes. Yes. Yes. Yes. [*He is affected too. We have the accumulated effect of these three acting strangely, to Priscilla's horror.*]

Priscilla: This is like a nightmare – Gran!

Gran: [*Dancing.*] You make me dance alone . . .

Priscilla: No, no, I can't stand it, I – [*Tries to rouse Billy.*] Billy! [*He slumps down.*] No, no – [*Runs off and straight into Mr Pluto who is just arriving. He is obviously taken with her.*]

Pluto: Well, what do we have here? Even Mr Pluto's heart might melt at such a sight.

Priscilla: Someone – help me.

Pluto: Help such a beautiful lady? Why of course. Madame, Mr Cornelius Pluto, chairman of nasty Plutonium Ltd. At your service. A Rolex watch, a diamante tiepin, a twenty-two-carat necklace. And nuclear power for the nation. [*To the audience.*] What wouldn't I do to make her mine? [*Takes her hand and kisses her up the arm. She is quite overcome.*]

Priscilla: Oh – that aftershave . . .

Pluto: A splish there, a splash there. Tell me, am I close to the Utopia Estate.

Priscilla: I live there

Pluto: You? [*Again to audience.*] But that means, this beautiful creature, possibly is affected. No. [*To Priscilla.*] Then you must leave.

Priscilla: Leave?

Pluto: Immediately. I will pay for the removal van.

Priscilla: But leave?

Pluto: Quietly, you understand. No fuss, not a word.

Priscilla: But my family?

Pluto: [*To the audience.*] What do I care about her family? How soon could you be ready?

Priscilla: What?

Pluto: Such beauty. Must be preserved. Not to be put in danger.

Priscilla: Danger?

Pluto: Did I say danger?

Priscilla: Yes, you did.

Pluto: A slip of the tongue. Well?

Priscilla: Well, what?

Pluto: Are you ready?

Priscilla: [*To the audience.*] I think he's taken with me. How flattering. After Billy. Maybe I should . . . [*She is tempted.*]

Pluto: One word, my dear, and Mr Pluto will do the rest.

Priscilla: Mr Pluto?

Pluto: Chairman and Managing Director of Nasty Plutonium Ltd.

Priscilla: [*To herself.*] Nasty Plutonium Ltd. And he mentioned danger? Now what was it Jessica said? [*Enter Jessica to repeat the previous warning.*]

Jessica: 'This estate was secretly built on a load of radioactive waste by Nasty Plutonium Ltd. It is now leaking out and getting into the fruit and vegetables. That's what's affecting you.' [*Exit Jessica.*]

Priscilla: Mr Pluto, what are you doing here?

Pluto: I have – shall we say – a little business to attend to.

Priscilla: Business?

Pluto: Nothing to worry your pretty little head about.

Priscilla: But you said people might be in danger?

Pluto: Business of my nature, highly confidential. Have no fear, I shall smooth is all over. Well, my desired one, what do you say? Mr Pluto can offer you anything you wish. Money. Luxuries.

Priscilla: I seem to have heard all this before. From the Lottery man. [*To Pluto.*] I'm not sure. [*To audience.*] He won't tell me anything.

Pluto: This is what I suggest. By this time tomorrow all this business will be cleared up. I shall meet you here. And we shall fly. Well?

Priscilla: I – I have to think about it.

Pluto: Think then. Until tomorrow. But no further. [*Kisses her arm again.*] What Mr Pluto wants, Mr Pluto gets. [*Exits.*]

Priscilla: I'm all in a tizzy. What's to be done? Billy! Billy! [*Enter Billy, drunk.*] We've been blind Billy. To everything. And Jessica was right about warning us. Billy? Billy! Creepers – give him some black coffee! [*Creepers summons servant to pour black coffee down his throat.*]

Priscilla: Billy, I do believe we are all being poisoned!

Billy: Poison? Poison? What's your poison? Mine's a vodka.

Priscilla: More coffee, Creepers! Sober him up! Andrew! [*Enter Andrew crying into a large hanky.*] Andrew, you have to help your mother.

Andrew: [*Blubbing.*] No one loves me. They take my money, then laugh at me. Why do they all laugh at me?

Priscilla: Andrew? Oh – Steven! [*Enter Steven, fiddling with a camera.*] Steven, I –

Steven: That film director's camera – it's bust. At last I have something to fix!

Priscilla: You can fiddle later, Steven. Everything is suddenly becoming clear to me. But my family must help, and –

Steven: Move that sprocket there, fiddle with that cog wheel here, a slight adjustment to the flange . . .

Priscilla: Why will none of my family listen to me?

[*Enter Freya, followed by more new-age travellers.*]

Freya: There they stand – our enemies! The privileged and the pampered!

Others: Yes!

Freya: We demand what is ours! Before we leave this site.

Others: Yes!

Freya: What you will not give – we shall take!

Others: Yes!

[*Billy has sobered up and gets to his feet.*]

Billy: What's this scruffy lot doing here?

Freya: Property belongs to the people. On behalf of the people, we claim it.

Billy: Clear off, you flea-bitten scroungers! You're a disgrace to decent honest people. Take your mangy caravans and get out!

Freya: Do not push us too far.

Billy: Listen, pet, with my money, I could push you off Mount Everest.

Freya: You hear his insults? Shall we stand for them?

Others: No!

Billy: Are you bunch of toe rags threatening Billy Wight, and his eighteen million quid?

[*There is a general sense of confrontation. Enter Wisdom from behind the travellers' ranks.*]

Wisdom: Enough of this!

[*Enter Gran from behind the Wight family.*]

Gran: My thoughts exactly. [*Taken with Wisdom.*] My, but that's a canny waistcoat. Pleased to meet you, Nelly Wight, Leam Lane Estate, born and bred.

Wisdom: I am Wisdom, new-age traveller.

Gran: Do you dance?

Wisdom: Of course. [*They begin to dance.*]

Gran: I think my family need a bit of sorting out.

Wisdom: There is also badness running through my family.

Gran: Why don't you and me see to it?

Wisdom: After you.

Gran: Right. [*Grabs hold of Billy.*] Call yourself a son of Nelly Wight? You've become a drunken, greedy, narrow-minded, selfish oaf. You've been ruined by easy money [*Throws him off. Next is Andrew.*] You think a fat wallet can buy you love, and you're taken in by every sweet smile and dab of lipstick. Grow up! [*Next is Steven.*] Steven? You could be an incredibly talented engineer, and you're just wasting your time on this estate, tinkering with silly things. Do something real. And you, Priscilla –

Priscilla: You don't have to tell me, Gran. We've all been poisoned in more ways than one.

Freya: What is all this talk? We need action!

Wisdom: Freya. You are a brave and spirited woman, and you can inspire our small band. But you are acting through envy, and malice, and resentment. Which is not the way.

Freya: People like us, and people like them can never be together!

Wisdom: No? [*Claps his hands. Enter Zoot and Jessica.*] Then you must tell that to these two. [*This has an effect on the other travellers.*] When I gave up my work with Nasty Plutonium Ltd, it was for a more simple life, and one which exploited others less, not for war.

Priscilla: Nasty Plutonium Ltd? Then you know Mr Pluto?

Wisdom: Because of that man, I came to this group of people.

Priscilla: Let me tell you two something. [*Takes Gran and Wisdom into a huddle.*]

Billy: What's going on here?

Andrew: Hang on, Dad.

Billy: Hang on?

Steve: Gran's trying to sort things out.

Billy: You mean – she's not – doolally?

Freya: What's going on, old man?

[*They come out of the huddle.*]

Gran: I reckon that should fix it nicely.

Priscilla: But you two are brilliant!

Wisdom: Your mother in law and I seem to have a certain –

Gran: Steady Wisdom. There are children present.

Wisdom: Wight family! Fellow travellers! If we forget this dispute among ourselves, tomorrow we can strike a blow against a real enemy. And without a fist raised in anger. What do you say?

Freya: Why should we?

Andrew: Why not? [*Obviously some attraction between these two.*]

Priscilla: Well, Billy?

Billy: Well what?

Priscilla: Are you going to help with this, or have another can of Scotch?

Billy: I don't understand what is going on.

Priscilla: I'll explain to you later. Meantime, let's just say richer can make you poorer. Well?

[*Billy picks up another can of beer. Takes the top off. Looks at it and then tosses it away. Family cheers, travellers cheer. All exit. Enter Mr Pluto carrying flowers. He takes a little time preening himself while he speaks.*]

Pluto: There. Everything settled. A word in the right ear, a little 'persuasion' with the appropriate authorities. And what's left? Only rumour. So a few people get ill, maybe die, a mystery bug . . . these things happen . . . two o'clock. She should be here. [*Enter Priscilla.*] Here she is. What a vision of loveliness. For you, my dear! [*Hands over the flowers.*]

Priscilla: How lovely. And how beautiful they smell.

Pluto: You are ready to go?

Priscilla: Well, not quite.

Pluto: No?

Priscilla: You are a very important man, Mr Pluto.

Pluto: This is true.

Priscilla: A very powerful man.

Pluto: Some men are born to be powerful.

Priscilla: Such an important powerful man, it must be something important that brings you all this way.

Pluto: Merely business, my dear.

Priscilla: What kind of business?

Pluto: Like I said, nothing you need worry your pretty little head about.

Priscilla: But Cornelius – I can call you Cornelius? – I don't want there to be any secrets if we are to be . . . friends.

Pluto: Or possibly more than friends?

Priscilla: Possibly. If there are no secrets.

Pluto: I really don't think that matters, my dear.

Priscilla: How can I feel close to a man who keeps secrets from me?

Pluto: [*To audience.*] I must make her mine – and yet . . . [*To Priscilla.*] Merely a small inconvenience in this area. All cleared up now.

Priscilla: An inconvenience?

Pluto: Yes.

Priscilla: [*Singing.*] 'You're my world. You're every breath I take . . .'

Pluto: Sing on! Sing on!

Priscilla: Tell me, Cornelius. Then I'll sing on.

Pluto: Yes but –

Priscilla: Just tell me

Pluto: Very well. But you must promise never ever to repeat what I am about to say. Not to anyone.

Priscilla: I promise.

Pluto: On your life and that of your family!

Priscilla: I promise on my life and the life of my family, never to repeat to anyone what you are about to tell me.

Pluto: I am here because something my company buried.

Priscilla: Buried?

Pluto: Beneath this estate, some years ago. Some toxic material. We buried it, then built the estate.

Priscilla: And?

Pluto: And now it appears to be leaking a little. What does it matter?

Priscilla: I'm still a bit confused, Cornelius. Do tell me again, simply.

Pluto: Very well. Here it is, then let's forget it. Some years ago my company, Nasty Plutonium Ltd, faced with a large amount of toxic radioactive material to dispose of, bought the land here through a subsidiary and disposed of the material as we laid the foundations for Utopia Estate. We were able to bury it under the very eyes of the authorities, and no one knew. It should have been safe but now, well, perhaps not. It appears some of that waste is seeping up through the fruit and vegetables. I have made sure that nobody will ever discover the truth.

Priscilla: Made sure?

Pluto: Not a word you understand? You swore?

Priscilla: I agree

Pluto: Important men in my position, powerful men can – influence other people.

Priscilla: Bribery?

Pluto: Whatever word you wish.

Priscilla: So you have bribed people to ignore your buried toxic waste?

Pluto: That's more or less it, my dear. It's the world. Now sing, and we'll be off. [*Starts to sing.*] 'You're my world, you're every breath I take . . .'

[*Enter Steven with the movie camera who has been filming all this. Also the Film Director.*]

Film Director: Cut!

Steven: I think that's what they call a wrap.

Film Director: Every word captured on camera.

Pluto: What? [*Enter Police Officer with handcuffs, which he clasps on Pluto.*]

Police Officer: I'm afraid you're nicked, sunshine. Good and proper.

Pluto: Treachery!

Priscilla: I'll keep my promise, Cornelius. I'll not repeat a word. Why should I? It's all on film.

Pluto: You betrayed me! [*Enter Wisdom.*]

Wisdom: Just like you and people like you have always betrayed people, Pluto. Playing with people's lives.

Pluto: Wisdom? Ha – I should have known. Look at you, a tramp!

Wisdom: Maybe. [*Enter Carstairs.*]

Carstairs: You and Nasty Plutonium betrayed me as well Pluto. You let me and other people live on Utopia Estate, knowing the dangers.

Wisdom: Fortunately, according to my calculations, things have not gone too far as yet. But the material must be contained. I have given the requirements to Steven. He says he can build an effective container.

Steven: It'll cost mind – keeping this stuff safe doesn't come cheap.

Wisdom: Total cost, including demolition of the Wight house, and relocating them to a place of their choice, about eighteen million.

[*Enter Billy and Andrew and Gran.*]

Billy: It's Gran's fault. She's persuaded me to use the Lottery money. I must be mad!

Gran: It came easy, son, it goes easy.

Wisdom: So far it has brought you only misery.

Billy: I'm not going back to Leam Lane Estate, mind. We want somewhere better than that.

Priscilla: Billy – you're sober. [*Comes over and embraces him.*]

Billy: Hadaway, man, you'll embarrass us. People are looking. [*Enter Jessica and Zoot.*]

Jess: Yes, Dad, we're looking.

Andrew: Me and Steven, Dad – we're looking too.

[*They watch as Billy kisses Priscilla back.*]

Pluto: You fools. You think you can get rid of that stuff? You think you can get rid of people like me?

Wisdom: We can only try, Pluto. [*Police Officer takes him off in handcuffs.*]

Gran: Now then, Wisdom, have you finished your calculations on that container?

Wisdom: I have, yes.

Gran: And will it work?

Wisdom: Who can tell, when humankind created such nightmares?

Gran: Well, let that Steven get on with it.

[*The glowing waste matter now reappears in the same open frame and from the same ceiling or floor as we saw in the Prologue. The sides of the container are brought in and placed in position so that the material is sealed in. The container is then lowered down the trap or raised up. Again dramatic music is used for this process, which should give an echo of the Prologue. The container slowly disappears as all watch it.*]

END OF PLAY

The World
According to Sharon

Hedworthfield School, South Shields,
September 2002

Most of the plays in this book were created as individual projects, but *Sharon* was part of a greater whole called *Aliens.* Three writers worked with different schools on South Tyneside, inspired by that general title, which could apply to non-terrestrials, immigrant workers or whatever. Kitty Fitzgerald (who organised the project) and Anne Orwin were the other practitioners, and the end product was the trio of short plays presented in one programme at The Customs House, South Shields. The project was funded by TEDCO Enterprise in Education, under the leadership of Liz White.

Creating plays gives you a licence for the imagination, so in *Sharon* we had a 'stage' alien, a ghost speaking only lines from Shakespeare, the burger man Ronald McDonald and a double-glazing entrepreneur with the wonderful name of Harry Pilchard. The eponymous Sharon dreams of escaping the drudgery of the everyday world via theatre, a dream which produces unexpected consequences. As in many of these plays we had a family unit at the centre, and though our characters were often comic caricatures, they were usually based on people from the children's own lives, again giving the plays an individual flavour.

We were lucky that the project gave the children the chance to perform in a real theatre – The Customs House, South Shields is a modern, well-equipped venue. There's a magic and a sense of self-esteem for youngsters to be operating in such a place, to have free access to those areas reserved normally for professional actors, and to sit in a dressing room or stand in the wings and feel that nervous sense of excitement as the audience gathers. It's very special.

Character List

News Vendor

Military Person

News Reader

Alien/Sharon

Drama Teacher

Elaine

Mum

Dad (*The ghost of Sharon's dad*)

Bank Manager

Supermarket Manager

Edward

McPeople

Ronald McDonald

Government Spokesperson

Harry Pilchard

Customer

Time: Present day

Location: Tyneside

THE WORLD ACCORDING TO SHARON

[*Empty stage. We hear a siren. Commotion. People run in panic down central aisle as if being pursued. Dramatic music. Once on stage people point to skies and run off. Enter News Vendor.*]

News Vendor: Extra! Extra! Alien invasion! Metro Centre occupied! Extra! [*Exit. Enter Military Person with megaphone.*]

Military Person: Do not leave your homes! We repeat, do not leave your homes! Do not panic! We repeat, do not panic! Matters will soon be under military control! Matters will soon be under military control! [*Does a bunk. Focus on News Reader.*]

News Reader: Tyneside has today been invaded by aliens. Up to fifty large silver spacecraft appeared in the skies this morning and were immediately fired on by the armed forces. The craft appeared to suffer no damage, and have now all landed in the Metro Centre, which has become their base, with the main activity seeming to be centred at Marks and Spencer. Some reports claim the aliens attempted to communicate with humans, but were met with hostile fire. We are now getting reports of a giant mothership landing on both carriageways of the Western Bypass, which will be closed to traffic until further notice. News on Newcastle United transfer latest follows shortly. [*More sirens and general mayhem. Finally a fanfare. Enter the main alien who proceeds to address the human race.*]

Alien/Sharon: It has been decided that humankind's domination over Planet Earth must now cease. The human race has shown itself incapable of managing the affairs of this planet, and the cosmic balance must be maintained. The planet has suffered severe damage: wars, pollution, exploitation, destruction of the eco-system . . . As from now, human beings will be a subservient species. Just as, until this time, cats, dogs, horses and other animals have been subservient to humans. The new order for Planet Earth will be established shortly. Go in peace. [*Drama Teacher, who is in audience, stands up.*]

Drama Teacher: Thanks very much, Sharon!

Sharon: Eh?

Drama Teacher: We'll leave it there for now. We'll try to fit in another rehearsal Friday.

Sharon: But I was just getting into it!

Drama Teacher: Sorry – School hall's booked for line dancing. Thanks everybody! [*Sharon is left alone on stage holding her alien mask. Enter Elaine.*]

Elaine: You make a great alien, Sharon.

Sharon: I know I do.

Elaine: Dead lifelike. I like being one of the panicking masses. Don't have to learn lines.

Sharon: It's funny, Elaine, when I put this mask on, it's like –

Elaine: What?

Sharon: Oh never mind.

Elaine: What about that Rob Matthews? A cracker.

Sharon: Suppose so.

Elaine: Gotta go – *Eastenders*. [*Exit. Enter Mum.*]

Mum: You're late for tea, Sharon. Been messing about acting again, I suppose. I've got some of those Kwik Save fish fingers. Guaranteed five percent fish.

Sharon: You will come and see the play, Mam?

Mum: As if I've got time for some stupid play.

Sharon: You've always got time for stupid television.

Mum: Less of the cheek. You sound just like your father.

Sharon: I wish he was still here.

[*Enter Dad. He can only be seen by Sharon.*]

Dad: 'When we are born, we cry that we are brought to this great stage of fools.'

Sharon: I mean properly around, Dad. More than just a memory.

Mum: I don't like to speak ill of the dead, Sharon, but in your father's case, I'll make an exception.

Sharon: I miss him.

Mum: Your father thought he was Laurence Olivier.

Dad: 'To be, or not to be, that is the question.'

Mum: There he was, Westerhope Amateur Dramatics. Fancied he was with the Royal Shakespeare Company. A dreamer, head in the clouds. He couldn't even mend a fuse.

Dad: Your mother's right, Sharon. I'd never knocked a nail straight in my life. Who are you in this play anyway?

Sharon: I'm the Chief Alien.

Dad: 'An actor must become the role. Every breathing living tissue, every gesture, every nuance.'

Sharon: That's the problem, Dad.

Dad: Problem?

Sharon: Sometimes the alien's more real than me.

Mum: Talking to yourself again. Now listen. My wages at the bread shop don't stretch very far.

Dad: 'Alas, now must I from this place, hence.' [*Exits.*]

Mum: Your brother Edward's contributing to the house-keeping now, and it's time you did. You'll be done with all that school soon. Time for some interviews. [*Enter Bank Manager.*]

Bank Manager: A career with International Bank offers security and, for the right applicant, excellent chances of promotion. Hours are nine to four thirty, five days a week, optional work on Saturday mornings. Dress must be smart, the company rule book must be obeyed. Employees are given twenty paid days holiday a year, plus a contributory pension scheme. There is an opportunity for fiscal, managerial and personnel training schemes. Trainers are not allowed.

Sharon: [*Adopting alien persona.*] Money-making institutions will be rendered obsolete.

Bank Manager: I beg your pardon?

Sharon: In the new order of this planet, the corrosive and destructive role of currency will be abolished.

Bank Manager: Next applicant, please. [*Exit Bank Manager.*]

Mum: So the bank turned you down?

Sharon: What? Oh – yes, I suppose they did.

Mum: Well see if you can do any better with Pricerite Supermarkets. [*Enter Supermarket Manager.*]

Supermarket Manager: An exciting career awaits new applicants with Pricerite. Staff are allowed four-minute tea breaks, and toilet visits – two per day – must not exceed one hundred and five seconds. We have a rapid-turnover situation and while conversation with check-out customers is deemed beneficial to the corporate image, these interchanges must not exceed thirty seconds, the better to facilitate point-of-sale efficiency. Staff training will consist of rapid-product identity skills, and knowledge of each product's location in the individual store.

Sharon: [*Alien persona again.*] Food is the gift of the planet, and should be made freely available to all the planet's inhabitants without recourse to the profit motive or commerce.

Supermarket Manager: Your application is for trainee sales assistant, I see? Perhaps I should acquaint you with Pricerite's activities. We are a multi-national company with annual turnover of more than £500 million, and more than 25,000 employees. Any questions?

Sharon: Of all the species of Planet Earth, only humankind required such artificial and exploitative methods of keeping its members fed or, in the case of 60 percent of its members population, hungry.

Supermarket Manager: Yes, I see. We'll let you know. [*Speaks into intercom or some such.*] Application rejected. File under subversive. [*Exit Supermarket Manager.*]

Mum: Another one you've thrown away! Why can't you be more like your brother Edward? [*Enter Edward.*]

Edward: May I be of assistance?

Mum: At least you went out and got yourself a proper job to help your poor old mum, Edward. Not like some.

Edward: At the call centre, the temperature is automatically controlled. Calls are dealt with at twenty-five per hour. All procedures are perfectly understood.

Mum: You're such a good boy, Edward.

Edward: I'm such a good boy. Hello, can I be of assistance? [*Exits.*]

Mum: See, our Sharon? I want you to get a job, I want you to keep it. I want you to have some security.

Sharon: But you don't understand me, Mam. Sometimes when I'm listening to those people, the alien takes over and –

Mum: Oh, I understand all right. You expect your mother just to keep on supporting you, and feed you and house you, and you just faff on and on. Like your father.

Sharon: It's not that, it's –

Mum: Him sitting around all day, spouting Shakespeare, and the rent still not paid. A laughing stock we were.

Sharon: I like acting, Mam.

Mum: And I like fur coats. Now I want you to get down to that new branch of McDonald's, see if there are any jobs going. [*Exit Mum. Enter three people in McDonald's uniforms.*]

[*They are doing a stylized job of slapping burgers into buns then handing them over to customers. As they do so, they have this rhythmic chant.*]

McPeople: Have a nice day! Have a nice day! Have a nice day! [*One of the three drops a burger on the floor. There is stunned silence. Enter Ronald McDonald.*]

Ronald McDonald: You have dropped a cheeseburger on the floor! A delicious unique McDonald's cheeseburger dripping with succulent tasty cheese, topped with a sun-ripe juicy tomato, a flavour-bursting dill pickle, shredded lettuce and creamy mayonnaise, on special offer with a soft drink of your choice, this week only £2.99! Get out! [*Guilty one is sacked. Immediately another one joins the line. Same ritual.*]

McPeople: Have a nice day! Have a nice day! Have a nice day! [*They exit, still chanting.*]

Ronald McDonald: [*To Sharon.*] Can I help you, young lady?

Sharon: I, er – well, that is – my mother thought there may be a job for me here.

Ronald McDonald: Are you bright? Can you show initiative? Do you know the difference between a Big Mac Special and a Premium Meal Offer? Can you ladle French fries – medium or large portions – without spillage? Can you say 'Have a nice day?'

Sharon: Well, I –

Ronald McDonald: Can you say, 'Have a Nice Day?'

Sharon: I suppose I could, that is – [*Goes into Alien.*] Part of humankind's downfall was its contamination of the planet's natural foodstuffs. Much of the planet starved, the rest gorged themselves on addictive polluted junk food.

Ronald McDonald: Can you say, 'Have a Nice Day?'

Sharon: [*Still as Alien.*] This helped them turn obese and aggressive.

Ronald McDonald: You cannot say, 'Have a Nice Day!' Application rejected. [*Exit Ronald McDonald. Enter Mum.*]

Mum: Three jobs thrown away! You're doing this on purpose, I swear.

Sharon: Mam, it's not that, it's –

Mum: Course it's not. It's all a game to you, our Sharon. Well it's not a game to me, five and a half days a week at that bread shop.

Sharon: Sometimes, Mam, it's like it's not me talking.

Mum: Is this some more nonsense?

Sharon: It's like the alien takes over.

Mum: Oh my God – what have I done to deserve this?

[*Weeps in frustration. Enter Dad.*]

Dad: 'All the world is a stage, and we are but players . . .'

Sharon: This is your fault, Dad.

Dad: 'Art begins when living itself is not sufficient for life.'

Sharon: I must have got it off you. My imagination takes over.

Dad: 'Art is ruled uniquely by the imagination.'

Sharon: That's not much good to Mam, though, is it. Look at her.

Dad: I was no good for you, man, Sharon. I'm sorry.

Sharon: I don't know what to do.

Dad: The world never knows what to do. That is why we need art, music, theatre.

Sharon: But what do I do now, Dad, this minute?

Dad: Do the play, Sharon. Do the play.

Sharon: Look, maybe I'd best just sort it out for myself.

Dad: I am to be banish-ed?

Sharon: Just go, Dad. I'm confused. [*Exit Dad.*] Mam, do you like your life?

Mum: Like it? What the hell do you think?

Dad: [*Voice off.*] Do the play!

Sharon: See you later, Mam. [*Mam exits one side, Sharon the other. Sharon re-enters, starts psyching herself up for rehearsals. Enter Elaine, watching her.*]

Elaine: What are you doing, Sharon?

Sharon: Rehearsals start in five minutes.

Elaine: You mean you don't know?

Sharon: Know what?

Elaine: You've got your head in the clouds, you. The play's cancelled.

Sharon: Cancelled?

Elaine: The drama club's been disbanded. Part of the cutbacks.

Sharon: What are you talking about?

Elaine: Part of the new National Policy apparently. [*Enter Government Spokesperson.*]

Government Spokesperson: In the current economic climate, priority must be given to core curricular activities which best equip pupils for the world of work. Vocational subjects will be given preference over such activities as art, drama and music which, in some circumstances, may have to be curtailed immediately. [*Exit Spokesperson.*]

Sharon: But what about my alien?

Elaine: Not much left of your alien now. [*Holds up an alien mask which is ripped in half.*] Don't look so upset. It was only a play. Hey, do what I did. Get yourself a lad. Look who I landed. [*Enter Edward.*] Hey Edward, what shall we do tonight?

Edward: You may choose from the following options.

Elaine: I love the way your brother talks. Fly me to the moon, Edward!

Edward: I'm sorry. That last request did not compute.

Elaine: He's a real star. And open to anything, aren't you, Edward?

Edward: You may record your message anytime.

Elaine: Love it. I'm having a ball, Sharon!

Sharon: And what about the play?

Elaine: Who needs a play, when you've got Edward? [*Enter Mum.*]

Mum: They make a lovely couple. Edward's such a hard-working boy. In ten years at that call centre he could even become a section manager.

Sharon: I want my alien back.

Mum: Now don't start with that Sharon.

Sharon: They can't just kill off my alien, like they try to kill off everything else in the world.

Mum: Sharon, you're talking nonsense. It's time you grew up.

Elaine: Time you grew up.

Edward: Grew up.

Sharon: I want my alien!

Mum: There is no alien, Sharon.

Elaine: No alien.

Edward: No alien.

Mum: But I'll tell you what there is. There's short time at the bread shop. So never mind your alien. How about getting a job?

Elaine: My friend works for Harry Pilchard's double glazing. His picture's in his firm's adverts every week in the Herald. He's a real go-getter.

[*Enter Harry Pilchard. During his speech Elaine, Mum and Edward exit.*]

Harry Pilchard: You want the best? Pilchard IS the best. Draught-free, trouble-free. Windows fitted in three days, satisfaction guaranteed. Estimates free of charge. [*Notices Sharon.*] You look like a smart girl. Smart girls can go far in this firm. Know what I mean? Make me a cup of tea, darling. And phone the wife. Tell her I'll be late. Not that she'll be bothered, the cow. New motor – what do you think? Turbo-charged, nought to sixty in five seconds. Like a bit of fun, do you? Everyone likes a bit of fun. Know what I mean? Need a new private secretary. The more private the better, get my drift? Book me a round of golf with that JP. Double-glazing. Cut-throat business. Dog-eat-dog. Survival of the fittest. That's me. Harry Pilchard. I like the top, darling. Nice bum. Get on with it.

Sharon: Hello, Mr Pilchard's secretary? One moment please. Hello, Mr Pilchard's secretary? No, I'm afraid he's in a meeting. Hello, British Airways, I'd like to book a ticket for Mr Harry Pilchard please . . . [*Enter Mum. Sharon hands over some housekeeping money.*]

Mum: I'm so proud of you, Sharon – a proper job. Look what I've got to celebrate. Sainsbury's fish fingers. Guaranteed a minimum 50 percent fish.

Sharon: Thank you, Mother. Hello, Mr Pilchard's secretary?

Mum: I'm so pleased for you, Sharon.

Sharon: Yes. Hello, Mr Pilchard's secretary? [*Enter Elaine.*]

Elaine: Great, eh, Sharon?

Sharon: Yes. Hello, Mr Pilchard's secretary? [*Enter Edward.*]

Edward: A satisfactory resolution.

Sharon: Yes. Hello, Mr Pilchard's secretary? [*Re-enter Pilchard.*]

Harry Pilchard: See this, Sharon? My own little private pad. Overlooks the Tyne. With a wife like mine, you need somewhere on your own. Know what I mean? Feel free to come any time. Great view. All the girls say so.

Sharon: I'm bored, Harry

Harry: Bored?

Sharon: Answering the phone all day. I'm wasted.

Harry: So what could you do?

Sharon: I could do anything.

Harry: So I'll promote you. How does Sales Executive sound? [*Enter Mum.*]

Mum: Sales executive?

Harry: You her mum?

Mum: Yes.

Harry: More like her sister. Sharon's a bright kid. Lots up top, if you get my meaning.

Mum: Not sure as I do.

Harry: Single parent. Hard going eh?

Mum: Her Dad's long gone.

Harry: That's men for you. Some of them. She could be out there, selling double glazing, Sharon. Do you like Italian?

Mum: Italian?

Harry: Romano's. Best tagliatelli on Tyneside. We fitted his windows. Wine? I'd go for the Valpolicelli.

Mum: You're a bit of a charmer, Mr Pilchard.

Harry: It's a lonely world, darling. And we all need some loving. Sharon, this is how it works. First out, salesmen do doorstop calls – cold canvassing. Interest? About five percent. Show them the product, warm them up. Times was you could get them to sign the contract there and then. Now the government insists on a few days to think about it. Bastards. When they've had time to think we send Sharon in, lovely, sexy, lively Sharon. Think you can do it? Course you can. Go sell some windows. [*Exit Sharon.*] Enjoy the meal, darling?

Mum: It's a long time since a man treated me like this.

Harry: Like I say – we're not all bad. I like to save the best for dessert. Know what I mean? [*Enter Sharon.*] How did you get on? [*She hands over some contracts.*] Ace. You're a natural. £100 commission on every sale. Can't be bad. Life's sweet, eh?

Mum: And I'm proud of our Sharon.

Sharon: I'm good, aren't I?

Harry: You're ace.

Sharon: When I turn it on they can't resist me.

Harry: An Oscar-winning performance.

Mum: And a new fridge-freezer for the house

Harry: Two beauties. That's what you are. To the future! [*They all drink. Enter Customer.*]

Customer: That double glazing you sold me. It's leaking.

Sharon: What?

Customer: Leaking. It fits really badly.

Harry: One minute. When did the work take place?

Customer: September of last year.

Harry: Seven months out of guarantee. Sorry.

Customer: Those windows cost me £4000!

Harry: Read the small print. Guaranteed six months.

Customer: You're a crook!

Harry: I'm a businessman.

Customer: [*To Sharon.*] Can't you do something. You talked me into it.

Sharon: Harry?

Harry: Get off my property, you miserable little wretch. [*Getting rid of Customer.*] Don't you worry your pretty little head about this, Sharon. It happens all the time.

Sharon: How do you mean?

Harry: The suckers never bother to read the small print. See, I know our windows will never go wrong before those six months are up.

Sharon: But that's –

Harry: It's the law, darling. *Caveat emptor.* Let the buyer beware.

Sharon: But they could change the law.

Harry: Let them. The Harry Pilchards of this world will always be one step ahead.

Sharon: Mother?

Harry: Your mother's fine, darling. I've just topped her up, if you know what I mean. Fancy one up the golf club later? [*Exit Harry and Mum.*]

[*Enter Elaine and Edward. Elaine proudly shows off her engagement ring.*]

Elaine: What do you think, Sharon? A hundred quid at Northern Goldsmiths.

Sharon: Elaine, the aliens are coming.

Edward: I'm sorry. That does not compute.

Elaine: You all right, Sharon? The wedding's a year next March.

Sharon: It's their time, everything will change. The aliens are coming. I know it!

Elaine: Maybe we should get a doctor, Edward.

Edward: Please select the appropriate option.

[*Enter masked Alien. Same mask as was in the play. Only Sharon can see it.*]

Sharon: So this is it then.

Alien: Soon.

Sharon: We've blown it, haven't we – us lot?

Alien: Yes.

Sharon: How will it happen?

Alien: A long peaceful sleep.

Sharon: And when we wake?

Alien: All will be different.

Elaine: Sharon – who are you talking to?

Edward: Please identify the relevant extension.

Sharon: And you chose me. To tell. Why?

Alien: You spoke to us. [*Alien removes mask, it is Dad.*]

Sharon: Dad – is it you?

Dad: Yes.

Sharon: Not the alien?

Dad: The alien too.

Sharon: But I don't understand, I mean –

Elaine: I'm really spooked now, Edward. She's lost it. Mrs Charlton! [*Enter Mum.*]

Sharon: Mother, you don't have long.

Mum: What?

Sharon: The aliens. They'll be here soon.

Mum: Oh my God, not that again. First she chucks the

job. Now this. What's the matter with your sister, Edward?

Edward: At this juncture, we have been unable to identify the source of the problem.

Sharon: You see, Dad and the aliens, all part of the same thing. Speaking to me.

Mum: Voices – she's hearing voices! I'll get some Prozac.

Sharon: And somehow Dad's become part of them.

Alien: [*With mask back on.*] We can embrace your dad. [*Halfway through the following speech, Sharon joins in with alien.*] Only a small number of humans were aware of the aliens coming. These were not the powerful and the mighty, but the often unsung. They understood what was to happen, understood their own species had failed the planet, understood that the human race would, without bloodshed, become something different. They understood how inevitable this was, just as to the rest of the human race this change seemed bewildering, inexplicable, and a course of events that has simply never crossed their minds.

Sharon: You don't have to be afraid, Mam.

Mum: What I'm afraid of is a daughter who's going bonkers. Can't you see Sharon, all this nonsense is in your imagination?

Sharon: What?

Mum: Your Dad, aliens – all made up.

Sharon: But they're here now. Dad, and the alien.

Mum: How come I can't see them? How about you, Elaine?

Elaine: I can see a brick wall.

Mum: Edward, can you see my deceased husband and some bug-eyed monster?

Edward: The question does not compute.

Mum: See? Come here, pet. Your mam'll forgive you for chucking the Pilchard job, and all the rest of the rubbish. You're my daughter. I just want you well again. We all do, don't we?

Elaine: We're just here to help Sharon. Aren't we, Edward?

Edward: Our operators can offer full assistance. Please hold.

Mum: Maybe it's my fault. Maybe I've not been fair with you. But we'll sort it out. You'll see. [*Puts her arm round Sharon. Others comfort her.*]

Edward: Please hold. Please hold. Please hold. [*Alien spreads his arms wide. The sound of warning sirens is heard.*]

END OF PLAY

Croak, The King, and a Change in the Weather

Himmeh Elementary School, Shatila, Beirut,
December 2008

This play was a somewhat different experience. The performance was outdoors, 8.30 on a Monday morning in Shatila
Palestinian Refugee Camp in the troubled Middle-Eastern
city of Beirut, Lebanon. It was performed in English by fourteen Palestinian girls aged eleven and twelve whose first
language was Arabic. It is also the only piece in this collection which is not totally original, the short play being based
on my book of the same name, published in 1997 by
Flambard and IRON Press with illustrations by Gaynor
Devaney. Simultaneous with the publication of this book, a
full-length stage version (also by me) did a six-week tour of
the North of England in a production by *Théâtre Sans*
Frontières, based in Hexham, Northumberland.

I lived in Shatila for two months in 2008, with the main
purpose of writing a book about the experience of such
extreme culture shock. *Camp Shatila – a Writer's Chronicle*
was published in 2009 by Five Leaves Publications. While
on camp I decided I'd try to create theatre with the Shatila
children. This threw up enormous cultural, administrative,
social, religious and practical problems and was probably
the hardest task I have ever undertaken in more than a
quarter of century of theatre work. By the time I'd obtained
the necessary permissions from the UN agency UNRWA,
we had a little more than a month to create and perform
a play. The children's limited English, plus ten thousand
other reasons, meant the normal process – i.e. starting with
a totally blank page – was simply unfeasible.

I decided that a shorter stage version of *Croak* might fit
the bill. Via an interpreter I related the story to the girls – it
is a fable about how the high and mighty are undone by

natural forces – and the response was enthusiastic. I went off, wrote a simplified seven-page script, which kept dialogue to a minimum, and also used movement, mime and dance. Rehearsals were bizarre. At times I was denied access to the school building. Other times hardly anyone turned up, the room was locked, or the children were inexplicably whisked away after ten minutes. At one stage it was announced that five of the cast were unable to make the dress rehearsal. All this was down to the upheavals caused by a Western playwright suddenly landing himself on a Muslim school and totally disrupting the syllabus. Luckily Himmeh School had a sympathetic head in Samiha Yazbeck, who, through all the creative chaos, kept faith in the project's value and steered me through the regularly occurring crises.

In the school playground we built a ramshackle stage from breeze blocks and hardboard, and scrounged sound equipment from a Beirut retailer. The school's art teacher, with no budget, made some ingeniously striking costumes; props were cobbled together by other members of staff.

One remarkable incident occurred towards the end of rehearsals. In the original published story (and the full-length play), the spoilt and greedy King and his sidekick Croak both perish at the hands of the same natural forces they foolishly believed they could control. Via the head teacher Samiha, the children requested that these two characters should be saved and given a second chance. And this from a refugee camp whose blood-splattered history is one of violence, death and retribution. We incorporated the changes into the play.

On a bright December morning we gave two performances in the playground, the first for the school pupils, the second for the intrigued if slightly bemused Shatila camp residents, most of whom (like the children) had absolutely no previous experience of theatre. In 2009 we brought the production, with the same cast, to the North-East of England for eight performances; one critic hailed it as 'Outstanding – a truly humbling experience' (*Shields Gazette*). In Spring 2011, a revised version, with live musicians, a choreographer, and a new male and female cast, was first produced at Theatre Monnot, Beirut, before touring the UK with performances at two Tyneside theatres, plus venues in Liverpool and Edinburgh. At present a Shatila Trust is being established with the object of creating further cultural interchanges between Shatila Camp and artists from the North-East of England. Throughout the Shatila experience my mantra was the quotation of the late Palestinian academic and writer, Edward Said: 'not the culture of power, but the power of culture.'

Character List

Narrator

King

Queen

Croak

The Girl

The Wind *(non-speaking)*

The Sun *(non-speaking)*

Servant One

Servant Two

Servant Three

Servant Four

Five Royal Soldiers *(non-speaking)*

Time: As appropriate

Location: The Land Where Nothing Has Ever Changed

Music Used in this Production:

Beethoven's Sixth Symphony (Pastoral)

'Just to Play' by Midnight Movies

'The Life Song' adapted from 'Every Time We Touch',
by Carly Simon

CROAK, THE KING, AND A
CHANGE IN THE WEATHER

[*Music. Enter the Narrator.*]

Narrator: Ladies and gentlemen, welcome to our little play! [*More music.*] Which includes [*introduces in turn*] the palace servants! [*Enter, stand to one side in line.*] The Royal Soldiers! [*March on, march off.*] The Queen! [*Same.*] Croak! [*Same.*] The girl! [*Same.*] And the King! [*Enter King. Stays Centre Stage.*] Now this King was very rich and very greedy. Everything the King wanted was brought to the palace for him. [*King now calls for and is provided with, in turn, the following, or services thereto.*]

King: My fan! My fingernails! My hair! My grapes! My cloak! My crown! My throne! [*Sits in the same.*]

Narrator: The King had never been outside the palace, and knew nothing of the poor people out there who provided him with all his luxuries.

King: Poor people? Ha ha, ha ha!

Narrator: The King's deputy was called Croak. [*Enter Croak.*] He was very sly and very nasty. Croak was very polite to the King, but very nasty to the servants. [*Croak does this.*] The Queen also lived in the palace. She was very sad and dreamed of living somewhere else. [*Enter Queen, who passes along line of servants who reach out to her. One brings on throne next to King, which she sits on.*] One day the King called for his midday meal of roast deer, hunted by the royal dogs. [*Enter servants bearing empty plates, which the king looks at.*]

King: Croak – where is my roast deer? [*Croak examines the plate then questions the servants. Slaps them and then* *dismisses them.*]

Croak: There has been some snow, Your Majesty.

King: Snow? What is snow?

Narrator: Outside the palace for the very first time it had snowed, and covered up the scent of the deer, which the royal dogs could not now hunt. No one in the palace had ever seen snow. The King told Croak to get rid of it, and Croak ordered the royal soldiers to do it. [*Soldiers now take wheelbarrows and shovels and go from the palace to get rid of the snow.*]

Narrator: No matter how much the soldiers cleared, there was always more snow. And then it snowed again. [*More snow. Exit soldiers.*]

King: I want my roast deer! Who can get rid of the snow? [*Enter Girl.*]

Girl: I can get rid of the snow. If I do it, will you give me a reward?

King: Yes, yes, now do it!

Narrator: The girl was a friend of the sun, and called on the sun to melt all the snow! [*Enter the Sun, which melts the snow. Girl returns to the King.*]

Girl: Where is my reward?

King: Reward? Reward? Reward? Bring on my roast deer! [*Servants do so. King eats.*] Throw this girl out, Croak! [*Girl seeks Queen's protection but Croak throws her out.*]

Narrator: The next day, the King called for his evening meal of baked pheasant shot from the skies by the Royal Archers. [*Croak instructs servants to bring it on. The plates are empty.*]

King: Croak, where is my baked pheasant? [*Croak asks the servants, who tell him. Croak hits them.*]

Croak: There has been – fog, Your Majesty.

King: Fog? Fog? What is fog?

Narrator: No one had ever seen fog. But now it had come, and the Royal Archers could not see the pheasants in the sky to shoot them down, so there was no evening meal for the King.

King: Croak! Get rid of this fog! [*Croak now sends the soldiers out with jam jars, with which they try to trap the fog.*]

Narrator: No matter how many jam jars the soldiers filled there was still more fog.

King: I want my baked pheasant! Why is this happening, Croak? And who will rid me of this fog! [*Enter the Girl.*]

Girl: I will. If you promise to give me a reward.

King: Yes, yes, yes, yes!

Girl: You promise?

King: Yes, yes, yes – just do it!

Narrator: The girl was a great friend of the wind. And when she called on the wind, it blew and blew and soon all the fog was gone. [*Wind comes and get rids of the fog. Girl goes back to the King.*]

Girl: My reward please, Your Majesty. [*Enter servants with pheasant.*]

King: My baked pheasant! [*Starts eating.*]

Girl: My reward please, Your Majesty.

King: Reward? Throw her out, Croak! [*Girl appeals to the Queen who cannot help her. Croak throws her out.*]

Narrator: The next morning the King prepared for his Royal bath. [*Enter King, also Croak and servants with towels etc. King tries to get into bath but there is no water.*]

King: No water, Croak! There is no water, Croak! Where is the water?

[*Croak asks the servants, then hits them.*]

Croak: There is ice, Your Majesty.

King: Ice? Ice? What is ice?

Narrator: The Royal Lake had frozen and turned to ice. There was no water for the Royal bath. No one had ever seen ice. The King wanted the ice gone.

King: Get rid of the ice, Croak! Now! [*Croak instructs the soldiers to go out. They go to the lake, kneel down and breathe on the ice. It makes no difference.*]

King: The King must have his Royal bath! You have failed, Croak! Who can get rid of this ice? [*Enter the Girl.*]

Girl: I can get rid of the ice, Your Majesty.

King: Good! Do it!

Girl: But you must reward me. And you must not trick me a third time.

King: Yes! Yes! Just do it!

Narrator: So the girl called on her friend the Sun again. And the Sun melted all the ice. [*Enter sun. Melts the ice.*]

King: Hurray! My bath! [*The King starts bathing. His servants help. Enter the Girl.*]

Girl: Where is my reward?

King: What? Oh, throw her out, Croak! I'm bathing!

Narrator: But this time, Croak decided they should get rid of the girl. She was too powerful. He persuaded the King to chop off her head, the next morning at dawn. [*Croak talks to King.*]

King: Yes! Yes! Lock her up! Then chop off her head!

[*The Girl again appeals to the Queen, who does her best to protect her. But the King and Croak get the servants to take the Girl and put her in the palace dungeons and the King gets on with his bathing. Night time. The Girl is in the prison. The Queen enters with a key with which she unlocks the cell door.*]

Queen: Go from this terrible place.

Girl: They must be punished – both of them.

Queen: I know. Now go!

[*The Girl makes her way through the corridors of the palace and escapes. She now does a dance to summon up the powers of nature and exits. Next morning, enter servants rushing about.*]

Servant One: The snow!

Servant Two: The fog!

Servant Three: The ice!

Servant Four: The sun!

Servant One: The wind!

Servant Two: The girl! [*Enter King and Croak.*]

King: My roast deer! [*Croak cannot help.*] My baked pheasant! [*Again.*] My Royal bath! [*Again.*] The girl! [*We see empty cell.*] Fetch the girl!

Narrator: But the girl was nowhere to be found. And there was no deer, no pheasant, no bath. Only snow and fog and ice. [*Servants and soldiers can do nothing. The King gets angry with Croak.*]

King: You have failed, Croak! Failed!

Narrator: But the Queen had a clever plan.

Queen: Who is the most powerful person in the land?

King: I am.

Queen: Who controls everything?

King: I do.

Queen: Who is the only person who can get rid of the snow, the fog and the ice?

King: Me!

Queen: Then go out there and do it.

King: Yes! Get ready Croak!

Narrator: Croak did not want to go outside the palace gates, where they had never been. But the King's mind was made up.

King: Open the Royal Gates! [*These are opened. The King and Croak pick a shovel and jam jar each and go into the outside world. Movements now choreographed to music as they try to get rid of first the snow then the fog then the ice. When they are attempting to do the last, the Sun emerges and begins to melt the ice, and the water begin to rise. At the moment they are about to drown, the Narrator enters.*]

Narrator: We, the children of of Shatila, have decided that the King and Croak should be allowed to live, and be given another chance. [*Waters are now lowered. Enter all cast, bring up music for the play's finale.*]

END OF PLAY

Triple Act

Star of the Sea RC Primary School, Whitley Bay,
December 2009

One important source of funding for longer-term drama
projects in schools has been the agency Creative Partnerships,
which, by the time this book is published, will probably
exist no more, given the recent slash-and-burn government
policy towards such valuable social and cultural institutions.
I was invited by Elaine Beard, Creative Partnerships agent
and joint-founder of Dodgy Clutch Theatre Productions, to
create a play with Star of the Sea. I'd worked with Dodgy
Clutch a good deal over the years, nearly always with children's theatre, and two of their practitioners, Adam and Sara
Riley, were on board for this project. Adam rigged our
lighting and Sara made props and sets with the children.

Star of the Sea is a Catholic school, and the play we
produced was due for performance as part of the school's
Advent evening in Saint Edward's Church, Whitley Bay, some
relevance to Christmas was requested. As a lapsed Catholic
and now an agnostic, I wondered if the nature of the school
or location might have a restraining influence on how the
piece evolved. Not so. Head teacher Mike Willcock has a
big commitment to the creative arts (the excellent choir is
much in demand for concerts), and there was never a hint
that the play should in any way be vetted. The piece opens
with a frenetic cops-and-robbers chase up and down the
church aisles, which raised a few eyebrows in the packed
pews. Mike asked for just one change to the script, that
of 'bent' copper to 'crooked' copper. This seemed reasonable. Catholicism did have an influence, though, in that the
play made animate the powers of good and evil, one of
the main thrusts being the central character's dilemma in
choosing between the two. We all know the devil often gets

the best tunes, which may not be fair but makes for interesting drama.

Our heroine Florrie, the only girl in her class without a new mobile phone, comes across a bag of stolen loot dumped by a fleeing burglar. Does she hand it in, or use it to buy the much sought-after mobile? Enter those same good and evil powers (which we called Lionel and Cyril), representing her good and evil sides, one at each of Florrie's shoulders tugging her first one way, then the other. Sometimes the two fight it out as our young heroine goes through her personal journey of discovery. Plays for young people can look at serious issues while having a lot of fun, and this *was* a lot of fun. The Year Five children were enthusiastic and as bright as buttons.

Creating a play with youngsters is an unpredictable affair, and you rely greatly on the allotted teacher. If the attitude is restrictive or over-authoritarian, it rubs off on the pupils, and making the play can prove a nightmare. I was lucky at Star of the Sea to have Mary Cave. Mary kept a firm hand on the tiller, but nurtured and encouraged the children's efforts with a humour and enthusiasm that helped us build up a real creative head of steam. Allow me to quote two illuminating examples.

In the first get-together, I talked about original ideas for plays and how they might come about: characters, plots, locations, themes etc. I asked for suggestions and scribbled each one on a large sheet of paper, which was then stuck on the wall. After two hours no fewer than fourteen separate plot lines had been proposed and the room was fully papered!

Two days before opening, I decided on a 'speed run'. In this, the actors sit in a circle and deliver at high speed the entire script, without any of the usual reminders that comes from being on stage. If actors can negotiate a speed run, they're on top of their scripts. Here something remarkable happened. It soon became obvious that every one of the twenty characters knew their own part word-perfect. But there was more. A few minutes in, characters began joining in with other characters, reciting their lines as well as their own. By halfway through the play every youngster in that circle of actors was chanting the script. Never in a quarter century of working with professional, amateur and youth theatres have I experienced the like. Every actor could recite every single line of the play.

Triple Act played to a packed church, and like most plays in this book there was a sadness when it was so quickly over. Yet when planning this book, the publishers and I thought it a good idea if one piece could be reprised to mark publication. In the case of Star of the Sea the original cast were still there in the summer term 2011, and more than eager to do an encore. This took place at the school in July.

Character List

Mum

Dad

Florrie

Pyeclet (the dog)

Tracey

Jake

Lionel – *Florrie's conscience (negative)*

Cyril – *Florrie's conscience (positive)*

Nicket

Police Officer One

Police Officer Two

Police Officer Three

Sharon

Joe

Jack

Duane

Santa Claus

Shop Assistant One

Shop Assistant Two

Shop Assistant Three

Shop Assistant Four

The play takes place on Tyneside, present day

TRIPLE ACT

[*A whistle blows at the back of the audience. Shouts of 'stop thief!'. Along comes Nicket, the burglar, with a bundle of money pursued by three police officers. A bit of a chase around during which Nicket realises the game is up if he/ she is caught with the loot, and unseen by the police officers hides it somewhere. Nicket now walks off and is pulled in by the police officers.*]

Police Officer One: Right, where is it?

Nicket: Where's what?

Police Officer Two: Don't play games – that money you stole from that shop till!

Nicket: Don't know what you're talking about.

Police Officer Three: We know you, Nicket. Come clean!

Nicket: About what?

Police Officer One: Right – you're coming with us!

Police Officer Two: We'll get to the bottom of this!

Police Officer Three: You're nicked Mr, Nicket! [*Exit all three. Enter our heroine Florrie with her pet dog Pyeclet, which sniffs about in the area of the loot.*]

Florrie: If only I could afford one of those new iPhones, Pyeclet. Everyone else at school is getting one. It's not fair! [*Notices dog sniffing.*] What is it, Pyeclet? A bone? [*Pyeclet shakes its head.*] A rabbit? [*Again.*] A rat? [*Same.*] Let's have a look then eh? [*Finds the money. Counts it.*] £250, Pyeclet! That would solve all my problems! But it's not mine. What do I do? Maybe I'll ask my mam and dad. Come on, Pyeclet! [*Exit both. We go into main area, which* *is the house interior. Enter Dad who switches on the TV for the football. Sits down. Reacts to TV.]*

Dad: Come on, son! Pass it, son! Out to the right, out to the right! [*Enter Florrie and Pyeclet.*]

Florrie: Dad, I found this money in the street. £250! That would buy me that brand new top-of-the-range-phone I've been dreaming of. Should I keep it? What do you think?

Dad: [*Only has eyes for football. Wears giant spectacles.*] Offside by a mile, ref! Oh come on, you need glasses, man!

Florrie: Thanks, Dad. [*Enter Mum. She is painting her oversized fingernails and talking to herself.*]

Mum: So I sez to her, I sez, if you think I'm paying that much, you must be crackers, I sez. And she sez to me, well, she sez –

Florrie: I found this large amount of money, Mam. It's really tempting to keep it –

Mum: As for that other one, well, I sez, I wouldn't touch her with a bargepole, her and that fancy man of hers! Eh, I hope this new nail varnish doesn't chip!

Florrie: Or do I have to give it back?

Mum: It was recommended by that *Britain's Got Talent* singer, so it should be good!

Florrie: Thanks, Mam. [*Enter brother Jake playing his Game Boy.*]

Jake: Gerrin! Gerrin! Gerrin! Gerrin!

Florrie: Maybe my big brother can help. Jake, is it wrong to keep money you find in the street? Even a big amount?

Jake: [*Totally absorbed by Game Boy.*] Gerrin! Gerrin!

Gerrin! Gerrin!

Florrie: I mean, it's not like I know whose it is –

Jake: Gerrin! Gerrin! Gerrin!

Florrie: Thanks, Jake . . . [*Enter sister Tracey, talking into her mobile.*]

Tracey: Her? Leave it out? Donna? Nah! Karen? Doubt it! Yeah, yeah, whatever!

Florrie: Tracey, what would my big sister do with the money? Keep it, or hand it in?

Tracey: See you five o'clock then. Grey's Monument. Yeah. Nah, don't bring Kevin. He's a no-no.

Florrie: Finders keepers – is that alright?

Tracey: 'Cos I say he is, that's why. Yeah, see you! [*Walks off.*]

Florrie: Thanks Tracey. So what am I supposed to do with this money? [*Enter Lionel, stage left.*]

Lionel: Spend it. You want to be a loser all your life? [*Enter Cyril, stage right.*]

Cyril: It's not yours. So give it back.

Lionel: How else are you ever going to get that iPhone?

Cyril: Don't listen to him. Hand the money in.

Lionel: Yeah, so some crooked copper can have two weeks on the Costa Brava! Don't be an idiot.

Florrie: Hang on, who are you two?

Cyril: The name's Cyril.

Lionel: Lionel. We're part of you.

Cyril: Your conscience you might say. See, you're growing up. So you start making big decisions for yourself.

Lionel: Except if you listen to him, you'll have nowt. Stick with me, kid.

Cyril: Stick with him, and you have to live with being a thief.

Lionel: You also live with 250 beautiful smackeroonies!

Florrie: Is this some sort of joke?

Lionel: No joke. Watch this. [*Stands in front of TV.*]

Dad: [*Who clearly cannot see him.*] Get it up the field, Ameobi, man!

Cyril: Or this. [*Makes faces at Mum still doing her nails. She can see nothing.*]

Mum: So I sez to her, I sez, don't you take that tone with me, I sez –

Florrie: They really can't see you!

Lionel: Smart, eh?

Cyril: Sooner or later, everyone gets to meet us.

Lionel: And everyone listens to one of us. Generally, it's me. I'm more – persuasive, let's say. Seen my list of clients? Politicians, industrialists, bankers – very impressive! As for him, he's got losers like Mother Theresa, Nelson Mandela. Yuk!

Florrie: You're not real then?

Lionel: Real?

Cyril: We're real right enough. Take a look at the world around you.

Lionel: You'll see how real we are. Anyway, this £250. You're not really thinking of handing it in are you?

Cyril: Stolen money will never make you happy, Flo.

Lionel: She never stole it, dumbo – she found it!

Cyril: Someone's lost it, somewhere.

Lionel: So? Someone's been run over by a bus *somewhere* – big deal!

Cyril: Why don't you just –

Lionel: Yeah? [*They square up and start grappling. Florrie pulls them apart.*]

Florrie: Stop arguing, you two! I'm confused! And I'm tired. I want to go to bed.

Lionel: So what about us?

Florrie: Just clear off.

Cyril: Flo, listen –

Florrie: No, I've had enough for now. Goodnight! [*Exit Lionel and Cyril. Florrie goes to bed. Sleeps. Wakes the next morning. Looks around but no sign of Lionel and Cyril. Checks. She still has the £250. Eats a bowl of cereal. Enter Mum.*] Morning, Mum.

Mum: If I cash in these vouchers at Netto, that'll save me £2.65, and – [*Exit Florrie. Enter Dad, reading newspaper.*]

Florrie: Morning, Dad.

Dad: Change the name of the ground? They can't change the name of the ground, not St. James' Park! [*Exit Dad. Enter Jake on Game Boy.*]

Florrie: Morning, Jake.

Jake: Gerrin! Gerrin! Gerrin! Gerrin! [*Exit Jake. Enter Tracey reading Hello magazine.*]

Florrie: Morning, Tracey

Tracey: Katie Price has written another novel – the second this week! [*Exit Tracey. Florrie shrugs her shoulders and makes her way to school. Enter Sharon.*]

Sharon: This iPhone's great. Plays music and everything! [*Enter Joe.*]

Joe: Seen this one? All these free games! [*Enter Jack.*]

Jack: It's mint this iPhone – gets you straight onto YouTube! [*Enter Duane.*]

Duane: You just touch the screen – everything you want! [*To Florrie.*] Where's your iPhone?

Sharon: Yes, where's yours?

Joe: Where's yours?

Jack: Where's yours?

All: Where's yours? [*Enter Lionel.*]

Lionel: Yeah, where *is* yours, Flo? Top of the range iPhone – that would put this lot in their place! Got the £250 there, have you?

Florrie: Yeah. [*Shows it.*]

Lionel: Then come with me. [*Enter Cyril.*]

Cyril: It's a trap, Flo – ignore him!

Lionel: This way Flo. [*Florrie hesitates, then goes with Lionel who leads her into phone shop where Shop Assistant One is standing by.*]

Shop Assistant One: You want something cheap, do you?

Florrie: What?

Shop Assistant One: You look like you could only afford a cheap phone

Florrie: Oh yeah? What's your most expensive iPhone?

Shop Assistant One: £250 – why?

Florrie: Show it to me. [*Waves money.*]

Shop Assistant One: [*Impressed.*] Oh, yes, right. [*Produces*

phone. While Florrie looks at it another customer enters and Assistant tends to him/her.]

Lionel: Just take it.

Florrie: What?

Lionel: The phone, walk out with it. He's not looking.

Florrie: Steal it, you mean?

Lionel: Phone shops – they make a fortune. One phone less, they'll hardly notice.

Cyril: No! That's out-and-out thieving!

Lionel: Shut your face. Pick it up, Flo, then you've got the phone and still got the money!

Cyril: Flo, you mustn't –

Lionel: Shut it! [*Pushes him away.*] Now, Flo, now! Before he comes back!

Florrie: I'm not sure, I –

Lionel: NOW! [*Florrie grabs the phone and they run out of the shop. Outside they start laughing.*] Great! Proud of you!

Florrie: It was dead easy!

Lionel: Course it was! There's plenty more things too!

Cyril: Flo, you can't just take things and –

Lionel: I told *you* to shut it!

Florrie: Yeah, that's right, shut it! [*They both push Cyril away. Exit all. Music.*]

[*Enter Lionel and Florrie.*]

Lionel: All those suckers, getting up every day to go to those miserable jobs, scrimping and saving, and it's all there just waiting for you to take it! Try this jeweller's shop! [*They go into jewellers.*]

Shop Assistant Two: What would madam require? A diamond? A ruby? A sapphire?

Florrie: [*Waves money.*] I'd like to see the really expensive range you keep in the back.

Shop Assistant Two: Certainly, madam. One moment [*Goes to back. Florrie robs shop. Assistant emerges.*] Hey! Come back.

Lionel: How about a new bike, to keep you fit? [*Goes into bike shop. Waves money.*]

Florrie: Could I just try this one?

Shop Assistant Three: Of course, madam, give it a spin outside. [*Florrie rides off on bike.*] Come back here, you cheeky monkey.

Lionel: Digital camera?

Florrie: You're on! [*Goes into camera shop. Waves money.*] Show me the latest models please.

Shop Assistant Four: Certainly, madam. This is a very popular model. [*Produces camera.*]

Florrie: I'd just like to see it in the natural light if I may.

Shop Assistant Four: Step outside for a moment, if you wish. [*Florrie does so. Runs off.*] Hey, come back here! [*Florrie is up a height. Enter Cyril.*]

Cyril: Stop now, Flo, while you still can –

Lionel: You're looking a bit sickly, Cyril. Maybe you should just rest up a bit. [*Shoves him away.*] Not sure Flo has much use for you anymore anyway. Is that right, Flo?

Florrie: Yeah, I mean – [*Moves towards Cyril But Lionel pulls her away.*]

Lionel: Don't be a loser! Right?

Florrie: Right.

Lionel: Cracking. Keep up the good work.

Cyril: Please, Flo . . .

Lionel: [*Mimicks.*] '*Please, Flo . . .*' Get lost, wimp! Tell him!

Florrie: [*After hesitation.*] Get lost – wimp!

Lionel: That's my girl! Learning fast! Well, things to do. See you soon! [*Exit. Cyril now pulls a confused Santa Claus on stage.*]

Santa Claus: Hey, what the big idea?

Cyril: If you won't listen to me, Flo, listen to him! You're short of presents for the poor children this year aren't you, Santa?

Santa Claus: Yes, that's right. Someone keeps stealing them from the shops, but I don't see what –

Cyril: This is her – the thief.

Santa Claus: This young girl? It can't be!

Cyril: Tell him, Flo, tell him just how many presents you've stolen.

Florrie: It's nothing to do with him, or you. Get away

Santa Claus: You, stealing Santa's presents? Is it true? You? Taking the joy away from little children?

Florrie: I'm not feeling well. Get away! [*Pushes Santa offstage.*]

Cyril: You still won't listen to me. Then how about this one . . . [*Enter Nicket, escorted by three police officers.*]

Police Officer One: OK, so maybe we didn't find the money, but there were enough witnesses to send you down, Nicket!

Police Officer Two: Eighteen months, that what the judge said.

Police Officer Three: And eighteen months is what you'll serve.

Nicket Another Christmas spent in the nick! Away from me kids. And the plum pud's horrible in Dartmoor!

Police Officer One: You should have thought of that before you chose a life of crime.

Nicket: Yeah, well, I didn't, did I? You never do.

Police Officer Two: More's the pity. Take a good look around, Nicket.

Police Officer Three: It's the last you'll see of the outside for a long time! [*Leads him off.*]

Florrie: They wouldn't put me in jail!

Cyril: Why not? You're a common thief.

Florrie: Shut up! Shut up! I feel unwell. I'm going home.

Cyril: Yes, why don't you just do that? [*Goes home, followed by Cyril. Mum, Dad, Jake and Tracey are there. Florrie enters.*]

Florrie: Mam! Dad! Tracey! Jake! [*Reaches out to them and faints. One by one they approach.*]

Mum: Eeeh, Flo!

Dad: What's the matter with her?

Jake: She's fainted!

Tracey: Why?

Mum: Best get her to her room.

Dad: Suppose so. C'mon you two. [*All help to get Florrie to her bedroom, where they discover a huge pile of stolen goods.*]

Mum: Eeeh, look at that!

Dad: Where did our Florrie get all that lot? [*Florrie awakes.*]

Florrie: I stole it.

Tracey: Stole it?

Jake: All that lot?

Mum: What for?

Florrie: I don't know. I tried to tell you!

Dad: Did you?

Florrie: You wouldn't listen – any of you!

Mum: Wouldn't we?

Florrie: You've never listened to me! Ever!

Dad: Have we not?

Mum: Is that why you stole all this lot?

Florrie: No, I – I mean yes, I – I mean . . . [*Bursts into tears. Enter Lionel.*]

Lionel: What's this? Weakness? [*Enter Cyril.*]

Cyril: No. Just being human.

Florrie: Mam, I love you! Dad!

Dad: Blimey!

Florrie: I've always loved you, but –

Tracey: Maybe give her a cuddle eh, Mam?

Mum: You think so?

Jake: Maybe Tracey's right. A cuddle. [*Dad takes off his giant glasses. Mam puts down her nail varnish. Jake puts down his Game Boy. Tracey puts down her mobile. Slowly they move towards Florrie.*]

Lionel: Hang on – this is wrecking everything!

Cyril: Eh, you? Shut it! [*Bit by bit the family come to Florrie and cuddle her.*]

Mum: But, Flo, what about all this lot? [*Enter Santa Claus.*]

Santa Claus: Just leave this lot to me.

Dad: Blimey – so he *is* real!

Florrie: Maybe you can sort this out as well, Mr Claus? [*Hands over the money.*]

Santa Claus: No problem! I'll see it's returned. Well, busy time, things to do – tara! [*Exits.*]

Tracey: Eh, Flo, I do like your hair. When did you have that done?

Florrie: About a year ago.

Tracey: I never noticed!

Mum: Me neither.

Florrie: Well, you've noticed now. That's the main thing.

Lionel: Yuk! Happy families – it's enough to make you sick.

Cyril: Why don't you go and make trouble somewhere else?

Lionel: That's exactly what I'll do. Like I always have done. Like I always will do. You haven't heard the last of me. *Ever!* [*Exits.*]

Cyril: I've got somewhere to go too.

Florrie: If it wasn't for you, Cyril –

Cyril: Never mind all that. I think there's someone wants to talk to me.

Dad: Who's that then?

Cyril: A certain Mr Nicket. Bye! [*Exits.*]

END OF PLAY AND CURTAIN CALL

MUSIC AND ALL CAST DANCE

Sausages and Circuses

Spring Gardens Primary School, North Shields,
March 2010

The way this play came about was slightly odd. One of the Spring Gardens School pupils, Liam Office, won a poetry competition run by the Northumbria Association – and a fine poem it was too. The prize went to the school itself and it provided funding to work with a writer on a creative-writing project of the school's choice. The pupils had recently seen my Palestinian play *Croak, The King, and a Change in the Weather*, and, showing great taste and discernment, plumped for me. I made an appointment with the head, Stephen Baines, to discuss the project, which we did, while simultaneously listening to the exciting climax of an Ashes test. Men can multi-task too. England won.

Another odd aspect at Spring Gardens was that Class 13 (which led us to call the theatre group *Lucky 13*) included only two girls but more than twenty boys – a statistical freak which led to a fair bit of cross-dressing in the play. Sometimes it's good to use the pupils' own talents as a starting point. Our numbers included one boy, Angus Davidson, who loved break-dancing and a girl, Abbie Reid, with a talent for gymnastics.

Embracing these talents helped shape the plot line. This concerns a boy, Jake, who runs away to join a circus only to discover it is shortly to be shut down by the bank. With the help of his grandad, a one-time circus juggler, Jake manages to outwit the heartless bankers and keep the circus open. I was pleased with the play, as we managed to embrace the current financial crisis and also attitudes to the elderly in a storyline that allowed us a lot of fun, not only with our acrobat (Rubberene in the play) and break-dancer (Bodypoppa) but also a strong man, a tightrope walker, a juggler, and a clown, so that the piece put many demands on the young cast. This was probably the most physical piece of theatre of all eight. Plus which, learning to juggle in a few weeks, then needing to do it in front of a live theatre audience, takes a bit of nerve. And we had a huge cast of thirty-four! Of which nineteen were speaking parts.

It was often a challenging journey at Spring Gardens, and several of the young actors went through minor crises in attempting to come to terms with their roles. There were occasional tears from the cast, and teacher Deborah Wilson and I suffered an occasional bumpy ride in the struggle to reconcile different attitudes towards presenting theatre. This is one risk of such ventures, and the well-worn but true maxim, 'the play's the thing', is always worth remembering. Ultimately we all *did* serve the play, and the two performances (at the school itself) went down splendidly, so much so that The Northumbria Association plan to repeat the project in 2011 with Ravensworth Primary School in Birtley, Gateshead.

Character List

Mum (Margaret)

Dad (George)

Grandad (Harry)

Grandma (Bella)

Wheelo, the Unicyclist
(*non-speaking*)

Darren

Lucy

Binky, the Clown
(*non-speaking*)

Bodypoppa,
the Street Dancer
(*non-speaking*)

Jake

Teacher

Milk

Trumpet

Gurgle

Shoulder

Dipstick

Chicken

Fizzle

Big Hat

Pelican

Circus Master

Circus Audience (four)
(*non-speaking*)

Drummer
(*non-speaking*)

Weight Carriers (three)
(*non-speaking*)

Carl, the Crusher,
Strong Man
(*non-speaking*)

Tightrope Tommy
(*non-speaking*)

Rubberene, the Acrobat
(*non-speaking*)

Bojangles, the Juggler
(*non-speaking*)

Circus Owner

Banker

Bank Employee
(*non-speaking*)

Time: Present Day

Locations: The Lawson kitchen, the school, the circus

SAUSAGES AND CIRCUSES

Scene One

[*The family living room, breakfast time. Mum is busy at the cooker, but also grooming herself, holding her hand mirror. Enter Dad.*]

Dad: No burnt sausages, mind.

Mum: What?

Dad: Yesterday's sausage was as black as coal.

Mum: What?

Dad: If you stopped looking in that mirror, we might get our sausages a bit quicker. [*Sits down. Enter Grandad with a stick.*]

Grandad: Did someone say sausages?

Dad: Here comes the ancient relic.

Mum: Don't be rude to my father, George.

Dad: If you'd only put him in a home, where he belongs, I'd be as nice as pie to him. [*Grandad sits down. Enter Grandma.*]

Grandma: Cooey!

Dad: You could stick her in a home and all.

Grandma: Morning, everybody!

Grandad: I once had a tasty sausage when the circus was in Bridlington!

Dad: Oh no, not more tales of the Big Top . . .

Mum: You know how much Dad likes remembering his

175

circus days.

Grandad: We had this unicyclist called Wheelo! [*Enter Wheelo to do his act and exits. Grandma sits down. Mum meantime has been neglecting the frying pan for her mirror.*]

Dad: Do we get to eat these sausages this year or next?

Mum: Sorry, just checking this anti-ageing cream.

Dad: Let me have a look. [*Examines her face.*] It doesn't work. [*Mum attends to sausages.*] Where are those children of ours? It's time they were at school. Jake! Darren! Lucy! [*Enter Darren. Likes to think he's a rock musician. Plays air guitar.*]

Dad: Look at the state of him.

Darren: It's cool, man – my favourite riff.

Dad: Riff? What's a riff when it's at home? Will these sausages be much longer? I've got a hardware shop to run, in case you've forgotten. [*Enter Lucy.*]

Lucy: We haven't forgotten, Dad – how could we? [*Quotes sarcasticly.*] 'Lawson's Hardware Store' – *The coast's biggest stock of plastic flanges!*

Dad: *And* three-centimetre rubber washers!

Lucy: Whatever . . .

Dad: Your dad's a successful businessman. You should be proud of that.

Grandad: Then there was Binky, the Clown! [*Enter Binky with a pie on a plate. Looks as if he's about to shove it in someone's face, but Grandad shakes his head and Binky exits.*]

Grandad: And I remember that Bodypoppa – what a street dancer! [*Enter Bodypoppa. Does his stuff. Exits.*]

Dad: Yes, well, I've got more important things than circuses to worry about.

Grandma: No sausages for me.

Mum: No?

Grandma: I'm going out. There's a rally on. [*Puts on motorbike helmet and walks out.*]

Dad: It's time she grew up. They'd both be happier in an old people's home. [*Enter Jake.*]

Jake: Grandad, tell me again about the circus fire-eater, Inferno!

Grandad: Inferno could blow fire the length of a bus, or the height of a house!

Jake: And what about the human cannon ball, Plumbum?

Grandad: They could shoot Plumbum so high, he'd hit the roof of the Big Top!

Dad: Filling the lad's mind with rubbish. Where's his head for business? You've got to have a head for business!

Grandad: If only I hadn't fallen off that high wire. That was me, finished.

Dad: Good job too. Jake needs to get a nice steady job. Like in a bank.

Jake: A bank?

Dad: Yes, a bank.

Grandad: I was a plate spinner too, and a juggler – I loved juggling!

Dad: Where *are* those blooming sausages? [*Looks at Mum, who is checking her nails.*]

Mum: Coming up! [*Darren does his air-guitar bit again. Starts singing. He's terrible.*]

Darren: Whoa . . . whoa . . . whoa . . . whoa . . .

Dad: Somebody save us . . .

Mum: Does this mascara make me look like a film star?

Dad: Yes, Godzilla. Where are those sausages!

Mum: Any minute!

Jake: Bet I could learn to juggle.

Dad: Pass me that newspaper, Jake. I need to check if Lawson's advert is printed correctly. [*Jake picks up newspaper. Spots something.*]

Jake: [*Reading.*] '*For Three Nights only – on The Town Moor. Billy Botto's Unique Family Circus. All the thrills of the Big Top!*'

Dad: The newspaper, Jake!

Jake: [Still reading.] '*Opening Monday July 10*' – that's today!

Dad: [*Snatches it from him.*] Thank you!

Lucy: Eeeh, Jake, you've gone all funny looking!

Grandad: I remember Billy Botto's Circus. Nice big blue tent, and red lorries . . .

Jake: [*Comes forward.*] The circus is here today!

Lucy: You alright, Jake?

Jake: The tightrope walkers, and the jugglers, and the clowns . . .

Mum: He's gone a very funny colour.

Jake: And the acrobats, and the trapeze artists, and the strong men . . .

Dad: He's talking nonsense – quick, give him that sausage!

Jake: And the ringmaster, and the Big Top . . .

Darren: I think Jake's gone into a comma!

Lucy: You mean *coma*, dumbo!

Grandad: Dumbo the Elephant – that was its name!

Jake: Got to go!

Lucy: You've got ten minutes yet, Jake.

Jake: Gotta go!

Dad: Remember – a head for business! [*Exit Jake.*]

Mum: Sausages, anybody? [*All look at one another.*]

Scene Two

[*The school. Enter nine pupils, who stand in a line. One gap in middle. Enter the Teacher with a register.*]

Teacher: Answer your name when called, thank you! Milk!

Milk: Here sir!

Teacher: Trumpet!

Trumpet: That's me, sir! [*Teacher looks at him.*]

Teacher: Gurgle!

Gurgle: Right, first time sir! [*Again Teacher looks.*]

Teacher: Shoulder!

Shoulder: On the button, sir! [*Teacher looks.*]

Teacher: Dipstick!

Dipstick: Got it in one, sir! [*Teacher looks.*]

Teacher: Chicken!

Chicken: [*Clucks.*] Bull's-eye it is, sir!

Teacher: Fizzle!

Fizzle: Zippety doo-dah, sir! [*Teacher looks.*]

Teacher Big Hat!

Big Hat: Raring to go, sir! [*Puts on big hat. Teacher looks.*]

Teacher: Pelican!

Pelican: [*Makes bird noise. Teacher looks.*]

Teacher: Lawson! [*Silence.*] Lawson! [*Silence.*] Where is Jake Lawson? [*Walks along the line.*] Well? Milk?

Milk: Fast asleep in bed, sir?

Teacher: Trumpet?

Trumpet: Fell down a big hole, sir?

Teacher: Gurgle?

Gurgle: Abducted by aliens, sir?

Teacher: Shoulder?

Shoulder: Run down by a steamroller, sir?

Teacher: Dipstick?

Dipstick: Turned into a werewolf, sir?

Teacher: Chicken?

Chicken: [*Clucks.*] Teamed up with Ant and Dec, sir?

Teacher: Big Hat?

Big Hat: On *Big Brother*, sir?

Teacher: Pelican?

Pelican: [*Makes bird noise again.*]

Teacher: Fizzle?

Fizzle: He went to join the circus, sir!

Teacher: What did you say, Fizzle?

Fizzle: Jake Lawson, sir. [*To the others.*] All together now!

ALL: *He went to join the circus – sir!*

Scene Three

[The circus. Enter four members of the circus audience, plus Jake, who all stand downstage and respond to the events. Enter Drummer who gives a drum roll for everyone who enters. Enter Circus Master to introduce the acts in turn.]

Circus Master: Carl, the Crusher, the world's strongest man!

[Drums. Enter Carl. Two people carry on his dumb-bells with great difficulty, and put them down in front of him. He makes big show of straining, then lifts. Puts down, then lifts again – this time with one hand. Motions carriers to take them off. They do so, again with great difficulty. Exit Carl to applause.]

Circus Master: Tightrope Tommy!

[Drums. Enter two people to lay down a length of rope. The four members of the circus audience look up into the air and point. Enter Tightrope Tommy with long pole who walks across it as people continue to look up and point, and finally applaud when Tommy completes the walk. Exits.]

Circus Master: Rubberene, the Acrobat!!

[Enter Rubberene. Acrobatics. Exits to applause.]

Circus Master: Bojangles, the Juggler!

[Enter Bojangles with juggling act. After applause, audience exits. Enter Circus Owner. Jake approaches.]

Circus Owner: So you want to join the circus, do you?

Jake: Yes! I can learn things, like my Grandad!

Circus Owner: The circus is about to close down – forever.

Jake: What?

Circus Owner: Nobody comes to the circus anymore. They're all playing on their computers. We need money to attract people back. But the banks won't lend us any.

Jake: Why not?

Circus Owner: They say they need it for other things. [*Enter Banker.*]

Banker: Kindly bring in my annual bonus! [*Enter Bank Employee with wheelbarrow full of money. Banker starts counting it.*] Fifty thousand . . . one hundred thousand . . . One hundred and fifty thousand . . .

Jake: You don't need all that money!

Banker: Oh, but I do!

Jake: What for?

Banker: I need to keep counting it of course . . . two hundred thousand . . . two hundred and fifty thousand . . .

Jake: [*To Circus Owner.*] How much do you need to save the circus?

Circus Owner: One million pounds.

Banker: Five hundred thousand . . . one million pounds! [*Finishes counting.*] My annual bonus – very good.

Jake: [*To Banker.*] How would you like the chance to double that one million pounds?

Banker: Double it?

Jake: Just imagine, counting to TWO million pounds every day!

Banker: That would be very nice, yes.

Jake: Grandad! [*Enter Grandad.*] How long since you last juggled?

Grandad: Years and years and years and years.

Jake: You've got to do it again – for me, and for the circus.

Grandad: But I'm an old man now, my bones are all stiff and my eyesight's bad, and I've got the shakes. [*Enter Grandma wearing crash helmet, which she removes.*]

Grandma: Do you love me, Harry Taylor?

Grandad: Course I do, Bella. I've always loved you.

Grandma: Then get juggling!

Jake: [*To Banker.*] I bet you your million pounds that this poor old man can juggle three clubs.

Banker: Him? This old ruin? He could hardly cross the road, never mind juggle!

Jake: You'll be taking a good bet then.

Banker: He should be in an old people's home, wrapped in a tartan blanket, with weak tea dribbling down his chin.

Jake: You'll take the bet, then?

Banker: Two million pounds! I could count it every day. Imagine! It's a bet!

Jake: Clubs please, Mr Circus Master. [*Enter Circus Master with three clubs.*]

Grandad: But I can't – [*Enter Mum.*]

Mum: You can do it, Dad – I'd bet my eyeliner on it!

Grandad: I'm not sure, I mean – [*Enter Darren and Lucy.*]

Darren: Rock on, pops!

Lucy: Mint, Grandad! [*Enter Dad.*]

Dad: Well – you may as well give it a go . . . [*Enter all the circus to watch. They start chanting.*]

All: Grandad! Grandad! Grandad! [*Enter Drummer to give a dramatic drum roll. Grandad picks up the clubs. At first he can't do it.*]

Banker: Just as I thought!

[*Grandad tries again. Eventually he juggles the clubs.*]

Banker: But that's impossible – I mean –

Jake: I'll take that wheelbarrow, thank you. [*Does so. Wheels it over to the Circus Owner.*] One million pounds. That should sort the problem. And keep the circus open too. Now, when can *I* start learning to juggle?

Circus Owner: Any time you like – what's your name?

Jake: Jake.

Circus Owner: Jake, the Apprentice Juggler – you're hired!

Dad: Just a minute, Jake. How did you manage that bet? You never had a million pounds to bet with!

Jake: Course I didn't, Dad – but he didn't know that, and like you've always told me, you've got to have a head for business! [*Music. All dance.*]

END OF PLAY

CAST LISTS

DOROTHY DAYDREAM

Some parts were taken by different actors in different performances.

Dorothy	Emma Giles/Alison Wharton
Teacher	Katie Grice/Deborah Bevan
Sally	Laura Newman
Michael	Jill Anderson
Second Teacher	Laura Whitfield
Bonkers	Paul Carr
Machine	Ashleigh Elliott, Elise Young, Neil Burrell, Blair Nichols
Clock	Rachel Hardie
Mr Tenpercent	Lee Peters
Bodyguard	Paul King/David Clark
Rodney	Blair Nichols
Director	Peter Mortimer
Producer	Jen Scott
Puppets	Eilean Hares
Set	Dodgy Clutch
On Script	Sharon Robe
Stage Manager	Neil Burrell

INVASION OF THE DIRTIES

Some parts were taken by different actors in different performances.

Jackie Kleene	Claire Chapman
Feather Duster	Jessica Tully/Ashleigh Elliott
Bossyboots	Karly Holland
Slimeball	Andre Cunningham
King Dirt	Serena Cook
King Dirt's Army	Sharon Robe, Deborah Bevan, Lee Peters, Rachel Hardie
Clock	Ashleigh Elliott
Director	Peter Mortimer
Producer	Jen Scott
Puppets	Eilean Hares
Set	Dodgy Clutch
On Script	Elise Young
Stage Manager	Neil Burrell

THE MAGIC SHELL

Dad	Mark Callaghan
Mum	Jodie Carter
Boy	Peter McCartney
Girl	Michelle Tighe
Friend	Abbie Wilkie
Villain One	Aaron Smith
Villain Two	Wafa Osman
Shell	Loma Simms
Security Person	Claire Anderson
Pilot	Dale Thompson
Co-Pilot	Steven McCormick
Stewardess	Victoria Mitchell
Passengers	John-Paul Henderson, Paul Turnbull, Emma Watson, Hayley Dunn
Announcer	Michael Clark
King	Christopher Blakey
Queen	Claire Anderson
Bodyguard	Alan Baker
Islanders	John Hopkins, Kerry Campbell
Singer	Joanne McCormick
Director	Peter Mortimer
Sets	Lesley Davies
Consultants	Miles Clarke, Judith Bremner, Kate Sanderson, Ada Kennedy

WHITER THAN WIGHT

Pluto	Callum Murray
Billy Wight	Stewart Pringle
Priscilla Wight	Emma Robson
Steve	Peter Drydon
Andrew	Craig Bell
Jessica	Rebecca Nixon
Gran (Nelly)	Rachel McConachie
TV Voice	Claire-Louise Kirsopp
Creepers	Gareth John
Flunky One	William Armstrong
Flunky Two	Alan Tweddle
Flunky Three	Marc Findlay
Maid	Jennifer Peadon
Film Director	John Dockray
Bank Manager	Mark Shafto
Shipping Magnate	Marc Findlay
Businesswoman	Louise Clough
Car Salesman	Alan Tweddle
Jewellery Assistant	William Armstrong
Farah	Michelle Golightly
Marie	Emma Goodfellow
Carstairs	Morgan Jeffs
Travellers	Mark Finday, Louise Clough, Jenny Drydon, Alan Tweddle
Zoot	Tom Dodds
Wisdom	Simon Doxford
Freya	Laura Turnbull
Bailiff/Police Officer	Jamie Eales
Woman Police Officer	Jennifer Peadon
Director	Peter Mortimer
Producer	Anne Brown
Co-Producer	George Welton
Props	Jan Hutchinson
Costumes	Christine Doxford
Set Design	Sheila Peace
Effects	Howard Pringle, Ian Robson
Technical Advisor	Andrew Biscoe

THE WORLD ACCORDING TO SHARON

News Vendor	Ashleigh Brennan
Military Person	Liam Alcock
News Reader	Paula Charles
Alien/Sharon	Michaela Stewart
Drama Teacher	Kayleigh Woods
Elaine	Christine Gauntley
Mum	Jessica Lees
Dad	Martin Coser
Bank Manager	Ashleigh Brennan
Supermarket Manager	Rebecca Arkley
Edward	Liam Alcock
McPeople	Kayleigh Woods, Robyn Frame
Government Spokesperson	Kayleigh Woods
Harry Pilchard	Martin Coser
Customer	Paula Charles
Director	Peter Mortimer
Technical	Customs House Crew

CROAK, THE KING, AND A CHANGE IN THE WEATHER

King	Fatima Ghazzawi
Queen	Sereen Kayyal
Croak	Reeham Farra
The Girl	Nrmeen Hazeeneh
Narrator	Iman Kallam
Servant One	Duaa Bisher
Servant Two	Kholoud Ismail
Servant Three	Duaa Ahmad
Servant Four	Malak Hussein
Soldier One	Hanadi Mahoul
Soldier Two	Baheeja Masri
Soldier Three	Fatima Qassem
Soldier Four	Mirvat Abboud
Soldier Five	Sara Hamad
The Sun/The Wind	Dina Shaaban
Director	Peter Mortimer
Producer	Samiha Yazbeck Shehadeh
Assistant Producer	Najeeba Khatib
Stage Manager	Mohammad Ahmad
Costumes	Hanan Leila, Mariam Nejem
Sound System	Ahmad Haleema (PARD)
Staging	Mahmoud Othman

TRIPLE ACT

Mum	Eden Wilkinson
Dad	Joe Logan
Florrie	Beth Tullock
Tracey	Chipo Mashiri
Jake	Jack Hartley
Lionel	Connor Physick
Cyril	Gabriel Dempsey
Nicket	Jordan Horner
Police Officer One	Joseph Myers
Police Officer Two	Anna Short
Police Officer Three	Thomas Craig
Sharon	Kate Gonsalez
Joe	Matthew Morley
Jack	Joe Dorr
Duane	James Wilson
Santa Claus	Tom Swinney
Shop Assistant One	Lille Downs
Shop Assistant Two	Joshua Caroline
Shop Assistant Three	Charlotte Bloomfield
Shop Assistant Four	Christelle Gatchalian
Pyeclet (a dog)	Joshua Caroline
Director	Peter Mortimer
Producers	Mary Cave and Lee Hall
Props	Sarah Riley
Lighting	Adam Riley

SAUSAGES AND CIRCUSES

Mum	Ellie Orton
Dad	Liam Office
Grandad	Russell Utterson
Grandma	Hannah Galley
Wheelo	Karl Ferguson
Darren	James Smith
Lucy	Dena Kerrigan
Binky	Harry Chatten
Bodypoppa	Angus Davidson
Jake	Daniel Anderson
Teacher	Jack Tully
Pupils	Tyrone Jeffrey, Harry Cardy, Corey Whitfield, Thomas Robinson, Daryl Penton, Luke Fletcher, Harris Scott, Liam Cervantes, Karl Ferguson
Ringmaster	Jonathan Young
Circus Audience	Tyrone Jeffery, Daryl Penton, Karl Ferguson, Liam Best
Carl, the Crusher	Connor Colquhoun
Tightrope Tommy	Thomas Boast
Rubberene	Abbie Reid
Bojangles	Shelby Geddes
Circus Owner	Kristian Knudsen
Banker	Christopher Sword
Bank Employee	Katelyn Cottingham
Director	Peter Mortimer
Assistant Director	Deborah Wilson
Technical Assistant	Angus Davidson
Programme	Kristian Knudsen
Lighting	Whitley Bay Explorer Scouts
Props	Mrs Keady

WRECKING CREW

DEMOLISHING THE CASE AGAINST STEVEN AVERY

5TH-ANNIVERSARY EDITION WITH UPDATED CONTENT AND AN EXCLUSIVE NEW INTERVIEW WITH STEVEN AVERY

JOHN FERAK

WILDBLUE
P R E S S

WildBluePress.com

Wrecking Crew published by:
WILDBLUE PRESS
P.O. Box 102440
Denver, Colorado 80250

This book is a 5-year anniversary update of the original edition, published in 2018.

WILDBLUE PRESS is registered at the U.S. Patent and Trademark Offices.

ISBN 978-1-960332-62-2 Trade Paperback
ISBN 978-1-960332-63-9 eBook
ISBN 978-1-960332-61-5 Hardback

Interior Formatting and Cover Design by Elijah Toten
www.totencreative.com

WRECKING
CREW

NOTE

Any grammatical errors found in quoted text and testimony are attributable to the original authors and should not be considered errors by the author or publisher.

TABLE OF CONTENTS

INTRODUCTION

When a Midwest farm girl named Teresa Halbach went off to college in Green Bay, Wisconsin, she found her calling holding the camera. A short distance from Lambeau Field, she started making money as a part-time photographer at Green Bay's west side shopping mall.

To her family, Teresa Halbach was the happy-go-lucky aspiring photographer. She took photographs at weddings and also snapped children's photos.

But after graduating college, Teresa started dabbling in more risky, provocative photography. She had a wild and crazy side. Future employment prospects with X-rated magazines such as Hustler and Penthouse were not out of the question.

"I gave my permission to Miss Halbach on a number of occasions to use my photography studio for nude portraits of her clients. In fact, a portion of my own business was taking nude photographs of my clients," reflected Tom Pearce, owner of Pearce Photography.[1]

During Teresa's last year of life, she was sucked into some of the darkest corners of the web. Her business, "Photography by Teresa," was out hustling for new sexually explicit photography clients, people who needed someone to capture them in more daring and provocative poses.

"Photography by Teresa is Adult Entertainment Products and Services, Photography, Portrait Photography, Professional Photography, Special Occasion Photography,

---

1. Affidavit of Thomas E. Pearce; April 21, 2017. All quotes from Pearce in this book are from affidavit.

Visual Arts Company. Get in touch with Photography by Teresa with contact details ..."[2]

Many years after his understudy's untimely and gruesome death, Pearce was asked to review Teresa's business profile advertising her adult-oriented photography services.

"Based upon my personal knowledge of Ms. Halbach's business (that) is an accurate depiction of the services offered by Ms. Halbach in the regular course of her business," Pearce said.

Besides her nude photography business, Halbach also hit the backroads for Auto Trader Magazine. She snapped photos of cars, trucks, and vans that people desired to sell. This work was concentrated around the Green Bay area, including Sheboygan and Manitowoc Counties to the south. With Auto Trader, a number of the men she encountered found she had sex appeal. They were attracted to her small frame and wanted to experience her wild side.

"In March 2005, Ms. Halbach told me that a male Auto Trader client made sexual advances toward her and invited her into his residence," Pearce recalls. "Teresa told me that this advance made her feel uncomfortable. After this incident, Ms. Halbach did not mention any problems with Auto Trader clients. Specifically Ms. Halbach never expressed concern about going to the Avery property."

Yet before she disappeared, on Halloween 2005, Halbach had reason to be apprehensive.

Her life was in grave danger.

"I was aware that Ms. Halbach was getting phone calls from someone who was harassing her," Pearce said.

At the same time, a messy divorce case at the Brown County Courthouse in downtown Green Bay was also preoccupying her time.

A husband and wife who lived near Green Bay had used her nude photography services at her Green Bay studio on

---

2. Exhibit from Affidavit with Pearce

Western Avenue. But when the couple's rocky marriage crumbled, Teresa began a romantic relationship with the man, who was almost a decade older than her. He ran a wedding disc jockey service and worked for a Green Bay television station.

"Teresa had taken nude photographs of Bradley and his wife ... after this, Bradley and his wife had broken up and Teresa started dating Bradley. Teresa and Bradley would only have sex, and Teresa did not have any feelings for him and it was only physical. Bradley and his wife were having problems at one time and he would confide in Teresa about his problems."[3]

On the day before she died, Teresa exchanged emails with a supportive friend who encouraged her efforts to grow her adult-oriented photography business.

"Hey Teresa, It was great to hear about your busy life! Sounds like so many things have changed for you in the last year. I'm so happy to hear that business is good. It sounds like you have many hobbies and things going on. It's great! I'm envious and wish I could make the time for that. ... I wouldn't have imagined Adrianne asking you to take nude photos of her. That's cool though that she is comfortable enough. Maybe we could pass your name around for porn shots."[4]

Five weeks earlier, a guy named Ken sent an email to Teresa's photography business thanking her for the letter and package she sent him. "AND the package, well, I think you take better care of me than my mother does, well, I think that's a good thing ... I wouldn't want my mom sending me a porn. I really appreciate everything and damn it I really want to talk with you ... I really miss you and REALLY thank you for sending me messages to my beeper ... I should

---

3. Investigator Mark Wiegert interview of Jolene Bain, Nov. 4, 2005

4. Exhibit 56 Correspondence regarding nude photography

be back online on Monday, hopefully we can talk. I miss you and thank you very much for the goodies. I'll let you know the results! Bye, Ken."

By November 4, 2005, four days after Teresa visited Avery Road in Manitowoc County for a scheduled photo assignment, the Calumet County Sheriff's Office opened a trunk inside her bedroom. She had recently moved into the two-story house on her family's dairy farm, near the town of Hilbert, population 1,100.

"I did locate in a trunk directly next to Teresa's bed several nude photos of a male and a female. Included with these photos were several negatives. There was a portrait order from Pearce Photography which had the name Bradley and Kaycee Czech."[5]

At that point, nobody knew whether these nude photos of the divorced couple were at the heart of her disappearance. The woman had taken out an emergency protection order to keep her ex-husband away from her and out of her life. The photographs recovered from Teresa's bedroom were a focal part of the bitter divorce case. Given Teresa's disappearance, the police would attempt to learn more about Teresa's sexual intimacy with the Green Bay disc jockey.

"By the end Teresa was pretty much leading a double life," Czech said.[6]

5. Wiegert's activity report for Nov. 4, 2005
6. Bradley Czech interview with private investigator Jim Kirby

CHAPTER ONE

TURNABOUT

Green Bay's television stations led off their newscasts with a chilling mystery on Thursday night, November 3, 2005. A fiercely independent, happy-go-lucky young woman from the heart of dairy country was gone. No one had seen or heard from her during the past four days. Television anchors painted a grim outlook as photos of Teresa Halbach flashed across the screen. Viewers were left uneasy and fearful of a worst-case scenario. Surely someone watching the distressing news would remember encountering Teresa over the past few days. At least, that's what the small-town Calumet County Sheriff's Office in Chilton, Wisconsin hoped.

But it was not Teresa's face displayed on the television screen that drew a red flag with one of the Manitowoc County residents. It was the image of her missing sports utility vehicle, a Toyota RAV 4.

During that time frame, Kevin Rahmlow lived around Mishicot, a small but proud Wisconsin town of 1,400 people of German, Swiss, and Bohemian heritage. Back in the day, Mishicot had six hotels, three general stores, a movie theater, a grist mill, and a brewery. By 2005, the community's three original churches still stood the test of time but Mishicot looked different. The town's gas station, owned by Cenex, was one of the local hangouts. People came there for fuel, a cup of coffee, and to buy their cigarettes. The popular business was at the corner of State Highway 147 and State Street.

Kevin Rahmlow vividly remembers when he pulled into the Cenex. It was Friday, November 4. Inside the convenience store, the missing person's poster caught his eye. Teresa Marie Halbach, the flier noted, was 5-foot-6, 135 pounds. Brown eyes and light brown hair.[7]

"I remember that the poster had a picture of Teresa Halbach and written descriptions of Teresa Halbach and the car she was driving," Rahmlow said.

As it turned out, Cenex was one of many small-town businesses, bars, and cafes where Teresa's concerned friends and family slapped up posters. They were desperate for answers, hoping somebody, anybody, remembered a sighting. And if the locals didn't see Teresa, perhaps they saw her Toyota RAV4. It had a large Lemieux Toyota sign on the back of her vehicle where the spare tire hung.

When Rahmlow saw the poster, he remembered something.

"On November 3 and 4, 2005, I was in Mishicot. I saw Teresa Halbach's vehicle by the East Twin River dam in Mishicot at the turnabout by the bridge as I drove west of Highway 147. I recognized that the written description of the vehicle on the poster matched the car I saw at the turnaround by the dam."

That Friday afternoon, Rahmlow happened to spot a man in a brown uniform. The man was sporting a badge. "While I was in the Cenex station, a Manitowoc County Sheriff's Department officer came into the station. I immediately told the officer that I had seen a car that matched the description of the car on Teresa Halbach's missing person poster at the turnaround by the dam."

After speaking with the uniformed deputy, Rahmlow went on with his life.

He had no idea whatever became of the matter. He later moved to another Midwest state. He even missed the initial

---

7. July 15, 2017 affidavit of Kevin Rahmlow

Making a Murderer craze on Netflix that captured world-wide attention.

When Kevin Rahmlow saw this flyer at the Cenex gas station in Mishicot, it triggered his memory surrounding Teresa Halbach's disappearance.

***

In December 2015, a true crime documentary about the Steven Avery murder case was released on Netflix, but Rahmlow didn't get swept up in the media frenzy. An entire year passed before he finally turned on Netflix to watch it. And as he watched *Making a Murderer*, the Minnesota man had a flashback. He remembered his encounter at the gas station in Mishicot from more than a decade ago. And besides being familiar with Manitowoc County, Rahmlow knew some of the key people who worked hand in hand with special prosecutor Ken Kratz to cement the guilt of Steven Avery. Avery, as the world now knows, was a previously wrongfully convicted man who lost eighteen years due to a barbaric daytime rape along the Lake Michigan shoreline during the summer of 1985. This was the crime that allowed dangerous sexual predator Gregory Allen to get away by the forces who ran the Manitowoc County Sheriff's Office, notably Sheriff Tom Kocourek, who was about forty years old at the time.

Fast-forward to 2007. Avery stood trial in Chilton for Teresa's murder even though the prosecution's evidence was like a piece of Swiss cheese. And yet despite his side's many holes, Ken Kratz overcame his murder case's numerous physical evidence shortcomings thanks to the unbelievable eyewitness testimonies from a number of unscrupulous people who very much had a stake, a big stake, in the desired outcome of an Avery guilty verdict.

December 12, 2016

Two weeks before Christmas, Rahmlow sent a text message to someone he recognized from *Making a Murderer*. By then, Scott Tadych was happily married to Steven Avery's younger sister, Barb. At the time of Teresa's disappearance, Barb Janda lived in one of the trailers at the Avery Salvage Yard compound, a forty-acre tract out in the middle of nowhere surrounded by large gravel pits. At the time of Teresa's disappearance, Barb and Scott Tadych were steady lovers and she was in the process of getting another divorce, this time from Tom Janda.

After watching *Making a Murderer*, Rahmlow informed his old acquaintance how "I need to get in touch with one of their lawyers."

Rahmlow explained in his text message to Scott Tadych how he recognized Teresa's vehicle as the one he saw by the old dam, either November 3 or 4. He also remembered having a conversation with a man whose face regularly appeared during the *Making a Murderer* episodes.

Scott Tadych did not respond.

Rahmlow reached out again, ninety minutes later. The second time, he texted his phone number to Tadych. He wanted to discuss the matter over the phone.

"OK, I will I am really sick now can hardly talk so I will call tomorrow," Tadych texted back.

But Tadych never did call back.

"I did not hear from Mr. Tadych the next day or any other day responsive to my request for attorney contact information for Steven Avery or Brendan Dassey," Rahmlow said. "I received another message from Mr. Tadych on December 19 (2016) at 6:10 p.m., which was not responsive to my request."

There is no doubt in his mind that Rahmlow saw Teresa's RAV4 along the rural stretch of two-lane State Highway 147 near the East Twin River Dam. The turnaround on the highway was barely a mile from Avery Salvage.

A licensed private investigator in Illinois and Wisconsin, James R. Kirby was hired by Kathleen T. Zellner & Associates to investigate Teresa's murder case.

"I requested abandoned and towed vehicle reports for the time period of October 31, 2005 through November 5, 2005, from the following agencies: Mishicot Police Department, Two Rivers Police Department, and the Manitowoc County Sheriff's Department," Kirby said.[8]

This, of course, was the period when Teresa was last seen in Manitowoc County, near Mishicot. On a Saturday morning six days later, under highly suspicious circumstances, her Toyota RAV4 turned up, double parked, on the far back ridge of Avery Salvage, near a row of junked vehicles. The spot of the find bordered the massive sand and gravel pit operated by Joshua Radandt.

The question lingered. Who moved Teresa's SUV to the far outer edge of Avery Salvage? Was it the killer working alone? Was it the killer working in tandem with an accomplice? Or was it somebody affiliated with the volunteer search party? Or was it one of the Manitowoc County Sheriff's deputies?

Incidentally, at the time of her disappearance, Teresa's RAV4 had no front-end damage. This small but critical detail is substantiated by the fact that the missing person fliers made no mention of any broken auto parts or wreckage. But when her sports utility vehicle surfaced on the Avery property, it showed heavy front-end damage. Weirdly, the broken blinker light from the driver's side was neatly tucked away into the rear cargo area of the murdered woman's auto. Why would the killer do something so strange? Of course, the logical scenario was that the killer had nothing to do with moving the vehicle to Avery's property, and that the mishap occurred, late at night, during the clandestine efforts to sneak the vehicle onto the Avery property without Avery or his family members catching on.

In any event, private eye Kirby's inquiry into the RAV4 spotted by Rahmlow on Friday afternoon, November 4, 2005, revealed the "Mishicot Police Department had no responsive records. Based upon the response of Two Rivers

---

8. Supplemental affidavit of James Kirby, Oct. 20, 2017

Police Department and Manitowoc County Sheriff's Office pursuant to my request, none of these agencies logged an abandoned vehicle on Highway 147 near the East Twin River Bridge."

Obviously, one of the most plausible scenarios for why the police did not log the abandoned vehicle spotted near the Old Dam on Highway 147 in rural Manitowoc County, which was Manitowoc County Sheriff's territory, was because the auto belonged to Teresa, and it got moved as a direct result of Manitowoc County's intercession.

CHAPTER TWO

BOBBY DEPARTS

The four Dassey brothers were: Bryan, twenty, Bobby, nineteen, Blaine, almost seventeen, and Brendan, sixteen. As mentioned earlier, the Dasseys occupied one of the mobile home trailers along Avery Road at their family's Avery Salvage Yard compound. Bryan, the oldest brother, worked in nearby Two Rivers at Woodland Face Veneer, a factory overlooking the scenic Lake Michigan.

Regarding the day in question, Oct. 31, 2005, Bryan Dassey told Wisconsin's Division of Criminal Investigation special agents Kim Skorlinski and Debra K. Strauss that he left for his job at 6 a.m. and visited his girlfriend afterward. He was not on Avery Road "except for waking up and going to work. Bryan said he got home sometime after supper but could not recall when that was."[9]

Eventually, the questions steered toward the missing photographer. She had been a regular visitor to the Avery Salvage Yard during the past year without any problems or hassles, unlike at some of her other unnerving Auto Trader assignments where men tried to proposition her or invite her inside their homes for an alcoholic beverage. Whenever Teresa visited Avery Road, she was given courtesy and respect.

"Bryan said he heard from his mom and Steven that Halbach was only at their residence about five minutes. He heard she just took the photo of the van and left. Bryan

9.   DOJ report of Bryan Dassey interview.

said the investigators should also talk to his brother Bobby because he saw her leave their property."

At Avery's five-week murder trial in 2007, prosecutor Ken Kratz chose to keep Bryan Dassey off his side's witness stand. Therefore, the jury deciding Steven Avery's fate never heard the following account:

"In October and November 2005, I lived with my girlfriend but I kept my clothing at my mother's trailer, which was on the Avery's Auto Salvage property. On or about (Thursday) November 4, 2005, I returned to my mother's trailer to retrieve some clothes, and I had a conversation with my brother, Bobby, about Teresa Halbach. I distinctly remember Bobby telling me, 'Steven could not have killed her because I saw her leave the property on October 31, 2005.'"[10]

Bryan Dassey's October 2017 sworn affidavit recalled how he was pulled over by police on November 6, 2005. He was behind the wheel of his uncle Steven Avery's Pontiac.

"My brother Brendan was in the car with me, and he was interviewed by other officers at the same time as me. I told the investigators that they should talk to my brother Bobby because he saw Teresa Halbach leave the Avery property on October 31, 2005.

"I was not called as a witness to testify at my Uncle Steven's criminal trial."

***

Most of the world who watched *Making a Murderer* fell in love with Steven Avery's private counsel, Dean Strang and Jerome Buting. The two criminal defense lawyers worked closely together, putting forth a heroic defense for

---

10. Exhibit G, Bryan J. Dassey affidavit, dated Oct. 16, 2017

their client at his murder trial, but even they now admit that, in retrospect, they overlooked some things along the way.

They had hired Conrad "Pete" Baetz, a retired police detective, as their investigator in preparation for trial. Baetz had moved back to his native Manitowoc County after his retirement in downstate Illinois. He had spent many years at the Madison County Sheriff's Office near St. Louis.[11]

"I have reviewed the police report of the November 6, 2005, interview of Bryan Dassey where he said that Bobby Dassey saw Teresa Halbach leave the Avery property on October 31, 2005. I was unaware of this report. I never tried to interview Bryan Dassey about Bobby Dassey's alleged statement. I was never instructed by trial defense counsel Buting and Strang to interview Bryan Dassey," Baetz said.

"Bobby Dassey was the key prosecution witness at Steven Avery's trial who testified that he saw Ms. Halbach walk towards Mr. Avery's trailer after taking photographs of his mother Barb Janda's van. Bobby also testified that when he left the Avery Salvage Yard, Ms. Halbach's vehicle was still on the property."

In hindsight, Baetz realized that the statement had major significance.

"If the trial defense counsel could have impeached Bobby Dassey with Bryan Dassey's testimony that Bobby admitted he saw Ms. Halbach leave the Avery Salvage Yard, it would have undermined the State's entire case against Mr. Avery, and there would have been a reasonable probability of him being found not guilty."

***

One week after the horrifying news of Teresa's disappearance, two key developments occurred. First,

11. Exhibit H, Affidavit of Conrad "Pete" Baetz, dated Oct. 18, 2017

Steven Avery, who was perhaps the second to last person to see Teresa alive, was taken into custody and jailed for her murder. This standalone event set the wheels in motion for the collapse of Avery's $36 million federal civil rights lawsuit against Manitowoc County whose insurance company had already chosen to deny coverage of the civil rights lawsuit based on Avery's allegation the misconduct on the part of former Manitowoc County Sheriff Tom Kocourek and prosecutor Denis Vogel was intentional, not just negligence on the part of these former county officials. The insurance company's denial of coverage served to greatly increase the pressure on the individual defendants who were named in Avery's lawsuit because they could have been bankrupted by an adverse jury award in the high-profile wrongful conviction case.

Second, nineteen-year-old Bobby Dassey, who may be the last person Teresa ever saw, was confronted by Wisconsin police investigators on November 9, 2005, a Wednesday afternoon.

"You're not under arrest. You understand that," said John Dedering, a middle-aged, bald detective for the rural Calumet County Sheriff's Office. "This isn't an arrest. But ... we need to hold on to you so we get our blood, our swabs, and our prints and such. Okay?"

Dedering had a search warrant for Bobby Dassey, who was 5-foot-10, 180 pounds, brown hair and blue eyes. At the time, Dedering and the other police officers trying to find Teresa did not know that Bobby Dassey was an awkward social misfit, a sexual deviant who had recurring sexual-fueled fantasies involving bestiality, mutilating naked women, torture, and drownings. Bobby's obsessions were being shielded from the police and the special prosecutor directing the murder probe. Obviously, Bobby was not about to volunteer such deviant information when he sat down for a formal face-to-face police interview regarding the events in question.

At any rate, the search warrant gave these Wisconsin investigators permission to get Bobby's DNA including a saliva and blood sample. Additionally, "Bobby A. Dassey is ordered to provide a forefinger and thumb print evidence. The physical person of Bobby A. Dassey shall be searched and documented including but not limited to scratches, bruises, and bite marks."

Manitowoc County Judge Jerome Fox signed the order on November 7, 2005, at 7:08 p.m. On a side note, Fox's legacy in the case would be his decision to sentence Brendan Dassey to remain incarcerated at a Wisconsin penal institution until at least 2048, when he will first become eligible for parole.

It's unclear why Dedering and the other investigators chose to drag their heels and not move with expediency to obtain Bobby's DNA samples on the night of November 7, 2005. After all, this was an open and unsolved murder. Nobody was arrested yet.

Of course, there may have been some discussions among the Manitowoc County Sheriff's officials who were quietly calling the shots and directing the Avery investigation because they wanted Avery's $36 million lawsuit to implode. Their professional livelihoods were at stake if Avery's civil suit was a success.

Sure enough, the next day, November 8, turned out to the most fortuitous day of the continuing murder saga at Avery Salvage. That Tuesday morning, the front and back license plates to Teresa's RAV4 suddenly appeared inside an abandoned station wagon that had its windows shattered. It was an easy place to plant evidence, especially when you consider that the station wagon was one of the several thousand wrecked cars that were searched by the police two days earlier, on Sunday, November 6.

But that initial police and volunteer firefighter canvass of the entire Avery salvage yard harvested no damning murder clues. No legitimate reason was given to explain why the authorities, at the recommendation of dubious Calumet County Detective Mark Wiegert, were summoned again, two days later, to search the same junked cars shortly after the crack of dawn.

Nov. 8, 2005, was also the same morning when the Manitowoc County Sheriff's Office's crackerjack evidence collection team of Detective James Lenk and Andy Colborn were back at Avery's. As far as they wanted the public to know, they had reached the conclusion that they just had not done a thorough enough of a job during their previous several days of constantly searching through Steven Avery's tiny bedroom and his book cabinet dresser for physical evidence. This time, this Tuesday morning, they were certain that disturbing clues fingering Avery for Teresa's murder were still being concealed inside their murder suspect's bedroom. Colborn maintained that he shook the wooden magazine cabinet near Avery's bed that contained all of Avery's Playboys. Then, out of nowhere, a single key, a spare key, shot out of the cabinet at an angle. The spare key landed softly on the blue carpet where the sharp-eyed Detective Lenk walked back into Avery's bedroom and exclaimed, "There's a key on the floor."

That afternoon, another Manitowoc County Sheriff's deputy, Sgt. Jason Jost, happened to be aimlessly wandering around the Avery property. Jost wrote in his reports that he had a suspicion from walking outside that perhaps some of Teresa's bones were here on the property waiting to be found. And Jost was right. He supposedly found a couple of large charred bones out in the grass in Steven Avery's backyard. Because the charred bones were not symmetrical, this raised questions about their baffling discovery. On top of that, the Manitowoc County Sheriff's Office chose not to capture any photographs or make any videotapes showing the condition and location of these human bones being recovered near Avery's burn pit. Instead, the authorities took photos of other things such as dried leaves and other debris used to ignite a bonfire.

In sum, the recovery of the spare key, the bent up license plates, and the backyard bones helped the Manitowoc County Sheriff's Office finally get even with their bitter enemy. Equally important, Steven Avery's arrest signified to Bobby Dassey that he was essentially off the hook as the prime suspect. He could breathe a sigh of relief, a deep sigh.

At the time of Teresa's disappearance, Bobby was proficient at dismembering the carcasses of wild animals, unlike Steven Avery, who didn't have much of an interest in hunting. And unlike most of Manitowoc County, Bobby was developing an appetite for devouring the flesh of road kill. Bobby claimed he came across a deer carcass on one of the roads near his house in the aftermath of Teresa's disappearance. Bobby claimed he grabbed the deer off the road and hauled it back to his family's garage to slice it up. How many nineteen-year-olds do you know who cruise around their gravel roads and side roads looking for dead deer to scoop up and take home for grub? And why all of a sudden during the first week of November, just days after Teresa vanished?

During a subsequent interview with police, Bryan Dassey, the oldest of the Dassey boys, was asked by the detectives "if he could remember anything strange that had stuck out in his mind during that time after Halloween." He said the incident "when Bobby had hung the deer in his mom's garage."

But back in November 2005, nobody was giving serious thought to the scenario that the deer carcass was a crafty ruse, a cunning way to mask the blood spatter and other evidence that may have pointed to Bobby instead of his always unlucky uncle.

Here were some of the key facts about Teresa's disappearance:

She vanished on a Monday afternoon after being on Avery Road.

In the wake of her disappearance, Bobby is on record as having been busy carving up and dismembering animals.

Teresa's incinerated bones actually turned up inside a burn barrel from Bobby's yard, a steel drum barrel that also included a mixture of animal bones.

One would think that an astute detective investigating a young woman's apparent murder would have a natural curiosity about such a coincidence.

"How long had you been hanging the deer, Bobby?" Dedering asked.[12]

"Since Friday night," Bobby answered, referring to November 4.

"Who hit the deer, you know?"

"No."

Bobby suggested he found the deer "right up the road."

"OK again, who claimed the deer?"

"I did. I trussed and hung it up that Saturday."

"Who skinned it?"

"I did."

After asking what Bobby did with the deer skin, Dedering, the bumbling detective from Calumet County, blurted out, "shows how much I've been in your garage, doesn't it?"

At that moment, Dedering's interview partner, Wisconsin DCI Special Agent Kevin Heimerl, made an observation.

"It sounds to me like you've skinned and butchered your own deer before?"

"Yeah," Bobby agreed.

"What would you normally do with the hide then?"

"We took them into town."

"Oh, OK."

---

12.   Bobby Dassey Nov. 9, 2005 interview with John Dedering and Kevin Heimerl.

Then Dedering wondered if the local butcher shop accepted deer heads.

"No. We just burn them," Bobby answered. "Over in the burning barrel."

At that point, Dedering admitted he wasn't familiar with Bobby's yard even though it was just a short walking distance from Steven Avery's trailer.

"In the burning barrels?" Dedering wondered.

"Uh-huh," Bobby agreed.

The conversation shifted back to Avery's skills as a hunter and rugged outdoorsman.

"He doesn't hunt that much," Bobby replied.

When Heimerl asked whether the deer's head still existed, Bobby responded by saying that the head was still right outside of his mother's garage.

"So which burn barrel do you guys normally burn the heads up?" Dedering asked.

"Uh, ours. This is the first one that we actually got our family ... the other one we took in to the butcher."

"Describe to me again, Bobby, where you hunt?" Dedering inquired. "How far is that from your house?"

His hunting spot was about two-and-a-half miles from home, he responded.

Dedering wondered whether Bobby knew the land owner in northern Manitowoc County.

"I don't know."

"But you know, what's his name, Scott Tadych?"

"Tadych," Bobby answered.

Bobby was asked if he and Tadych, the soon-to-be husband of Bobby's mother, hunted together.

"No. That's the first day actually that I hunted."

Now that Bobby's uncle was in custody, Dedering and Heimerl had a strong desire for Bobby to validate their murder theory. It was important for the reputation of Manitowoc County's tarnished sheriff's office to prove

Avery was a cruel diabolical killer who belonged in prison for the rest of his time on earth.

Ever a shifty detective, Dedering decided the best way to solicit Bobby's help in implicating Avery was to drive a wedge between Bobby and his uncle.

"Steve seems to think that he wasn't the last person to see (Teresa) but that you had. He says that you were the last person."

"No," Bobby answered.

"That you followed her out of the driveway."

"No. Her vehicle was there."

"Is that an absolute truth?"

"Absolute truth."

Bear in mind Dedering never seriously considered the young man sitting across from him in the interview as the more likely killer.

At the time of their interview, Dedering did not have a clue about Bobby's deviant sexual side. He knew nothing about Bobby's sadistic appetite for naked, drowned women and mutilated bodies. As a result, Dedering remained singularly focused that November afternoon. He needed to make Bobby mad, raging mad, at his uncle.

"I remember that we talked about why Steve would try to jam you up like that. Why?"

"That's a good point," Bobby agreed. "That's the kind of person he is."

"How does that sit with you?"

"It makes me angry."

"We're getting to the point where we're going to know everything. OK? You understand that we are going to know everything pretty shortly. Now, my concern is this, Bobby, that if you haven't been one hundred percent honest and truthful with me to this point, it's because of two reasons. One is that you're afraid something bad is going to happen to you and your family if you aren't, if you cooperate with the cops … What would be the other reason for you not telling me the truth? Well, I'll tell you, it would be because maybe you had some involvement with it. And like I said, you're shaking your head no, OK?"

Dedering asked if anybody told Bobby how to answer his interview questions with police.

"No."

"Nobody?"

"No."

"Your mom hasn't had any contact with you about this? You haven't sat down and had a family discussion about how all this should play out when that bald-headed, old buzzard starts hanging around and asking questions?"

"Nope."

"Nothing?"

"Nope."

Dedering wanted to believe Bobby had no role in Teresa's brutal killing.

"I'm kind of buying into the fact, and like I told you when I talked with you on Saturday, did I tell you that I thought I pretty much believed you then? I still think that pretty much too. OK?"

Still, Dedering wanted to know why Avery "would want to put you in a box? Why would he want to jam you up for?"

"Well, he don't want to go back," Bobby responded.

"You just said something. Something you might be on to," Dedering pondered. "You know maybe, you think maybe, he did this because he doesn't want to go back?"

"Yeah. I know as much as you do," Bobby replied. "You know more than I do. You guys know a lot more than I do."

"Yeah, but you know what you have that we don't have? You got family intuition, man."

"Yeah."

"So what's your gut telling you?"

"Steven's playing his hand."

"Who do you think did it?"

"I dunno."

"You don't know?"

"What I told you guys is all I know about it."

"So if you were a betting man, I'd bet that you didn't do it. Would you bet like that?"

"Yeah," Bobby wisely agreed.

CHAPTER THREE

ALIBI

After investing close to three years of her life reinvestigating Teresa's death, sinking hundreds of thousands of dollars of her law firm's own money into Steven Avery's post-conviction defense, world-famous exoneration lawyer Kathleen Zellner now believes the murder time sequence outlined by special prosecutor Ken Kratz was demonstrably false. According to Zellner, the cellular tower pings off Teresa's cell phone reveal the Auto Trader photographer left Avery's around 2:35 p.m. on Halloween 2005.

From there, Teresa retraced her route of travel from Avery Road. Teresa would have turned left on State Highway 147, traveling for a mile. When she got to the intersection of County Road Q, Teresa headed south. Then she met her disaster shortly afterward, probably along the seldom-traveled Kuss Road, a spooky dead-end road covered by a dense swath of woodlands along both sides of the road. The area's general terrain includes a patch of large sand and gravel quarries along County Road Q, including one enormous quarry that has been around for years, a parcel owned by Manitowoc County Government.

On the day of Avery's arrest, investigators Dedering and Heimerl peppered Bobby with questions about his own movements on the day Teresa met foul play.

"Now, I want to know again about when you left that day," Dedering inquired. "You remember about what time that was?"

"Right around 3 o'clock."

"Did you see anyone when you were leaving the driveway?"

"When I left?"

"Yes."

"No. I didn't see no one coming up the driveway."

"Were there any cars in the driveway?"

"Yeah. It's a little SUV."

"Now, you told me that you were nowhere near that teal colored SUV."

"Nope."

"Never?"

"Nope."

"Never there?"

"Never there."

"Never touched it?"

"Nope."

"Did you go anywhere that night after you got home from your hunting?"

"No."

"You stayed home?"

"Went to work."

Bobby worked at Fisher Hamilton in Manitowoc, a metal processing plant in town.

He told the police he left for work at 9:30 p.m., which is seven hours after Bobby was discretely eyeing Teresa from inside his trailer window.

"So what did you do when you were at home?"

"Napped … I came right home after hunting."

Suddenly, the interview took a change of direction.

Dedering wanted to boast about his credentials.

"I've been in law enforcement for almost thirty years, and I've done more than an interview or two. OK? … And what works for me is that, I'll be honest and then I find that usually people are honest in return, OK? I'm going to tell you something. OK? I can tell you that nobody from any sheriff's department planted any evidence anywhere. And that vehicle was found because we thought this through and we figured that something like this could happen ... we made sure that no Manitowoc city or county cop was on the property without another agency right alongside them so that anything that might be falling could be falling honestly."

Dedering wanted Bobby to understand his role investigating the homicide.

"Find the somebody that did something. I know you didn't. I'm pretty confident that you have no play in this. Am I right about that?"

Bobby mumbled something that couldn't be heard.

At that juncture, Kevin Heimerl bragged how he worked at the Wisconsin DCI, the same agency assigned in 2003, two years earlier, to review the Manitowoc County Sheriff's Office 1985 rape investigation spearheaded by Sheriff Kocourek, the one that put Steven Avery unjustly in prison for eighteen years for a violent rape committed by Gregory Allen.

"The Department of Justice, DCI. That's who I work for. We are here. We are in the middle of this thing, the same agency that would ask to review that first case. Those same cops, me and the guys I work with, the guys that are here, OK? Another thing I want to chew on ... people suggested that maybe, me and the people I'm working with, or any other cop like to make stuff up, twist stuff.

"I got it better. They rely on me. I got two kids that rely on me. You know what? There is no case more important to me. And I'm not going to jeopardize my family and my life for anybody and any investigation. OK?"

"That's where I am as well," Dedering added.

"Who is going put their career, because you know, you could be in insurance sales and do a rotten job at it and get fired," Heimerl reasoned. "You can get another job (in) insurance sales somewhere else. But you know, when a cop gets busted for lying, doing something illegal, they lose their job. They don't get another job. They don't get another cop job. OK?"

"OK," Bobby repeated.

"Because if we're not credible, we can't go into court," Heimerl maintained. "That's why. You can't be a cop, if we're not believed."

Dedering echoed those comments.

"Yeah, you know basically a cop whose word is worth nothing, isn't worth anything as a cop. You know. Because why go up on a stand, I swear to tell the truth and for the same reasons Kevin just insisted, I've got a family. I love my family. I need to have a few things to myself.

"You wouldn't lie or do anything illegal but your family comes first, doesn't it?"

"Yeah," Bobby agreed.

Transcripts of Bobby's police interviews show that almost all of his police interview answers were just one word answers.

Yet a bond was forming, between Bobby and the police. They wanted to use him to prosecute Avery. He could strengthen their case. For Bobby, the opportunity to help the police nail his uncle would solidify his purported alibi.

"Everybody else kind of takes a back seat," Dedering reminded Bobby. "You're not different than me. You're not different than Kevin. You're not different than any other cop. That's something that we all have in common. We all love our families. And we want to do the right thing for our families."

The temptation of planting evidence continued to come up.

But Bobby was not bringing up the topic. It was Dedering and Heimerl who kept dredging up the topic.

"It brings shame, humiliation, poverty, we wouldn't want anything like that," Dedering offered. "I'm not taking a chance ... I'm fifty some years old. How old are you?"

"Nineteen."

"You can walk down the street. And if there's a job to be, young, healthy, you could work here. You know what? I'm starting to be a liability, health insurance reasons. ... I can't do things wrong because there's too much writing on it for me. You believe that?"

"Yeah."

"I'm sure that the family would love to and probably does believe that there is some sort of conspiracy. But I'm here to tell you something ... You know what? Imagine how many people, how many police officers it would take to orchestrate a conspiracy of this size?"

"Yeah."

"One person could not do it, all right?

"Yeah."

"Do you think two people could orchestrate a conspiracy of this size?

"No."

"OK. Now you're talking more than two dirty cops within one police agency. All the supervisor's eyes and everybody else; the neighboring sheriff's department and state's special agents, and everybody else, and crime lab personnel. You know, you can't fool forensics."

"Yeah."

Dedering brought up the old motorcycle gang saying of how three people can keep a secret if two are dead.

"OK, that means if you don't want somebody else to know anything, you can't involve anybody else because somebody's going to give something up."

Bobby was told he "can believe what you want with your family about the conspiracy ... I can't tell you what to think. OK? But I can tell you that we do have a lot of stuff. I don't understand why Steve would tell somebody something like he wasn't the last one to see her. You know, I don't understand that. What do you think about that?"

Bobby: "I don't understand how?"

"OK. Do you get along with Steve pretty well?"

"Sometimes."

"What was the last thing that caused you to not get along with him?"

Once again, Bobby mumbled something unclear.

Eventually, Dedering asked Bobby whether he dated.

"Do you see anybody?"

"No."

"You are going to break a lot of young ladies' hearts."

"I don't have a girlfriend."

"Ha. You probably will die as a rich man if you keep that attitude. OK?"

Given that a couple of charred human bones apparently did turn up near his uncle's burn pile pit, the next question made sense to ask.

But Dedering had no idea whether his witness was being truthful or deceitful because authorities did not obtain any foot impressions near Avery's burn pit. In effect, it was a wasted question.

"Is there any way or any reason you can think of why your footprints might be near Steve's fire pit or was it Steve's burn barrel?

"No."

"No way that they'd be there?"

"I've been all over the place. Not by the burn barrels and fire pit."

"I just wanted to make sure, OK? Because if something like that'd show up, I worry you'd disappoint me."

Heimerl interjected.

"Well, if something like that would show up. It should potentially disappoint Bobby."

"Yeah," Dedering agreed.

Bobby sat there in utter silence. He knew if he could just sweat out a few more minutes, his interview with these two cops would all be over.

"We got a room available to get your swab, fingerprints and all that, so I think it's time to do that now. It's 3:51 p.m. on my watch. You nervous?" Dedering inquired.

Bobby did not answer.

"That was an eye roll," Heimerl remarked. "Yes or no?"

"No," Bobby responded.

CHAPTER FOUR

ZELLNER FACTOR

Just four days before the twelve-year anniversary of Teresa's mysterious Manitowoc County murder, the condemned prisoner made a prepaid collect call from his permanent residence behind the walls of the Waupun Correctional Center. The simple man had gained the unwavering support of millions of men and women across the globe, people whose lives were forever touched by the Emmy-winning documentary.

But their lives have never intersected with the plight of Steven Avery, a man unjustly imprisoned and snatched from society for eighteen long years, starting in his early twenties. This same man, at age forty-three, was on the verge of collecting a multi-million dollar federal lawsuit settlement at the hands of law enforcement in Avery's native Manitowoc County. Suddenly, just days before he got to sit inside the law offices for the sworn deposition of the man responsible for his disastrous life, retired Manitowoc County Sheriff Tom Kocourek, Avery found himself ripped away from his mother and father, Dolores and Al, his brothers Chuck and Earl, and his sister, Barb. This time, unlike the last time, there was a major news media marketing campaign, long before any trial, to brand Avery a demon, a sicko, a pariah, the pond scum of the earth. The people involved in this effort included the likes of Manitowoc Sheriff Kenny Peterson, Undersheriff Rob Hermann, Manitowoc County Special Prosecutor Ken Kratz, Calumet Sheriff Jerry Pagel, Calumet

County Sheriff's Investigator Mark Wiegert and Special Agent Tom Fassbender, worked at the Wisconsin DCI.

All six liked-minded men, between their forties and sixties, were in complete agreement. Steven Avery was going to go down hard for Teresa's murder and everyone in Wisconsin would be assured that he was a bloodthirsty monster.

The Steven Avery-is-guilty pretrial publicity mantra was bigger than a tidal wave. It was a typhoon, a monsoon. At the end of the day, after a few days of back-and-forth jury deliberations, including questions surrounding the testimony of Kratz's leadoff witness, Bobby Dassey, Avery was tried and convicted of the first-degree murder, though many people still had lingering doubts, even after trial had ended. Indeed, Avery was one of the last persons to see Teresa, but most people now believe what Avery has always professed from the get-go, that he is innocent, that he had nothing to do with her killing. What motive did he have to harm the freelance photographer from Green Bay? Rational people, objective people, people who are deep critical thinkers, struggle to find the motive.

Of course, there is another nagging question weighing on the minds of many. If Avery did not murder Teresa, then who did? And why?

Since January 2016, Avery has had a tireless advocate who dropped into his life from Wisconsin's dreaded rival, Illinois. Lucky for him, the suburban Chicago woman out of Downers Grove happens to be regarded as one the country's foremost lawyers in exposing police corruption and prosecutorial misconduct. She has achieved a miraculous streak of overturning more than twenty wrongful convictions since the 1990s.

"In 23 years, Kathleen Zellner has righted more wrongful prosecutions than any private attorney in America. No private attorney in the United States has successfully won for the release of more innocent defendants," her website proclaims.

As of September 27, 2018, the United States had 2,270 exonerations.

Suburban Chicago lawyer Kathleen Zellner has achieved more exonerations of wrongfully convicted prisoners than any other lawyer in the country.

"My interest in this area of law resulted in being appointed on a death penalty case, representing a serial killer. I represented an individual named Larry Eyler in the early 1990s and so I had to prepare a post-conviction. I had started my own law firm. I was the in-house counsel for a large HMO, and I was doing medical malpractice, but my clerks thought it would be interesting to see if we could tackle the complexity of a post-conviction case in 1992, with someone that everyone believed was guilty."[13]

---

13. Kathleen Zellner Sept. 27, 2018 at Maryville University, Peace and Justice Award lecture

Zellner said she made incredible discoveries that Eyler had only been convicted of one murder.

"I realized, as we were progressing, that we were really good at what we were doing and yet I'm getting ready to overturn the one conviction for someone that I know has committed twenty-one murders. So the dilemma I was in was to try to figure out how to turn it into something positive, something good.

"What I figured out was, my client was probably infected with the HIV virus, and I decided to have medical testing done, and I confirmed that he had a full blown case of AIDS. So I went to him ... I persuaded him to give to me the twenty-one confessions to all the murders he had committed, in tremendous detail. And I ended up helping to close all of those cases with three jurisdictions and the FBI ... and we closed all of the murder cases. I decided at that point that I would never represent someone again that I believe was guilty. I did not see myself as a criminal defense attorney, but I thought that our skill level on the Eyler case indicated that we, as small a firm as we were, could investigate and uncover evidence that the police had not and the prosecutors had not."

In 1994, Zellner took on her next case, the Joseph Burrows murder case.

The murder victim in that crime southeast of Kankakee, Illinois, was a frail eighty-eight-year-old retired farmer named William Dulin. The Iroquois County killing occurred on November 8, 1988. Dulin's bloody body was found inside his home. Four years later, in 1992, Joseph Burrows' murder conviction was affirmed by the Illinois Supreme Court, and he was scheduled to die by way of lethal injection, prior to Zellner's arrival on the case.

"I was called by the same group that had national funding and had given me the Eyler case so I really didn't want to take the call," Zellner said. "But they said to me, 'He's innocent. We're very sure he's innocent. And it's going to take a tremendous effort because he's facing the death penalty and he had an execution date set, within 120 days of when we took the case.'"

Zellner goes on explain how "we took Mr. Burrows' case and we began an intensive effort to save his life and vacate his conviction and because I had been with someone who was so profoundly guilty and evil, I became an expert in recognizing innocence. And I knew that Mr. Burrows was innocent, and this was not a DNA case. This turned on the testimony of his codefendant who had committed the murder."

As she dug into the case, Zellner realized the slaying was all about the ballistics from where the eighty-eight-year-old farmer was slain.

"After consulting with ballistics experts, I figured out that a woman had committed the murder, the murder of an eighty-eight-year-old farmer in downstate Illinois and there had been a struggle where shots had been fired into the ceiling, and I knew that the gentleman that was killed was so frail there wouldn't have been a struggle with my client, who was 6-foot-2 and weighed about 240 pounds."

The codefendant, Gayle Potter, age thirty-two, got a twelve-year prison sentence under a plea agreement with prosecutors where she fingered the thirty-five-year-old Burrows as the killer and another guy as an accomplice in the small-town robbery murder. Burrows and Ralph Frye, who was also wrongfully convicted of the killing, were actually about sixty miles away in the Champaign-Urbana area at the time of Dulin's death in tiny Iroquois County.

"And she was going to be out in about twelve months," Zellner said. "So I decided to focus all of my efforts on getting her, since I had become so skilled at getting confessions, getting her to confess to me that she had committed this murder."

Zellner said she knew that because of double jeopardy laws, Potter could not prosecuted for murder at that stage.

"So I visited her, fifty times. And we got to know each other and we talked about Mr. Burrows' children and the fact that he was months away from being executed and they were executing people in Illinois at that time. And she gradually came around to the position that she would testify at an evidentiary hearing which was in Kankakee, Illinois."

At that point, there had been hardly any death penalty cases in America that had ever been overturned by someone claiming to be innocent as Burrows.

"So I put her on the stand, not a lot of confidence in what she would do because she was very sociopathic. So the first question I asked her was 'Who shot William Dulin?' And she paused and she said, 'I shot William Dulin.' And it was that example of the narcissistic sociopathic, but the words came out of her mouth and it saved Mr. Burrows' life."

In the end, Potter was charged with perjury, and she served three more years of Illinois prison time. She never did get the death penalty.

"But I walked out the front door with him, and they took his handcuffs off, chains, we walked out the door, it was on the front page of the New York Times. And I thought to myself, this is what I want to do with the rest of my professional career. I have gotten big verdicts. I've won millions of dollars in verdicts, I know that I can convince a jury …but nothing in my mind topped the experience of thinking that you'd saved someone's life or you at least made a major contribution to saving a life."

Avery's crusaders believe it's only a matter of time before he will walk outside the Waupun Correctional Center in south-central Wisconsin as a smiling, teary-eyed free man, vindicated for a sloppy and corrupt murder investigation. But it took Avery eighteen years the first time around to convince the rest of the world of his innocence in the brutal attack that victimized Manitowoc businesswoman Penny Beerntsen in the late summer months of 1985.

Naturally, a second Avery exoneration would cause heads to spin in the Wisconsin criminal justice arena. Powerful politicians from both political parties, Democrats and Republicans, would be tarnished and shamed. For the time being, Wisconsin's judicial system, which does not have a reputation for honesty and integrity, is the last line of defense for the Avery-is-guilty faction. Wisconsin's politically connected people are uncomfortable with the latest worldwide *Making a Murderer* sequel. The first documentary was downright embarrassing enough. It exposed how Wisconsin's criminal justice system, how its small town police forces, still operate. Most of the dairy state consists of judges who are elected on popularity votes, not appointed after a rigorous interview and screening process as a number of states have established.

Although Wisconsin once had a proud reputation for being reform-oriented and one of the most progressive states in the country, it is not that way any longer. There are no meaningful reforms in Wisconsin to improve the state's blemished reputation when it comes to small-town police work, criminal forensics, and avoiding conflicts of interest in law enforcement. These are taboo topics that are not publicly talked about. And yet Wisconsin has an overabundance of unsolved murders and cold cases, because these crimes tend to occur inside the jurisdiction of largely untrained and inexperienced police agencies and sheriff's offices, people who are generally ill-equipped, inept, and simply not up to the task of solving complicated murder cases.

It is one thing for police cars to show up at the scene of the bloody murder and the killer is sitting on the front porch stoop with a cigarette dangling from his mouth, his hands in the air, and the bloody knife resting at the foot of his bloody sneakers. But what about the many unspeakable crimes of violence when the motive is not immediately apparent, when the killer is lurking in the shadows of society?

If these are the cards you are dealt, and you are a condemned but innocent prisoner, then you need a lawyer who can do more than just poke holes in the original testimony and evidence offered at your first murder trial. You need a lawyer who is not just regarded as an all-star in his or her neck of the woods, but a seasoned and skilled lawyer who has the reputation of being world-class, the most valuable player in his or her legal specialization. And you need that MVP lawyer who can get you access to an entire roster of internationally renowned experts, the cream of the crop, in complicated topics like biological and genetic science, criminal behavior, computer forensics, and prosecutorial misconduct.

If you are Steven Avery, you need the best of the best working on your side. You need someone such as attorney Kathleen Zellner from Illinois.

"Steven Avery started writing to me in 2011. I was in the middle of a civil rights case in Washington and so I really didn't have time to work on it and then his current girlfriend did contact me in September (2015). I did watch the documentary on Netflix. And the reason I took the case is because I felt that he had been discriminated against because his family was poor and they were uneducated. I know he's innocent. Now, I just have to prove it."[14]

But starting from scratch, trying to unwind a decade-old solved murder is no easy task. The Avery case is like climbing Mount Everest. It's wicked and nasty and there are numerous unexpected avalanches tumbling down the mountain trying to flatten Zellner and her crusaders in their quest for fairness and justice.

"I do not like people that are bullies," Zellner said. "I felt from a very young age that I was strong enough to protect people that were weaker or were victims.

---

14. Zellner interview with Newsweek, March 29, 2016

"Half of my exoneration cases have led to the apprehension of the real killer. I've probably solved way more murder cases than most homicide detectives. I think the good thing about the Netflix documentary was that it educated the public. Investigations can be corrupt, the evidence can be planted. Police officers can feel sufficiently pressured."

It goes without saying Zellner has few friends who are rooting for her to overturn Avery's murder conviction among Wisconsin's police law enforcement agencies.

This is hardly a surprise. In Wisconsin, it's quite common for police departments to keep their mouths shut and circle the wagons when someone in their profession gets outed for being a dirty, crooked cop.

Zellner is now in her third full year of providing free, pro bono legal representation to the world-famous Manitowoc County condemned inmate. Without Zellner's efforts, Avery is doomed. He has no chance for parole and will surely die inside of his lonely little prison cell and many of the deep, dark, and disturbing secrets regarding the true facts of the crime would remain bottled up forever.

But now, so it seems, Zellner is in her best position to expose the shenanigans, the evidence planting, the dirty tricks played by the likes of special prosecutor Ken Kratz. She is in prime position to pull down the curtains and show to the rest of the world the many instances where the evidence pieces magically appeared at the most opportune times of the murder investigation against Avery and later his sixteen-year-old developmentally disabled nephew, Brendan.

Given the international fervor generated by the Avery murder case, and given the backlash against the brave Emmy-award winning documentarians, Moira Demos and Laura Ricciardi, who have brought Wisconsin's boils to the rest of the world's attention, there is only one logical way for Avery to regain the freedom he lost on November 9, 2005.

Attorney Kathleen Zellner must be overwhelmingly successful in convincing America's judicial system that the person who killed Teresa, incinerated her body, and then cut her up into tiny pieces, was someone other than her client.

She must, in convincing fashion, put forth a compelling argument before the appeals court judges that the real evidence, the overlooked evidence, the concealed evidence, sheds light on the one or perhaps two culprits still roaming around and lurking in the shadows of society, bad people, terribly deranged, but people who still come and go freely in their Wisconsin communities to this very day, just as Manitowoc County's dangerous sexual predator Gregory Allen was allowed to do for another decade until he was finally captured and put in prison for life because he could not stop attacking and raping women during the 1980s and 1990s.

What if Zellner at this stage of the post-conviction process is on the right path?

What if she has uncovered the long suspected hidden truth, disturbing evidence that points to somebody other than Avery, but perhaps somebody who is still connected back to the family, somebody who was already familiar with the immediate landscape including Avery Road and Bear the dog?

Regardless of your opinion about Avery's guilt or innocence, you cannot deny that there were two strange people whose courtroom testimony helped sack Avery at his jury trial. One was Bobby, the nephew. The other was Scott Tadych, the abusive woman beater who is the current husband of Avery's dysfunctional sister, Barb, who has become an outcast within her family.

Tadych has a reputation of being a thug and a compulsive liar. Nothing out of his mouth can be trusted. He is regarded as one of the meanest monsters who live in the Mishicot-Two Rivers area, and he's behaved that way for years, court documents and police reports outline.

In November 2017, Zellner presented Wisconsin's circuit court with reams of evidence pointing at Bobby Dassey and Scott Tadych as being the most likely people involved in Teresa's death and dismemberment of her body.

"This new evidence establishes a reasonable probability that a different result would be reached at a new trial based upon the totality of the new evidence. In summary, this evidence consists of brand-new admissions from Barb Tadych and Mr. Tadych that they were aware that Ms. Halbach left the Avery property prior to her murder and an affidavit from Barb's stepson, Brad Dassey, that Barb tried to remove relevant and probative evidence from the Dassey computer before it was seized by police on April 21, 2006."[15]

---

15. November 1, 2017, Zellner's amended supplement to previously filed motion for reconsideration.

CHAPTER FIVE

SKINNY

On the day after Avery's arrest in Manitowoc for Teresa's killing, a strange, cryptic letter made it thirty miles north.

The "Green Bay Post Office pulled a piece of mail off their conveyor and reported it to Green Bay authorities." That piece of mail consisted of a letter without any envelope. It "was folded in thirds ... there was no stamp attached. The note, upon inspection, revealed that the writer indicated a body was burned up in the aluminum smelter at 3 a.m. on Friday morning ... the note was signed SIKIKEY ... the note was written in blue ink and had both printing and cursive writing in the body of the note."[16]

Indeed, the note was bizarre and baffling. One thing was certain. It was not Avery's handwriting. Was it from a crackpot or perhaps somebody with inside knowledge of Teresa's murder? The police were never able to decipher the letter's origin. Actually, they chose to downplay its relevance. After all, if the letter pointed at somebody else instead of Avery, that would have posed a public relations nightmare of epic proportions for Manitowoc and Calumet Counties as well as the Wisconsin Department of Justice. These agencies wanted Avery locked up and gone. They were tired of him being the public crusader for criminal justice reform in Wisconsin. None of the bad and incompetent cops of Wisconsin wanted anything to change. They wanted to maintain status quo and Avery's constant appearance in the

16. John Dedering activity report, Nov. 10, 2005 contact with Green Bay Police Department

press only reminded the public at large about the weaknesses and flaws in Wisconsin's fractured judicial system.

As it turned out, John Dedering, the Calumet investigator who interviewed Bobby, drew the assignment to follow up on the mysterious letter. He learned "the mail that was being sorted in Green Bay comes from Manitowoc, Two Rivers, Green Bay and De Pere. The Green Bay police officer, Fred Laitinen, advised that gloves were used to handle the piece of mail and the SIKIKEY letter would be held at Green Bay's Police Department."

Despite the intense statewide media feeding frenzy surrounding Avery's arrest, there had been no stories published regarding the prospect of Teresa's bones being burned. Then, two days after the mysterious letter, *The Herald Times Reporter* of Manitowoc ran a front-page newspaper article explaining "burned human remains, key to Halbach's SUV, found on Avery's land."

The mysterious letter writer had prophetically revealed, "Body was burnt up in Alunamon (sic) Smelter. 3 A M Fridy (sic) Morn. SIKIKEY."

The odd letter was not signed with the writer's real name. Rather, it ended with the following key identifiers: "Manitowoc Sherff (sic) Avery."

Finally, a dozen years later, private investigator James Kirby traveled to Manitowoc to interview Lisa Novachek, payroll employee at Wisconsin Aluminum Foundry. She also worked at the foundry in 2005 and has familiarity with her company's employees. The business has been a mainstay in Manitowoc since the early 1900s. It's tucked inside an old industrial neighborhood and remains a vibrant blue-collar operation to this day.

"I showed Ms. Novachek the 'SIKIKEY' note which was reportedly found during sorting at the Green Bay post office … Novachek told me there were twenty people who worked the night shift at the aluminum foundry in early November 2005 and that about half of them were illiterate or partially literate and that the 'SIKIKEY' note could have been written by one of them. Ms. Novachek told me that Scott Tadych's nickname at work in 2005 was 'Skinny' and that 'SIKIKEY' may be a reference to Scott Tadych."[17]

The Wisconsin Aluminum Foundry has been in Manitowoc for decades. It's where a portion of Teresa Halbach's bones and teeth may have been thrown into the industrial fire.

When Scott Tadych was twenty-nine, he was hauled into the Manitowoc County Jail on charges of battery, disorderly conduct, and criminal damage to property. And it would not be the only time he would end up in one of the local jails for criminal acts of violent tendencies.

According to the criminal complaint, officers in nearby Two Rivers met with a woman on July 7, 1997, at her residence. "She had an altercation with her live-in boyfriend, Scott Tadych. (She) stated Scott had accused her of seeing another male and she told him to leave the residence ...

17. Third supplemental affidavit of James Kirby, Nov. 16, 2017

Scott began packing up some clothing and personal items ... at one point she walked past Scott and he was swinging at the back of her head with his left hand but he missed her ... she told Scott that was the last straw and she went into the TV room to get his duffle bag and take it to the kitchen."[18]

At that point, "Scott went out of control and picked up the water cooler and slammed it down hitting the kitchen chair and the microwave cart ... she then called her mom and dad to come over because she feared for her life and her son ... Scott kept making comments to her and he pushed her two times."

Tadych decided to take out his anger and rage upon the woman's laundry.

"Scott went downstairs and threw all her laundry, clean and dirty, all over the basement floor and in the drain. Scott also punched her in the chest with his right fist. Scott walked back up the stairs and (the victim) was going to follow when Scott locked the basement door ... when she opened the door, Scott punched her again ... Scott's mother and father had arrived and both she and (his) mother had seen Scott strike her. Scott tried to push her down the basement stairs and shut the door."

When Tadych went into the garage, a fight erupted over the fishing rods.

"She was going to take the rods away from Scott, and he slapped her on the right arm. Scott filled up his car with his items and told his mom to get his brother."

As tensions escalated, Tadych drilled his girlfriend's son, who was only a boy.

"Scott punched (him) in the upper left chest with his right fist. (The boy) fell to the floor and was crying ... her son ... is 11 years old."

More chaos ensued.

---

18. State of Wisconsin vs. Scott A. Tadych 1997CF237

"Scott went outside and ripped the CB out of her truck ... She went into her truck to check for damage, and Scott was screaming at her and he pulled her hair ... after Scott pulled out the radio, her radio, clock, blinkers, and back up lights would not work. At no time did she give anyone permission to damage her property."

The victim's eleven-year-old son gave this account to Two Rivers Police: "he saw Scott pushing his mom ... Scott went downstairs to get some clothes and Scott began to throw clothes all over and Scott tried to rip up (his victim's) sweatshirts. (The boy) stated he was fearful Scott would hurt his mom ... Scott began screaming at him and calling him a lard ass and a fat ass."

Things got nasty when the child tried to stop Tadych from harming his mother.

"Scott went back upstairs and was pushing his mom around inside the kitchen ... he stepped between the two and Scott knocked him to the ground ... he fell to the floor and he was crying because it hurt."

Under a plea bargain, Scott Tadych was found guilty of criminal battery. On October 13, 1998, he was ordered to stay in the local jail for 135 days.

Seven years later, at the time of Teresa's disappearance, Tadych worked the overnight shift at the aluminum foundry near Manitowoc's downtown. All of a sudden, the SIKIKEY letter arrived in Green Bay suggesting Teresa's body was incinerated. Was the Wisconsin Aluminum Foundry plant in Manitowoc central to the missing photographer's dismemberment?

Was "SIKIKEY" an illiterate worker's best attempt at trying to identify Tadych by his nickname of "Skinny" at the foundry?

As of 2006, plant foreman Keith Schaefer had known Tadych for nine years.

"Keith went on to say he had been hearing Scott Tadych telling some of the workers in the plant about information on the Teresa Halbach murder/homicide investigation. Keith had heard that Scott had not shown up for work on October 31, 2005, however, he had heard he went to see his mother in the hospital. Scott had been telling people he had seen the fire on Halloween by Steven Avery and Scott, or the other people, made it sound like he had gotten out of the vehicle and actually talked to Steven by the fire. Keith also heard from other guys that Scott had noticed stains on the pants and shirts of one of Barbara's kids."[19]

As many people may remember, the prosecution maintained the infamous bleached blue jeans belonged to Avery's mentally disabled nephew, Brendan. Attorney Zellner strongly suspects that any cryptic conversations were not in regard to Avery's slow nephew. Rather, any phone calls made to Tadych at the Wisconsin Aluminum Foundry concerned Barb's other son, Bobby. After all, Brendan, sixteen, and Scott Tadych had nothing in common and had no real relationship whatsoever. On the other hand, Bobby and Tadych were tight.

After Teresa went missing, "Keith described Scott as being extra edgy lately, a short-tempered, angry person. Keith said he is a chronic liar and does not really get along with a lot of people at the plant and would never know when he would blow up at somebody. Keith felt Scott also knew more about the murder than he had told people, and Keith felt Scott could be very capable of the murder or knowing something more."

Yet, all the while, Tadych's romantic relationship with Barb remained fine.

"However, because of the case, he did seem disturbed by what was going on," Schaefer said. "After Steven was arrested, Scott had thought it had been a set up and that

19. Interviews of Keith Schaefer, Leonard Brouchoud, Thomas Culp, March 30, 2006, Investigator Wendy Baldwin

he was being framed; however, a week later, Scott did not believe this anymore and thought Steven was guilty."

CHAPTER SIX

AVERY'S PHONE CALL

Although he remained condemned to live out the rest of his days here on earth inside a Wisconsin Department of Corrections prison cellblock, Avery's spirits were high and his mood upbeat toward the end of 2017.

After all, his prospects of regaining his freedom or gaining a new trial were stronger than ever, thanks to Zellner's energy and fighting spirit. But back in Manitowoc County, the skies were dark and growing more ominous. People were becoming unhinged as the master at overturning wrongful convictions was starting to reveal her cards. As he remained at Waupun, Avery made a phone call to his sister, Barb, on October 24, 2017. Here's a synopsis of the call, which was recorded and included in the court record of Avery's post-conviction appeal.

The call concerned the personal computer inside the trailer of Avery's sister, Barb. This was the computer that her son Bobby used to fuel his wicked sexual fantasies involving gore, violence, and death.

"Why is all that shit on the computer?" Avery asked.[20]

"There was nothing on my fucking computer. All this, I didn't even have fucking Internet back then," his sister lied.

"Yes, you did."

"No, I didn't."

"What do you mean you didn't?"

---

20. Steven Avery call with Barbara Tadych on Oct. 24, 2017 and Scott Tadych transcript, amended supplement to previously filed motion for reconsideration.

"No, I didn't have Internet."

"You did."

"No, I didn't."

"At that time you did. Before that you did."

"No I didn't."

"You didn't? Well, it's on the computer."

"I did not have Internet."

"Well."

"Well nothing. I didn't."

Zellner has pointed out to the court handling Avery's post-conviction appeal that "Barb's vehement denial that her computer had access to the Internet at the time of Ms. Halbach's murder is probative because it is unequivocally false."

But why lie?

Was Barb lying to protect her older son Bobby? Was she content to see her youngest son, her feeble-minded son, Brendan, carted off to prison if it meant protecting someone else in the family for the murder?

Prior to the confrontational prison call, one of Zellner's expert witnesses, forensic computer expert Gary Hunt, conducted a forensic examination of Barb's desktop computer.

"The computer was used to access violent images of young deceased females, rape, torture, incest, and pedophilia on the Internet at times when only Bobby was home."[21]

Hunt's analysis also turned up evidence that someone inside the home had gone to great lengths to destroy information off the computer's hard drive. The computer record deletions were specific to the time frame of Teresa's disappearance and murder.

"Barb's denial is especially telling given that she took steps to delete the disturbing images before police seized her

---

21. 2017 affidavit of Gary Hunt, senior forensic examiner with QDiscovery LLC

computer on April 21, 2006. This is additional new evidence that supports Mr. Avery's claim that the recovered images on the Dassey computer meet the legitimacy tendency test established by Denny by implicating Bobby in Ms. Halbach's murder."[22]

Not only did Barb remove incriminating evidence against her son, Bobby, she also apparently knew that Teresa left the Avery property, alive, during the afternoon of October 31, 2005.

"Barb and Mr. Tadych have recently made admissions that Ms. Halbach left the Avery property before the murder," Zellner revealed.

These bombshell admissions came during the same recorded phone call of Avery and his sister Barb, October 24, 2017.

"Bobby's home," Steven Avery reminded his sister.

"He wasn't always home," she answered.

"Well, most of the time he was home."

"No."

Then out of nowhere, a male voice interjected.

"He doesn't know fucking shit."

It was the violent man from Manitowoc County who was eavesdropping. But why was Scott Tadych eavesdropping? Why was he so paranoid about his wife's conversation about Teresa's murder a dozen years afterward?

As Tadych listened intently, Avery informed his sister that Bobby saw Teresa leave the property.

"She left," Avery repeated.

"That's right," Scott Tadych interjected.

"Yeah. She left," Barb Tadych repeated.

"Yeah," Avery said.

"Yeah," his sister repeated.

"Well," Avery explained, "he didn't testify for that."

---

22. Steven Avery's amended supplement to previously filed motion for consideration, dated Nov. 1, 2017

Zellner now had tape-recorded statements from Barb and Scott Tadych agreeing that Teresa left the Avery compound on her final day of life, information that doesn't mesh with their original trial testimony.

"Mr. Tadych's response indicates either that Bobby had told him that Bobby observed Ms. Halbach leave the property or Mr. Tadych's response indicates that Mr. Tadych observed and or had contact with Ms. Halbach after she left the property."

But if Tadych and Barb were now admitting Teresa left Avery Road, not realizing their conversation was being recorded by the prison, what does that say for the crucial trial testimony served up by disgraced special prosecutor Ken Kratz's main trial witness?

Kratz highlighted Bobby's testimony, knowing full well it was sure to be the biggest televised criminal trial ever in Wisconsin.

"Barb and Mr. Tadych's admissions are crucial to Mr. Avery's defense because the most important eyewitness for the State was Bobby, who testified that Ms. Halbach was still on the Avery property and that he saw Ms. Halbach approaching Mr. Avery's trailer before he left."

On the other hand, if Bobby committed the murder, is it realistic to expect he would testify with truthfulness? Or, would he lie on the witness stand, realizing a guilty verdict against his uncle served his own needs?

Anyhow, here's how Tadych behaved during the October 2017 call between Avery and Barb where Tadych was eavesdropping the entire time.

"Let me talk to the cock-sucking loser. Fuck him. All you do is, the only evidence they got is against him, and he's trying to gasp for air to blame it on somebody else. He's a fucking loser. I wasn't even on that property that day, you goddamn idiot. That's how fucking intelligent you are. You want to get out yourself so you can get out and do something stupid again, you dumb fuck. I can't wait to kick your fucking ass. Fucking little fucker!"

Avery: "I ain't scared of him. I ain't scared of him."

Tadych: "You ruined my fucking life. You ruined my fucking name, dumb cock sucker. You fucking jailbird motherfucker!"

"Yep."

"I hate the cocksucker. You ruined my fucking life!"

"Yeah."

Avery reminded his sister how her husband was solely responsible for making outrageous false claims to the police suggesting Avery was molesting her sons including Brendan.

"It came from him. So he wanted the cops to put all the blame on me. So who would say something like, that I did something to the boys?"

"I don't know. I didn't read none of this shit, OK?"

"Yeah. That's why nobody wanted to read nothing and see about nothing. Any guilty person, uh, would say and try to blame it onto somebody else. Oh, I was fucking with the boys."

Now, the conversation fueled Tadych's rage.

"Yeah, fuck him, the cocksucker. He's a stupid fuck. Going down to fuck your family when he got out of prison the first time!" Tadych roared.

"Yeah? See. That fucker needs to be locked up. How about his mother?" Avery asked his sister.

Avery alluded to the fact that Tadych tried to attack his own mother during one of Tadych's domestics that resulted in an arrest.

"What about his mother?" his sister inquired.

This time, Tadych blew a gasket. He began screaming at Avery, loud as ever.

"Yeah, you talking about my mother, you cock-sucker? I'll put you in the fucking ground!"

"Yeah?" Avery asked.

"Fucking bastard," Tadych screamed. "I don't give a fuck. The cock-sucker's a loser. He's grasping for air. The only evidence they got is against him."

"Uh, his mother had to call the cops on him," Avery reminded his sister.

"He never touched his mother," Barb professed.

"You stupid fucker," Tadych yelled.

"I already asked her all of that," Avery told them both.

"Smart man you are. Thirty-six years in prison and you know the world. I hate him," Tadych shouted.

Avery's sister had enough.

"This needs to stop."

"It's gonna stop when it's over."

"It needs to stop now."

"I can't," Avery said.

"Well, like I said, you will end up with a dead sister because I can't take this shit no more."

"Well then shut the computer off then. Shut everything off. You don't need a phone. Just go to work."

"Yeah, OK, whatever."

From Zellner's perspective, the heated phone call was revelatory.

"Bobby and Mr. Tadych placed themselves in the same location as Ms. Halbach when she received her last phone call. Mr. Tadych's multiple inconsistent statements severely undermine his credibility at trial. His recent telephone call with Mr. Avery demonstrates his knowledge that Ms. Halbach had left the Avery property on October 31, 2005. The October 24, 2017 telephone call also demonstrates that Mr. Tadych has violent, homicidal propensities manifested by his uncontrollable temper. Mr. Tadych threatens to physically assault Mr. Avery and even more disturbingly, to put Mr. Avery 'in the fucking ground.'"

Back in 2007, special prosecutor Kratz glossed over the uncomfortable fact that the majority of Teresa's charred bones, supposedly burned at Avery's outdoor backyard pit on a cool autumn night, were never found. Practically all of her teeth were absent from Avery's burn pile pit. Meanwhile, some of the charred bones pointed to the neighboring property along Avery Road.

"It is an undisputed fact that some of Ms. Halbach's bones were found in the Dassey burn barrel," Zellner argued. "No credible explanation has ever been provided by the State as to why Ms. Halbach's bones would be in the Dassey burn barrel if Mr. Avery had burned her whole body in his burn pit."

CHAPTER SEVEN

COMPUTER BLUES

At the six month mark of the murder probe, Avery and his mentally challenged sixteen-year-old nephew, Brendan, were both incarcerated, but something wasn't right back on Avery Road.

Wisconsin police were becoming intensely focused on Barb's desktop computer. This was the home computer primarily used by her nineteen-year-old loner of a son, Bobby. The computer was kept inside his bedroom.

But before Wisconsin's police got a search warrant to seize the computer, Barb Janda was one step ahead of them.

"Mr. Avery has discovered new evidence that Barb hired a person to make deletions of incriminating evidence prior to the computer being seized by the police on April 21, 2006."[23]

Bolstering Avery's case, Brad Dassey shed light on a conversation he vividly remembers taking place during a drive to the Sheboygan County Jail to visit his half-brother, Brendan, back in 2006.

"My father Peter Dassey was with us. Barb stated that she had hired someone to reformat her home computer. She wanted to know if 'reformatting' would remove what was on the computer. Barb admitted her computer had some pornography stored on it, and she claimed the computer had 'viruses' on it. She had the reformatting done shortly before the authorities seized her computer. Barb commented that she did not think the person she hired knew what he was

---

23. Motion for Reconsideration, November 1, 2017

doing. She said she did not want anyone to get what was on her computer."[24]

Brad Dassey said he "thought that Barb was trying to remove evidence relevant to Ms. Halbach's murder. The authorities interviewed Brad after he reported this information, but he was not called as a witness, by either side, to testify at Mr. Avery or Brendan's trials."

In July 2017, Zellner's computer forensic expert, Gary Hunt, unearthed some, but not all, of the dirty little secrets from Bobby Dassey's home computer. The missing files only deepened the mystery surrounding Bobby and the time frame in question.

The home computer deletions were as follows:

August 23-26, 2005
August 28 - September 11, 2005
September 14-15, 2005
September 24 - October 22, 2005
October 23-24, 2005
October 26 - November 2, 2005
November 4-13, 2005
November 15 - December. 3, 2005

Of the computer files that were recovered, they paint a dark picture. Foremost, they undermine Bobby's incriminating trial testimony as Kratz's first witness.

"Bobby testified at Mr. Avery's trial that after he arrived home on October 31, 2005, from working the 10 p.m. to 6 a.m. shift, he went to sleep until 2:30 p.m. Bobby's testimony is demonstrably false. Mr. Hunt has determined that the Dassey computer was used to access the Internet at 6:05 a.m., 6:28 a.m., 6:31 a.m., 7 a.m., 9:33 a.m., 10:09 a.m., 1:09 p.m., and 1:51 p.m.

"Bobby was the only person home during those hours because his mother, Barb, was at work, Blaine and Brendan were in school, and Bryan lived with his girlfriend.

---

24. Brad Dassey affidavit October 30, 2017

"(This) is powerful evidence that Barb was aware that her computer had incriminating files on it that were relevant to Ms. Halbach's murder. Barb's efforts to delete the files before the computer was examined by authorities – in addition to her recent denials that she even had the ability to access the Internet during the time in question – reinforces this conclusion."[25]

In my 2015 WildBlue Press true-crime book, *Body of Proof*, nineteen-year-old Christopher Edwards of Omaha, Nebraska, emerged as the prime suspect in the disappearance of his missing girlfriend, Jessica O'Grady. The two worked at the Omaha Lone Star Steakhouse. Her body was never found, but the Omaha Police and Douglas County Sheriff's Office moved forward with an arrest in the hopes of achieving Omaha's first-ever no-body murder conviction before a jury.

One of the key pieces of evidence came from Edwards' laptop computer. The forensic examination of his computer determined that he was trolling the Internet in the days prior to killing his girlfriend, searching on medical websites for morbid details about the human body, including a Google keyword search for information relating to "arteries." The day after Jessica O'Grady disappeared, Edwards was caught on videotape at his local Walgreens store, where he purchased several bottles of white-out and cleaning supplies. When the police asked to look underneath his bed and his bedroom mattress, he initially balked at the idea, but then consented.

When his bedroom mattress was flipped over, it was saturated with blood. Later, the jury heard all of the evidence and found Christopher Edwards guilty of murder. He remains in the Nebraska Department of Correction. To this day, he refuses to reveal where he disposed of O'Grady's body.

---

25. Steven Avery's amended supplement, November 1, 2017

Meanwhile, Zellner also believes the computer forensics found on Bobby's computer can connect the dots for Teresa's demise and dismemberment.

"The forensic examination of Barb's computer performed by law enforcement did not permit law enforcement to detect Barb's efforts to delete computer records of eight periods in 2005. The missing records, which were presumed deleted, were only discovered using 2017 forensic technology."

Had that information been known at Avery's trial, it could have been a game changer for the defense. Unfortunately, Avery's lawyers Jerry Buting and Dean Strang were operating in the dark.

"Mr. Avery cannot be faulted for failing to detect Barb's efforts at concealment prior to his trial; in fact, as recently as October 24, 2017, Barb denied that she even had Internet during this period of time. The evidence is material because it supports Mr. Avery's theory of an alternative perpetrator … there was no evidence elicited at trial concerning Barb's efforts to remove evidence of the Halbach murder on her home computer," Zellner said.

But questions linger to this day. What had Barb come upon on her family's computer? Was she out to protect someone sinister in her family, someone the authorities had chosen to overlook? Was she willing to sacrifice her relationship with Brendan in order to keep her other more desirable family members out of law enforcement custody?

Had someone in law enforcement or the prosecution team tipped her off about the upcoming planned search of her family's computer?

"Shortly after my conversation with Barb I contacted the authorities because I thought Barb was trying to remove evidence relevant to the Teresa Halbach murder from her computer," Brad Dassey said. "I do not know who reformatted Barb's computer. I was interviewed by the authorities after I reported this information to them."

CHAPTER EIGHT

BOBBY'S OBSESSIONS

The mystery person Barb paid to obliterate data on the desktop computer stored inside Bobby's bedroom on Avery Road did a good job, but the computer tech was not perfect, as outlined by Gary Hunt, the senior forensic examiner with QDiscovery. He has been certified as an AccessData Certified Examiner since 2012 and a Certified Computer Examiner since 2013.

Gary Hunt is senior forensic examiner with QDiscovery. His work on the post-conviction process uncovered dark, violent pornography on Bobby Dassey's home computer.

"At the time of the 2006 investigation, there were three leading forensic examination utilities: Encase, Forensic Toolkit, and X-Ways. It is important to note that the platforms have significantly evolved since the 2006 investigation," Hunt explained. "FTK specifically added new features and parsing capabilities allowing for more efficient investigations and greater insight into the data at stake. Additionally, Internet Evidence Finder was not first released until March 22, 2009. The bulk of my analysis revolved around web activity which was streamlined by the use of IEF."

Approximately twelve years after Teresa's terrorizing death, Hunt uncovered startling new information on Bobby Dassey's home computer. This information was not[26] known to Avery's trial lawyers, Dean Strang and Jerry Buting. It also wasn't known to the producers and documentarians of the original *Making a Murderer*.

This information was uncovered by Kathleen T. Zellner & Associates, but not until 2017.

"There was a single user account on the computer named 'HP Owner,'" Hunt found out. "The HP Owner user conducted the following Internet searches on various dates: teen pussy, 11 year old sex, 12 year old sex, 15 year old girl, 15 year old girl naked, aaa teens, cute kid naked, fuck preteen girl, hot teen pussy, kid slut, kid sluts, naked teens, naked young girl, naked young pussy, nude teenage girl, nude teenage girls, pre teen sluts, pree (sic) teens naked, preteen boobs, preteen busty, preteen girl model naked, preteen girl nude, pre-teen girls naked, preteen naked, preteen pussy, preteen sex, preteen sluts, pre-teen girls naked, preteens naked, pre-teens naked, teen black pussy, teen girls naked, teen porn, teen pussy, teen redhead pussy, teen sex, teen twits, teen twat, teenage pussy, teens naked, teens spread wide open, wet teen pussy, young 13 girl nude, young 13 year old girl nude, young 13 year old naked, young 13 yr old naked, horsecum, car accident, car accidents, deseised (sic) girls, dessesed (sic) girls, diseased girls, drawned (sic) girls, drawned pussy, drowned girl, drowned girl nude, drowned pussy, fast car accident, gun to haed (sic), gun to head, knife

---

26. Affidavit of Gary Hunt, October 26, 2017

goes through skin, rotten girl, seeing bones, hot girls, and tempo car accident."

At the time of these repetitive searches, Bobby was nineteen and worked the 10 p.m. to 6 a.m. shift at the metal processing facility in Manitowoc, not too far from his home.

From Bobby's bedroom computer, Hunt recovered two pictures "in the unallocated space, the first showing Teresa Halbach and Steven Avery, the second showing only Teresa Halbach."

Both images were carved from the unallocated space of the computer hard drive. Since the files were recovered via data carving, there is no file system metadata available. In other words, the files' original paths, names, and creation dates, accessed or modified timestamps are not available.

"In conclusion, the computer was used to run Internet searches including but not limited to those identified in (the previous paragraph) and Exhibit B. Some images displayed as a result of the searches were clicked on by the user. Additionally, two pictures of Teresa Halbach were recovered from the unallocated space. These images do not have any date attributes or information suggesting how they arrived on the computer."

Meanwhile, a law enforcement heavyweight who dedicated his career to putting ruthless killers in prison also came to Zellner's aid in her quest to regain Steven Avery's freedom.

Gregg McCrary is a distinguished retired FBI agent who teaches policing at Marymount University in Arlington, Virginia. He is a nationally regarded violent crime behavioral expert. He signed a sworn affidavit on October 23, 2017.

"I have reviewed the Wisconsin DOJ report summarizing the forensic computer examination of the Dassey computer. It is my opinion, based on this report, in addition to the report of Kathleen T. Zellner & Associates' forensic computer examiner, that Bobby Dassey's Internet searches reflects a co-morbidity of sexual paraphilias. The sexual and violent content he was searching for and viewing should have alerted investigators to Bobby Dassey as a possible perpetrator of Teresa Halbach's murder.[27]

"The content of these images, combined with the obsessive use of the computer to view these images and Bobby Dassey's entanglement in the investigation into the murder of Teresa Halbach, should have alerted the investigators to Bobby Dassey as someone having an elevated risk to perpetrate a sexually motivated violent crime such as the violent crime perpetrated on Teresa Halbach."

In hindsight, McCrary found it troublesome that Bobby turned into a star witness against his uncle.

"The fact that Bobby Dassey became the key witness for the prosecution and that his testimony placed Teresa Halbach on the property 'walking over to Steven's trailer' after she completed her assignment, interjected himself into the prosecution in a way that should have raised the suspicions of reasonably trained detectives, if that testimony is untrue. Based upon the affidavit of Bryan Dassey, it appears that Bobby Dassey's testimony was untrue."

McCrary is regarded as a foremost expert witness in violent crimes. He worked at the FBI for twenty-five years. On the other hand, John Dedering, the Calumet County Sheriff's Investigator, who interviewed Bobby, had practically no real world experience handling murder cases because it was largely cow country.

In fact, Dedering even admitted during his questioning of Bobby how he had basically shied away from entering the Dassey's property off Avery Road. The investigator chose to keep himself away from the inside of Bobby's garage where Bobby was dismembering a deer carcass that he chose to grab off the road shortly after Teresa vanished. The deer carcass was taken home by Bobby after the Manitowoc

27. Second Supplemental Affidavit, Gregg McCrary, October 20, 2017

County Sheriff's Department had already made visits to Avery Road on successive days to interview his uncle, who denied any involvement in Teresa's disappearance and freely gave detectives permission to walk through his trailer to look for signs of foul play.

"In my opinion, a prudent investigator would have considered Bobby Dassey a suspect and would have investigated him as such," McCrary said. "There is no evidence that authorities ever investigated, much less eliminated, him as a suspect or investigated the discrepancies in his trial testimony."

***

After Dedering and Wisconsin DCI agent Kevin Heimerl finished their non-accusatory interview with Bobby on November 9, 2005, they led him down a hallway to undergo a physical examination with Faye Fritsch. She was a nurse at the Aurora Medical Center near Manitowoc.

Dedering noted he questioned Bobby Dassey regarding scratches on Bobby's upper back. Bobby Dassey stated these were due to his Labrador puppy jumping on his upper back.

"He stated he was bent down to put on his shoes (this morning) when the dog jumped up and scratched him," Dedering wrote. "I did examine Dassey's shirt and could find no obvious holes or tears."[28]

The investigator spoke with Dr. Laura Vogel-Schwartz to get her assessment.

"She stated it was not likely they were over a week old. She stated it is her opinion that the scratches were fairly recent. The scratches to Bobby Dassey's back were photographed. We did escort Bobby Dassey from the

---

28. Interview of Bobby Dassey by Investigator John Dedering, November 9, 2005

hospital. He was released, and I observed him speaking with his mother in the parking lot."

A baby Labrador puppy supposedly dug its claws deep into Bobby's back, so he claimed. Nobody in Wisconsin law enforcement ever bothered to follow up and investigate the veracity of Bobby's claim. After all, the case's lead investigators, who had no business lurking around the Aurora hospital, were intently focused on something far more important to them. They wanted to personally monitor the DNA collection from their new prisoner, Avery, who was being asked to submit fresh new DNA samples to the lead Wisconsin detectives even though he was only being arrested on a charge of being a felon in possession of a gun, not murder. Prosecutor Kratz would not charge Avery with first-degree murder and mutilation of a corpse until a week later, November 15, 2005.

But why did Mark Wiegert and his sidekick, Tom Fassbender of the Wisconsin DOJ, need to collect more DNA samples from Steven Avery? After all, Avery had given up his DNA samples to the state of Wisconsin when he was serving state prison time for Gregory Allen's crimes.

Nonetheless, Fassbender and Wiegert teamed up on the afternoon of November 9, 2005, to pick up Avery at his residence and bring him straight to the hospital where they could be inside the room as they observed the events unfold.

"Steven asked what the DNA samples were for," Fassbender's report showed. "He was essentially advised that samples were being obtained from everyone that has been around the area and that they are used for standards for comparison. He advised that they already have his."

Theoretically, if Wisconsin already had Avery's DNA samples on file in 2003, this raises a legitimate question. Why did Wiegert and Fassbender decide they needed to make a special trip to the hospital to take yet another DNA specimen from Avery? Also, why were Wiegert and Fassbender absent from the physical examination of Bobby and the collection of Bobby's DNA sample yet the two were inside the doctor's office as so-called passive observers when the nurse took an abundance of additional DNA from Avery?

"After the physical examination, Faye Fritsch did the buccal swabs on Steven Avery. The buccal swabs were taken from Steven Avery's mouth at 1:51 p.m. and I saw Faye Fritsch place the swabs into an envelope and seal the envelope. The envelope containing the buccal swabs was turned over to me by Faye Fritsch at 1:53 p.m.," Calumet Sgt. Bill Tyson's reports show.

From there, Avery was taken into another examination room for palm prints and fingerprints. A correctional officer handed off those prints to Tyson at 2:10 p.m.

Regardless of Avery's guilt or innocence, however, it appears that monkey business was going on at the hospital and that the registered nurse, Faye Fritsch, then thirty-five, of Two Rivers, was complicit.

"During the physical examination of my body on November 9, 2005, the nurse took two swabs near my groin at the request of Calumet County Investigator Wiegert," Steve Avery said. "I saw the nurse who took the groin swabs hand them to Investigator Wiegert as I was being taken out of the exam room by Agent Fassbender and the nurse. I saw Investigator Wiegert pretend to put the swabs in the hospital-type waste basket but I did not actually see the swabs leave his hands and fall into the basket."[29]

Fassbender's report noted there were numerous small scratches, scars, and sores documented on Avery's body. This was all understandable since Avery did metal scraping at the salvage business. "There was one particular wound that entailed a cut to Steven's middle finger on his right hand. The cut had scabbed over."

During the exam, Fassbender left briefly to fetch Avery a can of soda. "Fassbender asked Steven if he wanted

29. Affidavit of Steven Avery, November 23, 2016

something to drink, and he said he would take a soda. Fassbender left the room and got him a soda."

Unknown to Avery at the time, this was another way for Fassbender to obtain another DNA sample of Avery, without Avery's knowledge.

But Fassbender made sure he was back in the doctor's room, with Wiegert, when the DNA harvests were taking place. Both men kept their mouths quiet when the nurse carried on and began to take additional DNA samples from Avery that were totally unnecessary and outside the scope of their court-obtained search warrant. Incidentally, these were DNA samples that the same nurse would not attempt to take from Bobby that same afternoon.

"Towards the end of the examination," Fassbender's report reflected, "(Nurse Faye) Fritsch had the lights turned out in the examination room and utilized a Woods light to illuminate any secretions on Steven's body. Fritsch subsequently took two swabs in Steven's groin area. After that, she continued and was going to take more swabs when (myself) and Investigator Wiegert conferred and determined that the search warrant did not call for that type of exam.

"Investigator Wiegert immediately stopped Fritsch and the exam was concluded. Investigator Wiegert had Fritsch dispose of the two swabs into the Biohaz/sharps bin. Fritsch also took buccal swabs from Steven's saliva."

It's quite curious to look back years later and realize that both Wiegert and Fassbender thought it was crucial they needed to be sitting in the very same room as the Manitowoc nurse who collected Avery's DNA, only to mess up and obtain more DNA samples than necessary. But if being present to watch Avery's DNA collection was so essential, why did both Wiegert and Fassbender choose not to accompany Avery down the hall to obtain his fingerprints and palm prints as well?

"Agent Fassbender's report is not credible because Nurse Fritsch never mentions in her charting disposing of the groin swabs," Zellner said. "Agent Fassbender's report directly contradicts Mr. Avery's account of this examination as described in his affidavit.

"Contrary to Agent Fassbender's report, Investigator Wiegert told Nurse Fritsch that he would discard the swabs while Agent Fassbender escorted Mr. Avery into a separate room to get his fingerprints. As Mr. Avery followed Agent Fassbender and Nurse Fritsch out of the examination room, Mr. Avery heard investigator Wiegert tell Nurse Fritsch to give him the groin swabs and Mr. Avery observed Investigator Wiegert walk to the examination room receptacle as if to discard the groin swabs. Mr. Avery observed that Investigator Wiegert did not drop the groin swabs into the receptacle."[30]

The illegal collection of the groin swabs is yet another reason why Avery's murder conviction warrants being overturned, according to Zellner.

"Investigator Wiegert, as an experienced investigator, would have known that taking groin swabs was not authorized by the search warrant, which permitted only the collection of saliva and blood samples. It is therefore reasonable to conclude from this clear violation of Mr. Avery's Fourth Amendment rights that Investigator Wiegert planned to use the illegally seized groin swabs from Mr. Avery to plant Mr. Avery's DNA on other crime scene evidence," Zellner stated.

30. Zellner Motion for Post-Conviction Relief June 7, 2017

CHAPTER NINE

SHADY DEPARTMENT

Where there are shuttered factories and boarded up businesses, one of the most desirable jobs in an economically depressed blue-collar area is one that provides a shiny badge, holster, and loaded gun.

A fear factor and an intimidating law enforcement presence often keep the locals in check, and cast an eye of suspicion on the community's outsiders, notably minorities. In communities like this, a job as a county sheriff deputy means power and prestige. These jobs are hard to come by.

Positions in full-time law enforcement carry generous fringe benefits, enormous job security, and generous taxpayer-funded retirement pensions that most of the taxpaying public won't have in their line of work. Work in the public sector, particularly in law enforcement, and you tend to make above-average wages. Usually, there's a steady flow of overtime pay and built-in annual pay raises that most people in the private sector would envy.

Being a sheriff's deputy in a small town means something. It means clout. It makes you somebody. You are given enormous power to mess with somebody's civil rights and freedoms. Want to harass somebody? Want to make somebody's life miserable? Want to intimidate someone? Want to rough someone up? Most cops who operate on the dark side of the law know what they can get away with. Fortunately, most people in law enforcement are honorable, righteous, and truly want to do the public's good. They are our true public servants, and they try hard to keep our communities safe. For them we owe a debt of gratitude.

But not all cops are cut from the same cloth and that's just as true in Wisconsin. Around northeastern Wisconsin, the Manitowoc County Sheriff's Department gained notoriety on a number of cases involving strong suspicions of a police cover up.

Upon taking office in January 2007, Sheriff Rob Hermann promoted his younger brother Todd to the position of deputy inspector of operations – third in command of the entire sixty officer department. In effect, the sheriff put his little brother into one of the best paid positions and most powerful roles in all of county government.

During Rob Hermann's tenure as sheriff, his undersheriff remained Gregg Schetter. Schetter and the Hermann brothers all grew up together in southern Manitowoc County. In fact, Schetter happened to be one of the groomsmen in Todd Hermann's 1993 wedding, along the sheriff himself. Wouldn't it be nice to have your wedding party doing your performance reviews, setting your salaries and pay raises, especially in a county government job?

As for Schetter, he was sandwiched in the middle of both Hermann brothers in the upper administration. He was the boss of one and answered to the other. This was small-town cronyism at its finest, and this was the way the political movers and shakers of Manitowoc County preferred to run their downtown sheriff's office. The Manitowoc Sheriff's Office did not have an internal affairs unit for citizens to bring their complaints about corruption or abuse of power involving the sheriff's deputies. Instead, complaints from the citizenry were funneled to Schetter, and he decided what complaints were legitimate and which ones to dismiss.

The opportunity to wear the brown uniform and the shiny star as a Manitowoc County Sheriff's deputy was historically based on who you knew – not what you knew. Deputy candidates who may have been highly qualified but failed to have an inside connection were often part of the reject pile. Their job application materials often collected dust, and they would need to look elsewhere to pursue a career in law enforcement.

As far as the top of the administration was concerned, Sheriff Rob Hermann and Undersheriff Gregg Schetter were afforded a long-standing generous perk that was off-limits to virtually all other county government employees. They got a yearly fuel stipend to the tune of nearly $10,000 each just to drive to and from their office desk jobs in downtown Manitowoc. The generous stipend, approved by the Manitowoc County Board of Supervisors, came in addition to their annual salaries in the neighborhood of $100,000, all for managing a mostly rural sheriff's office, rarely ever handling serious crimes such rapes, kidnappings, bank robberies, and murders. Most of the serious offenses tended to occur within the jurisdiction of the Manitowoc Police Department, a city police agency that strived to hire more qualified police officers. The city department was regarded as being far more professional, ethical, and accountable to the residents, but it was often dragged down and sullied because it shared the same name as the county sheriff's office.

For those who desired to climb the ladder within the Manitowoc County Sheriff's Office, there were two easy ways to get there. One was to brown nose your way to the top. The other was to have dirt on your superiors. A number of employees who climbed to the top of the troubled department were skilled at both.

***

Back in the 1970s, Bob Hermann, president of Cleveland Auto Sales & Salvage Inc., helped elect a mediocre city cop in his thirties named Tom Kocourek as the new sheriff of

Manitowoc County. In 1978, Kocourek garnered the most votes in a crowded five-man political primary that ousted the incumbent sheriff. By all accounts, Bob Hermann was an all-around likeable fellow. He had recently retired from his position as a Manitowoc County traffic patrolman. On the other hand, Kocourek brought few redeeming qualities to the sheriff's office. Yet he would hold down the fort for the next twenty-two years, retiring in 2001, so he could start collecting his government pension as he went to work in Manitowoc's non-profit sector as a well-paid executive director of the Big Brothers Big Sisters organization.

As sheriff, Kocourek's legacy is that his name is synonymous with crookedness and corruption. Along the way, Kocourek made sure to mold a number of disciples within his sheriff's office. After all, he wanted some of the minions to follow in his footsteps and uphold his legacy.

Incidentally, just five days before Teresa vanished after visiting Avery Road, recently retired chief investigator of Manitowoc County, Gene "the sketch pencil" Kusche, was compelled to give a sworn deposition at a Manitowoc law office. During that late October afternoon, Kusche was asked to recall the circumstances of his demotion by Sheriff Kocourek during the 1980s. Kusche had been the undersheriff at one time, second in command of the entire agency, but then, out of nowhere, Kocourek removed him from the post.

"I asked him, 'Why did you do this?'" Kusche testified. "And he said, 'Because I lacked tact.'"

Kusche remembered his two-decade-old conversation with Kocourek like it happened yesterday.[31]

"I said, 'Tom, tact on your department was the ability to smile at someone's face while you stabbed them in the back.' I don't think he responded," Kusche smirked.

---

31. Gene Kusche, deposition in Avery civil rights wrongful conviction lawsuit, October 26, 2005

Actually, Kusche was no honorable cop himself. And that's why, despite his baggage, he was worth keeping around inside the Kocourek regime. Plus, Kusche acquired a special skill that no one else in the sheriff's office had. Kusche was a pretty good sketch artist. As people who watched *Making a Murderer* will remember, Kocourek used Kusche as one of his henchmen to accomplish the false imprisonment of Steven Avery, the bushy bearded young punk, age twenty-three.

On the hot summer afternoon of July 29, 1985, a prominent young businesswoman was badly beaten and viciously raped as she jogged in her bikini along the sandy shores of Lake Michigan. Sheriff Kocourek put himself in charge of solving the brutal rape, although virtually no investigation would be done. Within hours of the attack, Kocourek selected Steven Avery, a local rascal, as the horrific crime's scapegoat. That night at a local hospital, Kusche was furnished a recent jail mugshot of Avery. Kusche traced the mugshot on his sketch pad. His drawing was presented to the semi-conscious rape victim as she lay in her hospital bed, recovering from her near-fatal beating.

Before the clock struck midnight, the sheriff got on the phone with another of his henchmen – Kenneth Petersen, a sergeant in road patrol. Petersen, in turn, got a hold of traffic patrol deputy Mike Bushman.

In due time, Petersen and Bushman would both ascend into top level leadership positions – tokens of gratitude for their unwavering loyalty and ability to follow orders from their sheriff. As for Bushman, he grew up in St. Nazianz, a tiny German village in southern Manitowoc County surrounded by farms, hillsides, and wilderness. There, his family ran the Bushman Hardware Store. After high school, Bushman tried college, but he lacked ambition and dropped out. During the 1970s, he found a job as a local school bus driver, but driving a yellow bus wasn't glamourous. A job as a Manitowoc County Sheriff's deputy was way more appealing. Although Bushman had no prior law enforcement experience or special qualifications that suited him to become a cop, that would not be a problem.

When Bushman filled out the job application, the form asked for references. The first reference Bushman put on his application was Bob Hermann, the popular Manitowoc County traffic patrol deputy who ran the Cleveland Auto Salvage yard about fifteen miles from St. Nazianz. The name of Bob Hermann meant something in a county where law enforcement jobs were based on who you knew.

Sure enough, Bushman got the job. Now, he too was a full-time county road patrol deputy like Bob Hermann. Of course, Bushman owed a tremendous debt of gratitude to the Hermann family and that would not be forgotten.

As for Ken Petersen, he wasn't the type of guy you'd expect any reputable law enforcement agency would be begging to take a job, either.

Growing up in Manitowoc, Petersen had no ambitions to pursue a career in law enforcement. He graduated from Lincoln High School in 1968. From there, he attended Lake Shore Technical College in nearby Cleveland, Wisconsin, earning an associate's degree in marketing. But over the next six years, Petersen bounced from job to job. He struggled to find stable employment. Among his many low-paying jobs during the 1970s that did not pan out, Petersen worked at the Montgomery Ward retail store in Manitowoc. But in 1975, Petersen had a stroke of good fortune. He got hired by the Manitowoc County Sheriff's Office. For Petersen, 1978 was a transformative year that paved the way for his future success. That was the year Tom Kocourek was elected sheriff.

Three years later, in 1981, Petersen was involved in a big slip-up that made the daily newspaper. His actions involved a questionable death, possibly a preventable death.

Petersen was involved in a traffic crash that left dead a twenty-two-year-old woman from Manitowoc County's small community of Newton. The case may have ruined his law enforcement career had he worked for someone other than Kocourek. A number of sheriff's deputies who worked at the agency have said that Petersen was driving his squad car excessively over the speed limit in a reckless manner at the time he ran over the young lady during a thick, late night fog.

The fatality was chronicled in Manitowoc's newspaper on July 21, 1981:

"County Coroner Marion Cumming today identified the woman killed in a crash of two motorcycles early Monday as Gina M. Herzog, 22, Route 1, Newton. Cumming said the cause of death was a head injury sustained in the crash of the motorcycles. A squad car later collided with the wreckage and the victim."

Shortly after midnight, two young men on motorcycles left a bar out in the country as Petersen was gunning the gas on his squad car racing to the bar to investigate allegations of underage drinking. The motorcycles got tangled in the thick dense fog, causing the riders to tumble to the ground. Minutes later, Petersen's squad car came barreling down the two-lane highway. Fellow members of the Manitowoc County Sheriff's Department have said that Petersen was racing toward the bar like a madman when he struck and ran over Herzog, who may have been sitting on the side of the roadway, shaken up from the initial motorcycle tumble, according to other sheriff's deputies who worked for the county at the time of the tragedy.

Nobody else was seriously hurt during the motorcycle spill.

Two days later, a number of top public officials for Manitowoc County orchestrated a press conference. Deputy Petersen was absolved of any wrongdoing and negligence regarding the tragic loss of life.

According to the newspaper account, a coroner's inquest into Herzog's death was not even necessary. The Manitowoc press was assured the matter was cleared up even though it was unclear whether interview statements were even taken from the other motorcycle riders involved in the bike spill.

There was also no mention in the newspaper article regarding how fast Petersen was traveling. It was unclear whether any crash reconstruction occurred. The story in the paper was headlined, "Coroner says police car no factor in traffic death."

"The pathologist, Dr. John H. Fodden, said severe skull bone and brain damage caused the almost immediate death of Herzog and this was due to the motorcycle crash. Herzog also was injured internally after death and that could have been caused by a wheel of one of the motorcycles or an automobile. But, it was very, very, clear this was after she was dead," Dr. Fodden told the newspaper.

But was Herzog alive when Petersen's squad car ran her over? Since Petersen was barreling down the two-lane highway under the thick fog and darkness, he did not know. Was the young woman's death avoidable? There's not even a paper trail surrounding the crash in Petersen's personnel file.

My review in 2016 of Petersen's Manitowoc County employment file showed there was no mention at all of the fatality. There was no mention whether twenty-two-year-old Gina Herzog's fatality went before the sheriff's office accident review board even though it was standard practice to do so whenever one of the Manitowoc County squad cars sustained damage.

At any rate, both Petersen and the Manitowoc County Sheriff's Office escaped liability. Perhaps most telling, there were no more follow-up newspaper articles regarding Herzog's death after July 23, 1981. The local newspaper agreed to bury the story and nothing more was ever written about the infamous "Kenny Petersen incident." One sheriff's official told the author that Herzog's father was heartbroken and devastated by his daughter's untimely tragedy, but decided not to pursue a lawsuit against the Manitowoc County Sheriff's Department because nothing could change the outcome. A civil lawsuit against the county and Kenny Peterson would not bring the grieving man's daughter back.

As a result, the "Kenny Petersen incident" became a successful whitewash for Sheriff Kocourek. He was skilled at manipulating the local press to do what he wanted, and part of that skill also involved making sure that some stories that may have reflected poorly upon him and the Manitowoc County Sheriff's Office never saw the light of day.

As for the victim, Gina Herzog's newspaper obituary noted she was born in Manitowoc, a Class of 1977 graduate of Kiel High School, and she worked in Sheboygan for the state of Wisconsin's Division of Vocational Rehabilitation Office. She was survived by her parents of rural Newton, a sister, two brothers, and one grandmother.

The Herzogs had to persevere after the pain and heartache of their profound loss that many people blamed on Kenny Petersen's reckless driving.

As for Petersen, his law enforcement career hardly hit the skids because of the episode. In fact, his county sheriff's career would undergo a dramatic rise – three major promotions within the next eight years.

In 1982, Kocourek promoted Petersen to road patrol sergeant. In turn, Petersen became an obedient foot soldier. That was never more so than on July 29, 1985, hours after Penny Beerntsen's brutal attack on the Lake Michigan beach.

"That evening I would have received a phone call from Sheriff Kocourek informing me to arrest Steven Avery to see if he was at home and arrest him for attempted first-degree homicide," Petersen testified. "That night the only person I had any contact with was the sheriff. There was no one else that I was aware of."[32]

---

32. Deposition of Sheriff Kenny Petersen in Steven Avery's civil rights lawsuit, October 13, 2005

The previous winter, Avery had forced Sandra Morris, the wife of sheriff's deputy Bill Morris, off the road in front of Avery's trailer. Avery pointed an unloaded shotgun at her, accusing her of spreading false rumors that Avery had been outside naked on one of his cars laying down and masturbating on the hood of the car. The Sandy Morris incident was fresh on the minds of the Manitowoc County Sheriff's Office in the summer of 1985, and that made Avery a prime scapegoat for Sheriff Kocourek. He would look good to the community if he could take a heap of credit for single-handedly solving the rape of a prominent businesswoman in lightning quick fashion.

So that night, July 29, 1985, one of the deputies Petersen asked to tag along, to carry out the sheriff's wishes of arresting Steven Avery, was road deputy Mike Bushman. Thanks to Kocourek, Bushman was now serving as Manitowoc County Sheriff's Office's first-ever dog handler. Under Petersen's watch, Avery's arrest – for a brutal crime he was being framed for – went down without a hitch.

At his December 1985 jury trial, Avery provided more than a dozen witnesses who insisted he was doing concrete work at his family's salvage yard on the afternoon in question. Avery's public defenders produced store receipts from the ShopKo retail store in Green Bay indicating Avery and his wife were inside the store at 5:13 p.m., a mere seventy-five minutes after the time of the vicious rape north of Two Rivers. The jury of Manitowoc County residents rejected Avery's pleas of innocence.

The jury was in line with District Attorney Denis Vogel and Sheriff Kocourek. Avery was convicted of attempted first-degree murder, first-degree sexual assault, and false imprisonment. On March 10, 1986, Judge Fred Hazlewood sentenced Avery to spend thirty-two years inside a Wisconsin state prison facility. In August 1987, a Wisconsin appeals court rejected Avery's attempt to overturn his conviction, even though it appeared Avery was truly innocent of the awful crime.

In the back of his twisted mind, Sheriff Kocourek knew he had pulled a fast one. He had hoodwinked the entire Manitowoc community, a jury, and even the rape victim. He had tricked them all into believing Avery was the villainous monster who raped the woman who ran the popular candy store in Manitowoc. Now that Kocourek's career was going places, he needed other foot soldiers he could trust as part of his army.

On December 21, 1987, he typed a two-paragraph memo for Petersen's personnel file.

The subject was titled "PROMOTION."

"During the past twelve months at the Manitowoc County Sheriff's Department you have been in training for one of the most important positions at the department ... Because of the excellent job which you have been doing ... effective January 15, 1988, you will officially assume the duties of Deputy Inspector of the Operations Division. Congratulations on your new appointment and I look forward to working with you in your command position for many years to come."

On December 18, 1989, Petersen drew another huge promotion from the boss.

"As Inspector at the Sheriff's Department you will represent the Sheriff in his absence and supervise the day-to-day operations of the entire Sheriff's Department ... Your past work product in the various positions held by yourself at the Manitowoc County Sheriff's Department has always been excellent and I feel confident that this pattern of productivity will continue in your new position as Inspector ... I look forward to working with you and having you as my right-hand man here at the Manitowoc County Sheriff's Dept." – Sheriff Kocourek

Petersen's promotion to sheriff's inspector came with a nine percent salary increase and another exclusive perk given only to the top two sheriff's officials.

"As Inspector, he is now eligible for $100 per month car allowance plus 1,000 gallons of gas per year," Kocourek notified county personnel.

As for Bushman, documents contained within his employment personnel file from Manitowoc County government show he had wrecked one of Manitowoc County's new Chevrolet Caprice squad cars on September 4, 1989. Bids to repair the damage ranged between $2,004 and $3,792 – a lot of money by 1989 standards.

"Sgt. Bushman, while on patrol, observed what appeared to be a drunk driver. While watching this vehicle in his rear view mirror, Sgt. Bushman lost his bearings in relationship to the intersection. Sgt. Bushman was unable to stop the squad car before it ran off the road through the T intersection … The squad car, at just less than highway speed, struck the embankment and came to a rest … Investigation into the accident showed the case to be a result of inattentive driving. Accident investigated and written by the Wisconsin State Patrol."

Bushman's incident was presented to the sheriff's office's accident review board. One of the reviewers happened to be Petersen, who ran over Gina Herzog eight years earlier.

"We recommend Sgt. Bushman be issued a written reprimand relating to this accident," Petersen advised Sheriff Kocourek.

As Petersen knew from prior experience, a royal screw up as a Manitowoc sheriff's deputy was not necessarily a professional setback under Kocourek's leadership. Just a few months later, on February 9, 1990, Bushman received a memo in his personnel file from the sheriff.

"I wish to congratulate you and advise that you have been selected to fill the position of Lieutenant/Shift Commander … Your excellent service to Manitowoc and the Sheriff's

Department in your past positions of patrol officer and patrol sergeant have prepared you to assume the responsibilities of lieutenant, and I am sure you will do an excellent job as you have in the past."

In Bushman, Kocourek knew he had added another sheep to his flock.

***

Because the 1985 Avery prosecution was a sham from the get-go, the Manitowoc sheriff was growing increasingly paranoid. He was willing to target anybody who posed a threat at blowing his cover.

In 1990, as Avery was serving his unjust attempted murder prison sentence, Kocourek got wind of someone in town who was not convinced of Avery's guilt. Freedom of speech may be afforded by the U.S. Constitution, but the following information, obtained from a Manitowoc County Sheriff's police report, reveals the dangers of speaking out in a small town where law enforcement runs roughshod over the citizenry. One man in Manitowoc was threatened with arrest and felony charges if he made his beliefs known again about Avery's innocence.

In March 1990, Kocourek, the sheriff himself, wrote up a formal report, classifying the incident as "Harassment."

According to the sheriff, a customer of the Beerntsen's Confectionary candy store stopped inside and asked if co-owner Penny Beerntsen was there. She and her husband were out of town at the time. The customer, Erik Moen, thirty-three, told the store clerk he was a friend of Avery and that Avery was innocent of assaulting the candy store lady.

A week later, the sheriff of Manitowoc County made a personal visit to Moen's residence on South 38th Street in Manitowoc. "Erik stated that he was in fact at Beerntsen's Confectionary several days ago and had stopped in to purchase some chocolates. He stated that he meant no harm and only wanted to tell Penny Beerntsen that, in his opinion, Steve Avery was innocent," Kocourek's report reflected.

The sheriff who had framed Avery also knew about Gregory Allen, the dangerous sexual predator who was allowed to get away with the near fatal assault and remain a danger to the community at large. Yet this is how Kocourek summarized his exchange with Moen.

"Erik admitted that he had no new factual data that was not already brought out during the trial and that the belief of Steve Avery being innocent was only a personal belief on his part. I advised Erik that his presence at the store in attempting to contact Penny Beerntsen reference this case could be interpreted as a felony charge reference harassing a witness.

"Erik was warned that any future attempts to contact the Beerntsen family and discuss the matter would result in felony charges being brought against him. He was also informed that if he had any new information that was not already brought out at the trial, that he should contact the sheriff's department, which was the investigating agency, and we would be glad to look into that information. Erik stated that he understood," Kocourek wrote.

Obviously, Kocourek's report was a web of lies. He was not about to reopen the rape investigation, and he most certainly was not about to investigate somebody else as the rapist. Rather, the sheriff's face-to-face interview with the local man served a higher purpose. Kocourek had iced the concept of Avery's innocence from gaining traction around Manitowoc. For him, this was an important event, much more so than punishing real criminals.

In the days following the brutal attack along Lake Michigan's beach, the traumatized rape victim began receiving anonymous threatening phone calls at her house from the rapist, Gregory Allen, who was notorious for calling his victims afterward.

But Sheriff Kocourek convinced the candy store owner not to worry, she was just confused. Avery was already in jail, he informed her. Rather than trust her own instincts, she believed the sheriff.

Because the residents of Manitowoc County were in no position to rise up and oust Kocourek from office, he remained the most powerful politician of Manitowoc County for many more years to come. Finally, when the numbers lined up for him to collect his police pension, he decided to leave the office on his own terms. In 2000, he decided to pass the torch of corruption to someone else. But his heir apparent, Ken Petersen, still didn't know where all the bodies were buried and all the skeletons were being hidden. The Manitowoc County master needed to let his understudy in on one more devious secret. Once again, all things centered on the high-profile rape conviction of Avery, from the 1980s. At the time, Avery was pushing forty and in the middle of his prison term behind the walls at the Wisconsin Department of Corrections. As for the retiring sheriff, Kocourek was cutting cakes, receiving going away gifts, and bidding his farewells to fellow county government employees and local dignitaries as part of his grand farewell retirement send-off.

And now that Petersen had earned the outgoing sheriff's sacred trust, the time arrived to make Petersen aware of a secret document being kept inside a special safe, a safe to which only the sheriff of Manitowoc County had access. Although the sheriff's office had a large vault where it housed thousands of old records from major criminal cases over the years, this particular report was apparently off-limits to the rest of the sheriff's employees. The secret document turned out to be a letter, purportedly written by a prison inmate, outlining an alleged confession that convicted prisoner Avery gave to the inmate regarding the 1985 rape of Penny Beerntsen.

The letter was mentioned as part of Avery's $36 million civil rights lawsuit. It was more unflattering testimony about Kocourek and the topic of the letter's existence came up just a couple of weeks before Teresa vanished and was killed.

"He said somebody from, some inmate from Brown County sent it to him," Petersen testified. "That's all I know … I don't know if it came direct or where it came from. All I know is it was there."

Regardless of how it was contrived, the letter in the sheriff's safe was phony.

In reality, Avery never confessed to raping Penny Beerntsen.

He maintained his steadfast innocence since his arrest by Kenneth Petersen on July 29, 1985. On September 11, 2003, the gates of the Wisconsin Department of Corrections swung wide open as a large contingent of well-wishers shared hugs, kisses, and tears with Avery. Attorney Keith Findley of the Wisconsin Innocence Project had secured a DNA exoneration proving Gregory Allen was the real beachfront rapist, just as the more reputable City of Manitowoc Police Department suspected all along.

Two years later, during October 2005, Avery's tenacious civil lawyers from Milwaukee, Walt Kelly and Stephen Glynn, were pounding away at the tainted Manitowoc County Sheriff's Office. The agency's upper administration was uneasy and uncomfortable. The scrappy civil attorneys were making substantial progress as they assembled their case against Manitowoc County and Sheriff Kocourek, the suspected crook and mastermind of Avery's 1985 frame job.

That month, the following employees got pulled off the job and were paraded into a Manitowoc law office, where they were forced to raise their right hand and be subjected to an uncomfortable videotaped civil rights lawsuit deposition: Sheriff Ken Petersen, Lt. Detective James Lenk, road patrol Sgt. Andrew Colborn, former sheriff's deputy Judy Dvorak, and retired chief investigator Gene Kusche. Dvorak would reveal how she despised Avery, who had no history of any sexual violence but did have a solid alibi to account for his whereabouts during the time of Gregory Allen's rape.

At most of these lawsuit depositions sat a short stubby man who was not dressed in a suit and tie like the room full of lawyers and key members of the sheriff's office such as Petersen and Lenk. Avery's unsightly presence at the same table as members of the Manitowoc County Sheriff's Office had to be sickening to them.

The clock was ticking, ticking closer and closer to the scheduled deposition of the master himself, retired Sheriff Tom Kocourek.

What would he have to say for himself when he found himself seated at the same wooden table, sitting in the very same room, as the unfortunate man from whom he had stolen eighteen years of his life?

CHAPTER TEN

RAV4

One of the most shadowy figures to emerge from the Teresa Halbach murder probe was veteran Manitowoc County classic car buff, Andy Colborn.

Colborn belonged to various classic car clubs around northeastern Wisconsin, and he was fond of the 1950s-era Plymouths. Over the years, Colborn had walked the grounds of Avery Salvage on many occasions to find the right spare parts for his prized collection of old cars. And like so many of the rising stars in the Manitowoc Sheriff's Office, Colborn landed in law enforcement as a last resort. After high school he enlisted in the Air Force, on active duty, serving our country from 1976 until 1988. He was stationed in Nevada for much of his time. In his late twenties, he left the Air Force and found work in Las Vegas as an auto transmission mechanic. After three years as a grease monkey, Colborn left Nevada and returned to Wisconsin. That year, 1990, he found employment at the Waupaca Foundry, where he stayed until 1992. But in his early thirties, he set his sights on a new line of work. Manitowoc Sheriff Tom Kocourek offered Colborn a full-time job as a county jailer.

Colborn later gained infamy for his role in Avery's wrongful conviction case. Colborn was the dopey Manitowoc County jailer who spoke with one of the Green Bay area police departments around 1995 regarding the recent arrest of serial rapist Gregory Allen. Colborn was alerted that the police in Brown County had a rapist in custody who had confessed that someone else was imprisoned for a violent assault committed in nearby Manitowoc County.

Many people believe Colborn confided in Sheriff Kocourek about this matter. In the end, Manitowoc County ignored the call, preferring to let Avery rot in prison another eight years for a crime he did not commit. From the moment that Colborn disregarded the call that could have gained Avery his freedom many years sooner, Colborn's career path was on the rise under Kocourek and Petersen. Colborn was moved out of his less desirable job as a jailer and assigned to road patrol. He later was promoted to a shift sergeant. By the fall of 2005, Colborn had delusions of becoming the next sheriff of Manitowoc; Kenny Petersen was nearing retirement and the crooked agency's coveted top spot was opening up.

However, the month of October 2005 was becoming more and more stressful, all thanks to his sheriff's office's arch nemesis. Colborn was being dragged into the civil rights lawsuit of Avery, who was finally freed in September 2003.

Just three weeks before Teresa vanished, Colborn was in uniform when he showed up at the Manitowoc law office to answer a barrage of questions from Avery's civil attorneys of Milwaukee.

Colborn: "I gathered, yes, that they had someone in custody. I don't know if this person had commented directly to the person who contacted me or had commented to other people within that jurisdiction and this eventually got to my caller."[33]

Lawyer: "But the detective had indicated that there was a person in custody who had made a statement about a Manitowoc County offense, correct?"

"Yes."

---

33. Andrew Colborn civil rights lawsuit deposition in Steven Avery case, October 13, 2005

Lawyer: "And what that person in custody had said, was that he had committed an assault in Manitowoc County and someone else was in jail for it. Correct?"

"Yes, sir."

Lawyer: "And that much you're pretty sure of?"

"Yes."

Lawyer: "I mean, that's a significant event?"

Lawyer: "Right, that's what stood out in my mind."

After the newspaper coverage of Avery's exoneration in September 2003, Colborn had realized he was in a hot mess. He needed to confide in someone he trusted about his role in the Gregory Allen episode.

"You brought that up to someone else, correct?" Kelly asked.

"Yes, sir."

"And to whom did you bring that up?"

"To Lieutenant Lenk."

"There was also a conversation that followed that. You spoke to Sheriff Petersen, correct?"

"Yes sir … I remember coming into work and Sheriff Petersen was downstairs where our patrol division is, and I got the impression he was waiting for me to come into work. He initiated the conversation by saying he had spoken with Lieutenant Lenk, and he felt that it would be in the best interest of Lieutenant Lenk and myself and the sheriff's department, I would suppose, that if I was to give him a statement on the gist of our conversation, or what we had discussed. And I asked for clarification on that, you know," Colborn laughed nervously during his deposition.

"And he goes, 'Well what you discussed about a telephone call that you received when you were working in the jail' and I said, 'OK,' and before I went out on patrol I provided this statement."

In the coming days, Colborn realized his lawsuit deposition experience had negative overtones and perhaps lasting consequences that weren't good for him.

Would Avery's lawyers amend their civil rights case to add Deputy Colborn as one of their codefendants? Colborn also had to figure that those who ran the sheriff's office were not going down on a sinking ship. He was emerging as a logical fall guy, a prime scapegoat for Sheriff Petersen and the lawsuit's other codefendants, Kocourek and former District Attorney Denis Vogel.

The continuation and the publicity of Avery's civil rights lawsuit was bad news for Colborn's upcoming sheriff's candidacy. Colborn had been collaborating with Lt. Lenk about his eventual bid for sheriff. A Colborn victory put Lenk in line for a hefty raise and promotion to undersheriff of Manitowoc County.

However, the big election was still a year away but campaign season was just around the corner. But in 2005, there were far more pressing matters. The sheriff's office needed to deal with Avery.

"If we wanted to eliminate Steve, it would have been a whole lot easier to eliminate Steve than it would be to frame Steve, you know?" Sheriff Petersen told Green Bay television station Fox 11 in the days after Avery's arrest.

The Manitowoc sheriff went on to say, "If we wanted him out of the picture like in prison or if we wanted him killed, you know, it would have been much easier just to kill him."

***

One of the most dramatic moments from Avery's murder trial came when Colborn, then forty-eight, was on the witness stand during Avery's trial and defense attorney Dean Strang had a chance to cross-examine him.

"One of the things that road patrol officers frequently do is call into dispatch and give the dispatcher the license plate number of a car they've stopped or a car that looks out of place for some reason?"[34]

"Correct, yes, sir," Colborn answered.

"And the dispatcher can get information about to whom the license plate is registered?"

"Yes, sir."

"And if a car is abandoned, or there's nobody in the car, registration tells you who the owner presumably is?"

"Yes, sir."

"I'm going to ask you to listen, if you would, to a short phone call."

Manitowoc County Sheriff's Department this is Lynn.

Lynn.

Hi Andy.

Can you run Sam William Henry 5-8-2. See if comes back to (Inaudible.)

OK. Shows that she's a missing person. And it lists to Teresa Halbach.

All set.

OK. Is that what you're looking for, Andy?

'99 Toyota?

Yup.

Ok. Thank you.

You're so welcome. Bye. Bye.

When the call ended, Strang resumed his line of uncomfortable questions for Andy Colborn.

"And then you tell the dispatcher, oh, ''99 Toyota?'"

"No, I thought she told me that."

Strang replayed the audio for the jury and Sgt. Colborn to hear again.

OK. Shows that she's a missing person. And it lists to Teresa Halbach.

All set.

---

34. Feb. 20, 2007 cross examination of Andy Colborn by attorney Dean Strang

OK. Is that what you're looking for, Andy?
'99 Toyota?
Yup.
Ok. Thank you.
You're so welcome. Bye. Bye.

Colborn ducked his head toward the courtroom microphone. He avoided eye contact with Strang.

"Were you looking at these plates when you called them in?" Strang asked.

"No, sir."

Then he lifted his head, grimaced, and cracked his knuckles two times.

"Do you have any recollection of making that phone call?"

Colborn buried his head. He paused a few seconds before answering that he guessed he made the call on November 3, 2005.

"Probably after I received a phone call from Investigator Wiegert letting me know that there was a missing person."

November 3 was when Calumet and Manitowoc County first learned of Teresa's disappearance.

Strang followed up with another excellent question.

"Investigator Wiegert, did he give you the license plate number for Teresa Halbach when he called you?"

Colborn would not look up and answer Strang's question.

He was in his comfort zone keeping his head down and looking straight toward his microphone.

"You know, I just don't remember the exact content of our conversation. But he had to have given it to me because I wouldn't have had the number any other way," Colborn testified as he let out another nervous laugh.

"Well," Strang began, "you can understand how someone listening to that might think that you were calling in a license plate that you were looking at on the back end of a 1999 Toyota?"

"Yes," Colborn looked up and shrugged his shoulders.

"But there's no way you should have been looking at Teresa Halbach's license plate on November 3 on the back end of a 1999 Toyota?"

"I shouldn't have been, and I was not looking at the license plate."

"Because you're aware now, that the first time that Toyota was reported found was on November 5?"

"Yes, sir."

The turnabout near the Old Mishicot Dam along State Highway 147 is where several people saw abandoned Teresa Halbach's RAV4 in the days after her disappearance.

***

After the *Making a Murderer* hysteria, many fans presumed Colborn made his cryptic call after snooping around late at night, on his way home from work on November 3, the first night of the missing person's investigation.

That evening, Colborn spoke with Avery in person at Avery Salvage between 6:30 and 7 p.m. to get a statement from Avery about the missing woman's whereabouts. And later that night, Colborn met with Lenk, Manitowoc County Detective Dennis Jacobs, County Detective Dave Remiker, and Calumet County Investigator Dedering. The five men focused on Avery and another Manitowoc County residence Teresa visited on her last day of life, the property on County Road B belonging to George Zipperer. Colborn joined Dedering and Remiker at that house around 9:40 p.m. They made entry at 9:53 p.m.[35]

"I did review voice mail messages left on the answering machine and caller ID. I did locate a caller ID entry on October 31, 2005, at 2:12 p.m. from phone number 920-737-4731. I recognized this as being the cellular phone number of Teresa Halbach."

By all accounts, the Manitowoc County Sheriff's entourage called it a night around 10:30 p.m. No additional work was done to locate Teresa or her missing SUV during the overnight shift.

It's been established that Colborn drove home from sheriff's headquarters in downtown Manitowoc using his personal vehicle.

He testified he fell asleep on his living room couch at his home near Whitelaw. His work schedule had him off the next day, Friday, November 4. But there were other factors at play. Given Teresa's alarming disappearance and the zeal to pin the crime on Avery, Colborn had a lot on his mind.

But if Colborn chose to cross the line from good cop to bad, he had to reconcile these inner demons with his own conscience. After all, Colborn was a God-fearing man who was deeply involved in his Christian church. On one hand, a young woman from a good farm family was suddenly missing. Her worried family deserved the best effort from him and other police. On the other hand, Colborn considered

35. John Dedering report, Nov. 3, 2005 contact with George, Jason and Jo Ellen Zipperer

Avery a filthy no-good swine, a glory hound who was leveraging the Wisconsin media to undermine the reputation of the Manitowoc County Sheriff's Office with his constant press coverage regarding his wrongful conviction lawsuit. The lawsuit gnawed at Manitowoc County because it kept giving everyone a black eye. And get this: Avery was now on the verge of becoming one of the biggest millionaires in Manitowoc County. Would he use his exoneration lawsuit money to buy up the city's downtown businesses, own the local pool halls, and maybe a tavern or a strip tease club?

The idea of Avery being rich, filthy rich, was downright repulsive to the community's leaders. And if Manitowoc County's lawyers reached a large settlement as payment to Avery as reparation for all of his injustices, Colborn was a logical fall guy for the screw-up. The footsteps were getting louder and louder. Then, all of a sudden, there came along a golden opportunity for Colborn and others to restore their careers and destroy Avery's life once and for all.

"Just three weeks before Teresa Halbach's disappearance, both Lenk and Colborn were deposed in Avery's civil lawsuit about their own involvement in the failure to follow up an exculpatory lead which contributed to Steven Avery spending another eight years in prison before his eventual exoneration. Curiously, although Lenk and Colborn were aware that authority for the investigation of the Halbach disappearance was transferred to the Calumet County Sheriff's Department because of the conflict of interest arising from Avery's lawsuit, both officers volunteered to search Avery's personal residence and did not inform the Calumet County authorities that they had direct contact with the civil case or that they had themselves been deposed and had their conduct as to Avery called into question in the case a mere three weeks earlier."[36]

---

36. Zellner post-conviction motion 2016

Colborn's cryptic phone call to dispatch remained one of the biggest mysteries associated with Teresa's killing.

But new evidence Zellner uncovered in 2018 strongly suggests Sgt. Colborn, who by all accounts was conscientious about his job, was ambitiously working off the clock, so to speak, on Friday, November 4, because he did not want to let his comrades down.

Former Mishicot resident Kevin Rahmlow positively identified Colborn as the sheriff's deputy whom he alerted to the abandoned RAV4 being parked near the State Highway 147 turnabout.

"In the series, I recognized the officer who I talked to at the Cenex station on November 4, 2005," Rahmlow testified with confidence. "Having watched *Making a Murderer*, I now know that his name is Andrew Colborn."[37]

Zellner's filings from October 2017 reveal, "The eyewitness was also sure he shared his observation with the Manitowoc County deputy. But in that instance, Sgt. Colborn never made a report of this conversation."

During an August 2018 interview for this book, Zellner told the author, "I went to the old dam with Mr. Rahmlow and my investigator. He is absolutely telling the truth about seeing the Halbach vehicle. He is also telling the truth about the Cenex station missing poster in the window regarding Ms. Halbach and her vehicle."

When Colborn made his highly suspicious call into Manitowoc County radio dispatch, he was not utilizing his squad car's CB radio.

"Sgt. Colborn placed this call from his personal cell phone, not his squad car's radio," Zellner said. "Sgt. Colborn testified that, after completing contact with the Zipperers, he signed off at Manitowoc County Sheriff's Department, which would have included leaving his cruiser in the secure (police) lot and drove his personal vehicle home.

---

37. Kevin Rahmlow affidavit July 15, 2017

"If Sgt. Colborn was on duty and in his squad car, it would be reasonable to expect transmissions to and from Manitowoc County Sheriff's Department dispatch to come over the radio. Because Sgt. Colborn called dispatch from his personal phone, it is reasonable to conclude that he made the call on Friday, November 4, 2005, his day off."[38]

Kevin Rahmlow now believes he encountered Colborn at the gas station around 12:30 p.m. to let him know about the missing woman's vehicle.

"Sgt. Colborn confirmed the identity of Ms. Halbach's vehicle by calling ... dispatch on his cell phone around 7:30 p.m. on November 4 ... Realizing such a call would be recorded, Sgt. Colborn removed the license plates from Ms. Halbach's vehicle to conceal that he had actually located the vehicle at the point in time when he made the call about the license plates."

In the background of Colborn's call to Lynn, the Manitowoc County dispatcher, someone else's voice can be heard.

"Audible in a recording of Sgt. Colborn's call to Manitowoc dispatch regarding the victim's license plate number, a third-party states, 'It's hers.'"

Zellner also realized Colborn's license plate call was tendered to Avery's original trial lawyers Buting and Strang on a CD containing a total of thirty tracks of other dispatch calls in relation to the investigation.

"It is apparent that the recordings are organized chronologically on the CD. Sgt. Colborn's dispatch call was titled 'Track 3.' The preceding, 'Track 2,' is a call to Manitowoc dispatch from an unnamed officer regarding George Zipperer. The officer requested a criminal records check of George Zipperer from the dispatcher.

"It is reasonable to conclude that this call was placed by one of the Manitowoc County Sheriff's Office deputies

---

38. Motion for Post-Conviction Relief filed June 7, 2017

who were with Calumet County Sheriff's Office Detective Dedering before they proceeded to the Zipperer's on November 3, 2005. Therefore it follows that Sgt. Colborn's call to dispatch occurred after he responded to the Avery property to make contact with Mr. Avery and after he drove back to the Manitowoc County Sheriff's Office about his contact with Mr. Avery.

"Sgt. Colborn's explanation that he called Manitowoc County Sheriff's Office dispatch to confirm information obtained from Calumet County Sheriff's Office Investigator Wiegert is contradicted by the chronological order of the ... dispatch calls as produced to trial defense counsel. Sgt. Colborn testified that he placed this call to dispatch after speaking with Investigator Wiegert while he was driving from the Avery property to Manitowoc County Sheriff's Office after making contact with Mr. Avery. However, based upon the chronological organization of the Manitowoc County Sheriff's Office dispatch calls as produced to trial defense counsel, Sgt. Colborn called dispatch after meeting the assembled officers at Manitowoc County Sheriff's Office, long after leaving the Avery property and speaking with Investigator Wiegert," Zellner stated.

Given the uncontroverted facts dug up by Zellner, Colborn's murder trial testimony now appears seriously flawed.

"After departing the Manitowoc County Sheriff's Office for the Zipperers' property, Sgt. Colborn had no viable reason to call Manitowoc County Sheriff's Office dispatch regarding Ms. Halbach's vehicle," Zellner argues. "From the time Sgt. Colborn arrived at the Manitowoc County Sheriff's Office to the time he checked out and returned home, Sgt. Colborn was with at least Detective Remiker and Investigator Dedering, both of whom could have confirmed information regarding Ms. Halbach's vehicle."

A month before Avery's huge trial got under way, Strang and Buting informed Manitowoc County Judge Patrick

Willis of their client's frame-up defense in the murder trial. The lawyers for Avery planned to build their defense on the premise that Lenk and Colborn had falsified several pieces of evidence, namely blood, to secure Avery's arrest and conviction for Teresa's murder.

But Strang and Buting tried to stretch their theory like a rubber band and it never panned out as they envisioned.

They accused Lenk and Colborn of having planted an old vial of Avery's blood, a vial kept inside a cardboard box of files from Avery's wrongful conviction rape case, at the Manitowoc County Courthouse, which was next door to the sheriff's building.

With the trial looming, the prosecution team realized it needed to defuse this argument. In the days before Avery's February 2007 murder trial began, Calumet County Investigator Gary Steier was tapped to speak with Lenk and Colborn regarding their whereabouts during the week leading up to the discovery of Teresa's RAV4 by Pamela Sturm.

Steier's interviews of Lenk and Colborn were non-accusatory and consisted of softball questions that did not include any follow ups. This is understandable because Steier knew that his own head would be dished up like the head of John the Baptist if Wiegert and others discovered he was attempting to grill the two Manitowoc County sheriff's deputies and finding flaws with their interview statements.

Lenk and Colborn were questioned separately about their schedules for Sunday, October 30, 2005, through Saturday, November 5.

"Sgt. Colborn indicates he can recall where he was because his routine is fairly rigid. On Sundays, Sgt. Colborn indicates at 10:30 a.m. he would have left his house and went to his mother-in-law's house to check on her. Sgt. Colborn indicates every Sunday, prior to the start of his shift, he goes over to his mother-in-law's to make sure she is OK. Sgt.

Colborn says he would leave her house about 11:45 a.m. to go to work."[39]

Monday was Halloween, the date when Halbach met her end.

"Sgt. Colborn indicated he had worked a nine-and-one-half-hour workday and was done around 11:18 p.m." Colborn "would generally go home after his shift is over and watch TV, fall asleep on the couch, and then go to bed."

For Tuesday, November 1 and Wednesday, November 2, Colborn remembered he worked regular eight-hour shifts, finishing at 8 p.m.

"Colborn indicated generally he would have returned home or he would have watched TV and then gone to bed."

Thursday, November 3 was the start of the missing person investigation for Teresa. Colborn was the first officer to interview Avery, a face-to-face interview in which Colborn did not see any noticeable gashes or wounds to Avery's hands. "Sgt. Colborn indicated he had started at 11:45 a.m. where he had worked his eight-hour shift, plus three hours of overtime, assisting Calumet County Investigator John Dedering in speaking to the Zipperers about Teresa Halbach. Sgt. Colborn also remembers he was called to go check the Avery residence. Sgt. Colborn indicated he had concluded his shift around 10:50 p.m."

Next, it was time to ask Colborn about his whereabouts and movements for the next day, Friday, November 4. This time, Colborn claimed he had a foggy memory. He portrayed himself as having what's known in police circles as cop amnesia.

"On Friday, November 4, 2005, Sgt. Colborn indicated he was off. He could not recall what he had done on his off day."

---

39. Interview of Sgt. Andrew Colborn, Investigator Gary Steier, January 11, 2007

Colborn was just one day removed from the biggest day of police work in his career, and he was allowed to answer with a straight face that he simply could not remember anything about his activities and whereabouts the following day, on an open missing person's case, where the victim had not been found, her car was still gone, and the attacker remained at large.

It's also a little-known fact that Colborn was intricately involved in two other very strange discoveries of physical evidence surrounding Teresa's murder. Not far from the location where the eyewitnesses saw Teresa's RAV4 being hidden off Highway 147 at the turnabout, civilian searches also found a silver cellular phone in the ditch. And it wasn't an ordinary phone, either. The phone is commonly known as a burner phone. Burner phones are often used by two groups: people on a limited budget who use them to avoid the expensive entanglements with mobile companies, and the other element of people who use burner phones are criminals. There's a degree of privacy that make it nearly impossible for police to hunt down the caller's activities. A burner phone would be ideal for a drug dealer, a phone harasser, and for a stalker.

On Wednesday, November 9, ten days after Teresa vanished, a search party of Manitowoc County residents notified the police that they had made a suspicious discovery at 2:50 p.m. The find occurred along State Highway 147, just east of Ridge Road. Three police officers were called to the spot: Colborn, Lenk, and Calumet County Deputy Craig Wendling. "In the north ditch right along the gravel line was an Audiovox phone, silver in color. That item was found by a person searching, his name being John Campion ... After collecting the phone, we did return to the command post and all the evidence was kept in my exclusive possession in my squad. I then transported all the evidence to the Calumet County Sheriff's Office."[40]

The burner phone became an afterthought as the murder investigation focused squarely on Avery, who was also taken into custody that same day, November 9.

Incidentally, three days earlier, Colborn was also involved in the mysterious find at the creepy Maribel Caves Park. The secluded site is off-the-beaten path but it was located in the same general area where Teresa may have encountered her attacker. It was another example of Colborn being called outside the comfort zone of Avery Road to an off-site location to collect suspicious evidence that would quickly fade into oblivion as far as the police investigators were concerned.

"I was approached by Sgt. Colborn ... and informed he had left the crime scene to meet with a citizen at the Maribel Caves Park. Sgt. Colborn reported that the citizen found a piece of, what appeared to be, woman's blue jeans, and also found a plastic baggie containing a lubrication box ... I informed Sgt. Colborn he should get me all the information on the citizen and I would do an evidence sheet on that showing the exchange of custody."[41]

These mysterious blue jeans belonged to a female. Eerily, they had cut marks on them and bore a similar resemblance to the Daisy Fuentes clothing brand.

---

40. Deputy Craig Wendling, evidence collection from November 9, 2005, along with Manitowoc County's Sgt. Andy Colborn and Lt. Jim Lenk

41. Calumet County Sgt. Bill Tyson, November 6, 2005, supplemental report

Pieces of torn blue jeans belonging to an unidentified female were recovered from the creepy Maribel Caves Park property. It's the same general area where Teresa Halbach vanished.

CHAPTER ELEVEN

BATHROOM SINK

When Colborn interviewed Avery face to face on the evening of Thursday, November 3, one thing stood out. Colborn did not notice any gash or open wound on Avery's hand. The wound did not bust open until after Colborn left and went on his way back to the sheriff's office. If Colborn had noticed a bloody gash, he would have made a notation of such when he finally wrote up his first incident report of the event, eight months later.

"I, Sgt. Colborn attended a pretrial conference ... I mentioned that I had made initial contact with Steven Avery on Thursday, November 3, 2005. It was suggested to this sergeant on June 29, 2006, that I make an entry on this case narrative describing my initial contact with Steven on November 3, 2005."[42]

Colborn was the noon to 8 p.m. shift commander.

"I personally responded to Avery Auto Salvage initially to make contact with Charles 'Chuck' Avery in an attempt to locate the missing person. The Calumet Sheriff's Office had provided me with a (registered plate) which corresponds with a Toyota RAV4 registered to the missing person, as well as the name of the missing person, that being Teresa Halbach."

When he got to Avery Road, Colborn went to the main business office near Al and Dolores' trailer.

---

42. Manitowoc County Sheriff's Office summary, Sgt. Colborn entry, dated June 29, 2006

"As I exited my squad, again my intention was to walk to Chuck's trailer and make contact with him, however, as soon as I exited my squad, Steven Avery exited Allan and Dolores' trailer from the garage area and made contact with me. Steven inquired as to what I was at the property for. I asked Steven if a girl from Auto Trader Magazine had been on the property that day taking pictures of a vehicle they were selling. Steven replied that the female had indeed been on the Avery property and that she had been photographing a van which his sister was selling."

Even though Avery consistently told everyone that Teresa came between 2 and 2:30 p.m., Colborn chose to write down "it was somewhere around 3 p.m."

"He informed me that he did not speak with her and she had only been on the property five to ten minutes at the most … Steven stated that he did not speak with her and therefore would not know where she was going when she left the Avery property. Steven did volunteer the information that he glanced out the window of his residence and had observed her photographing the van. That is how he knew she was on the property."

When Colborn left the Avery compound, no evidence pointed to Avery as the abductor. Oddly, Colborn never went and spoke with Chuck Avery even though his report indicated visiting with Chuck was his main intention.

"As far as making contact with the Avery family or returning to the Avery property, no further action was taken on November 3, 2005, by this sergeant."

Here's what Avery remembers happened.

"After that conversation, I drove my Pontiac Grand Am from my parents' residence to its usual parking spot outside my garage. I got out of my car and walked to my sister's trailer, which was right next to mine. There, I broke open a cut on the outside of the middle finger of my right hand as I was attempting to unhitch my sister Barb's trailer. Before going to my trailer to put masking tape on my finger, I went into my Pontiac to grab my phone charger. I dripped blood in my Pontiac on the gearshift and other places. Anyone who looked through the windows of my Pontiac could have seen the blood on the gearshift and known there was a cut on my hand. I left my Pontiac unlocked."[43]

Shortly thereafter, Avery, along with his brother Chuck, drove into Manitowoc to buy supplies at Menards. Video surveillance from the store confirms this event.

"I remembered that I went to Barb's door to see if any of her sons wanted to go with me to Menards. Bobby and Blaine were home. I asked Bobby and Blaine if they wanted to go with me and my brother to Menards. I told both of them that a law enforcement officer had just left the property after asking me questions about Ms. Halbach's visit to photograph Barb's van on October 31, 2005. I noticed that Bobby was immediately nervous after I mentioned the visit by the officer. He said that he could not go with me to Menards and that he had 'things to do.' My memory is that Blaine said that he wanted to go to Menards and he went with Chuck and me."

But Avery had just split open his finger. That was troublesome and painful.

"Prior to leaving for Menards, I returned to my trailer to put tape on my bleeding finger. I entered my trailer through the south door because it was closest to the bathroom. I did not lock the south door of my trailer after I entered through it. A large amount of blood dripped onto the rim and sink and the floor of the bathroom. I did not wash away or wipe up because Chuck was waiting for me to go to Menards in Manitowoc with him. I quickly wrapped my finger in duct tape and left the trailer to meet Chuck. I left through the front door of my trailer."

The time they left was between 7:15 and 7:30 p.m. The skies were dark.

---

43. Affidavit of Steven Avery, November 23, 2016

"While we were leaving Avery property, driving a flatbed to Menards in Manitowoc, I saw taillights in front of my trailer," Avery remembers. "The taillights were further apart and higher off the ground than sedan taillights. I told my brother, who was driving, about the taillights. We turned around and drove to my trailer, but the vehicle was gone."

All told, Avery and his older brother were gone about three hours. They didn't make it back to Avery Road until 10 p.m. to 10:30 p.m.

"By the time we got home ... I was real tired. I went into my trailer through the front door and went straight to bed. I did not go back into my bathroom on November 3."

On Friday, November 4, Avery got up around 6 a.m. He walked down the hall to his bathroom to take a shower but was befuddled when he noticed his sink. "I saw that most of the blood on my sink, which I had not cleaned up the previous night, was gone. It seemed to me that the blood had been cleaned up. After reviewing more case documents and thinking about what happened on November 3, 2005, I do not believe that law enforcement broke into my trailer and took blood from my sink and planted it in Ms. Halbach's vehicle."

In retrospect, Avery now suspects the following events occurred after he went to Menards that night.

"I believe that Bobby removed the blood from my sink and planted it in the RAV4. Law enforcement would not remove the blood from the sink because they would not know that the blood belonged to me and would believe that it belonged to Ms. Halbach. Only the killer would know that the blood did not belong to Ms. Halbach and only someone who saw my finger bleeding would know that the blood was mine, so, I think that the only person who was there and knew my finger was bleeding and could have gotten into my trailer was Bobby. He would have taken the blood to frame me and save himself.

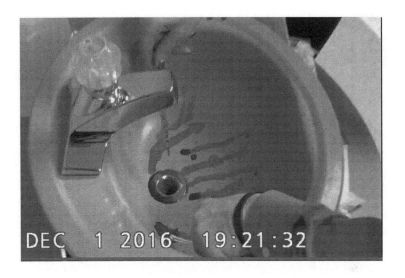

Steven Avery has always maintained that someone went into his trailer to remove blood from his bathroom sink shortly after his brother Chuck and he drove to Menards on Nov. 3, 2005.

"Bobby drove his Blazer to the front of my trailer and it was his Blazer taillights that I observed as Chuck turned on State Highway 147. I do not believe that the vehicle could have come from any other location than the Dassey-Janda place because the vehicle was gone in the two minutes it took Chuck, Blaine, and I to return to the trailer."[44]

Avery also pointed out, "the vehicle had to already be on the property when we left and Bobby's vehicle was the only vehicle that was present at the time we left. I believe that my trailer door was unlocked but even if it were locked, the Dasseys had a key to my trailer at their place."

By sheer coincidence, Zellner retained the services of Stuart James, one of the country's foremost experts on blood spatter and blood stain analysis. Earlier in this book, there was mention of the 2006 Omaha murder of Jessica O'Grady, the college coed who disappeared after telling her

---

44. Supplemental affidavit Steven Avery, June 29, 2018

apartment roommates she was heading over to the home of her boyfriend, who lived with his aunt. Although O'Grady's body was never found, the police in Omaha arrested Edwards and charged him with her murder. The prosecution's leading witness was James, the world renowned expert from Fort Lauderdale, Florida. His testimony left the jury from Omaha convinced of the boyfriend's guilt. This was the case where authorities found the defendant's mattress was saturated with blood from Jessica O'Grady. Tiny spatters of blood were found on the ceiling as well as the bedroom posts and nearby clock. Prior to being charged, Edwards was seen on store surveillance camera visiting Walgreens buying cleaning supplies to conceal some of the blood stains rampant throughout his basement bedroom at his aunt's home.

A decade later, James was putting his skills to use researching Teresa's slaying. One of his first experiments concerned the blood stains in Teresa's vehicle.

"Mr. James oversaw experiments that conclusively refute Mr. Kratz's argument that the 'sheer volume, the sheer number of places rule out that the blood in the RAV4 was planted.' The experiments demonstrated that it was actually a small amount of blood that was planted in the RAV4, and it was selectively dripped and one stain most probably was applied with an applicator.[45]

"Mr. James opines that the most likely source of Mr. Avery's planted blood was the blood deposited by Mr. Avery in his sink on November 3, 2005, and not blood from the 1996 blood vial. Mr. James, because of his familiarity with EDTA blood vials, opines that the hole in the top of the 1996 blood vial tube was made at the time Mr. Avery's blood was put in the tube, and the blood around the stopper is a common occurrence and does not indicate that the tube was tampered with."

---

45. Zellner post-conviction filings

Regarding the blood spatter in the RAV4, "Mr. James, based upon the experiments that he oversaw, opines that the blood spatter found in the RAV4 was selectively planted because the experiments demonstrated that if the State's theory that Mr. Avery was actively bleeding from the cut on his right middle finger was true, then blood would have been deposited in many more places in the RAV4 than where it was deposited.

"The blood spatter experiments conducted with actual blood on the subject's middle finger conclusively demonstrate that the blood would have been deposited on the RAV4's outside door handle, key, key ring, steering wheel, the gear shift lever, brake lever, battery cables and hood prop. The blood found in the RAV4 was only deposited in six places, not fifteen, and consisted of small drops of blood in the front of Ms. Halbach's RAV4 on the driver and passenger seats, driver's floor, and rear passenger door jamb."

At Avery's trial, Kratz speculated the blood in the back resulted when Avery picked up and tossed Teresa's dead body into the cargo area of her vehicle.

Stuart James' re-creation of the crime concluded Kratz got it wrong.

"Mr. James opines that the blood spatter on the inside of the rear cargo door was the result of Ms. Halbach being struck with an object consistent with a hammer or mallet while she was lying on her back on the ground behind the vehicle after the rear cargo door was opened."

"Mr. James opines that the State expert, Mr. (Nick) Stahlke, mistakenly described the blood on the rear cargo door as having been projected from Ms. Halbach's bloodied hair after she had been shot and as she was thrown into the cargo area of the vehicle. Mr. James, by overseeing a series of experiments, opines that the State's description of the cause of the blood spatter on the rear cargo door resulting from Ms. Halbach being thrown into the cargo area and blood being projected from her bloodied hair on the cargo door is demonstrably false.

"The erroneous blood spatter testimony of the State's expert Mr. Stahlke resulted in the State presenting a false narrative to the jury about the sequence of events surrounding the attack on Ms. Halbach. The State presented a scenario where Ms. Halbach was already fatally injured in Mr. Avery's garage prior to being thrown in the back of the RAV4. The experiments overseen by Mr. James demonstrate Ms. Halbach was struck on the head after she opened the rear cargo door. She fell to the ground next to the rear bumper on the driver's side where she was struck repeatedly by an object similar to a mallet or hammer."

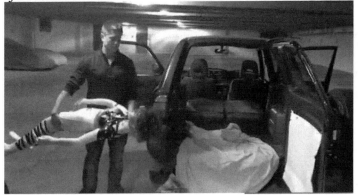

Stuart James oversaw several blood spatter experiments to demonstrate why special prosecutor Ken Kratz's theory about Teresa Halbach's attack had to be untrue.

After Avery was arrested and charged, he insisted to his lawyers, Strang and Buting, that his blood was planted in the RAV4, coming from his bathroom sink.

However, they ended up settling on a far more salacious theory. They decided to make Colborn and Lenk the culprits of their blood-planting defense.

In fact the following time sequence makes it virtually impossible for Sgt. Colborn to be the blood planter, according to Zellner's fact-finding probe.

"After Sergeant Colborn came to the Avery property on November 3 to speak with Mr. Avery around 7 p.m. he attended a meeting at the Manitowoc County Sheriff's Office at 8 p.m.," explained Zellner.

It takes twenty-three minutes to drive from Avery's to the Manitowoc Sheriff's Office headquarters next to the downtown courthouse.

If Avery, Chuck, and Blaine Dassey left for Menards at 7:15 p.m., Colborn only had twenty-two minutes to pull it off.

If they left at 7:20 p.m., then Colborn only had seventeen minutes.

If the Averys left at 7:25 p.m., then Colborn only had twelve minutes.

If they did not leave until 7:30 p.m., then Colborn only had seven minutes.

"It is therefore extremely improbable that Sgt. Colborn planted Mr. Avery's blood in Ms. Halbach's vehicle on November 3, 2005.

After devoting nearly three years to studying the psychology of Teresa's murder, Zellner surmises the killer realized there was a limited window to frame Avery. "The killer was familiar with the Radandt and Manitowoc County pits. He devised a plan to bring the RAV4 from the murder scene to the Avery property.

"He knew that he needed to put something with the DNA of Mr. Avery in the RAV4."[46]

When Steven left for Menards, his south door to the red trailer was unlocked because he didn't expect anybody to break in.

---

46. Post-Conviction Relief Motion, June 7, 2017

"The killer entered the trailer, intent on finding an item of Mr. Avery's with his DNA that he could use to plant DNA in the RAV4 to connect Mr. Avery to Ms. Halbach's murder. In the small trailer, the killer noticed fresh blood in the bathroom sink. The killer quickly collected the blood from the sink in Mr. Avery's bathroom and deposited the blood in several spots throughout the RAV4. The killer recognized that the blood had to be planted quickly, within fifteen to twenty-eight minutes and before it coagulated."

If Teresa's RAV4 was being stashed near the old dam, off Highway 147, it would only take Bobby one to two minutes to get there from Avery Road, do the deed, and get back home before his brother and two uncles returned from the Manitowoc Menards.

But if Bobby did the deed, the next logical question to ask is, how?

CHAPTER TWELVE

BLOOD DOCTOR

Born in 1941 in New York City, Stuart James obtained his bachelor's in biology and chemistry from Hobart College in New York in 1962. He later went on to graduate school at Elmira College where he studied bloodstain evidence, homicide investigations, and forensic microscopy. Among his many accolades, James became certified in 1997 as a competent forensic expert in the discipline of bloodstain pattern interpretation, and he was elected as a distinguished member of the International Association of Bloodstain Pattern Analysts in 2004. James has given consultation and testimony in the following places: Alaska, Arkansas, California, Connecticut, Delaware, District of Columbia, Florida, Georgia, Hawaii, Idaho, Illinois, Indiana, Kansas, Louisiana, Maryland, Massachusetts, Michigan, Missouri, Nebraska, Nevada, New Jersey, New Mexico, New York, North Carolina, Ohio, Pennsylvania, Tennessee, Utah, Vermont, Virginia, Washington, Wisconsin, Republic of South Korea, Toronto, Canada, St. Croix, U.S. Virgin Islands, and Mannheim, Germany.

The person's work he was asked to critique was that of Kratz, who had limited prior experience trying a murder case in Calumet County, according to a review of Westlaw filings.

Before conducting their analysis in Teresa's murder, James and Associates Forensic Consultants studied photos of the RAV4, bone fragments, the burn area behind Avery's garage, burn barrel contents, the burned cell phone, the garage and its contents, and blood stains on Avery's bathroom floor. Additionally, James reviewed the DNA reports, trial testimony, and arguments, including that from Kratz, anthropologist Leslie Eisenberg, and forensic scientist Stahlke. He also gave his undivided attention to the photographs of Teresa's cargo door, portions of the plastic dashboard of the RAV4, and chapters from Kratz's book, *Avery: The Case Against Steven Avery and what 'Making a Murderer' Gets Wrong.*

Stuart James is regarded as one of the country's most prolific blood-spatter analysis experts.

James found it noteworthy to mention how "Kevin Heimerl, special agent with the Wisconsin Division of Criminal Investigation, described there being no blood spatter in Mr. Avery's garage."

"I have reviewed the trial testimony of John Ertl, field response technician for the Wisconsin State Crime Lab. Ertl testified he had some experience as a bloodstain pattern analyst and that he saw no bloodstain patterns whatsoever in Mr. Avery's garage," James said.[47]

"To a reasonable degree of scientific certainty," James continued, "the absence of bloodstain patterns from a gunshot in Mr. Avery's garage is inconsistent with Ms. Halbach being shot in the head in that location."

As for Avery's red trailer, James found it telling that Ertl "found no evidence of bloodstain patterns in Mr. Avery's trailer. To a reasonable degree of scientific certainty, the absence of bloodstain patterns in Mr. Avery's trailer is inconsistent with a brutal attack occurring in that location. Further, the complete absence of Ms. Halbach's blood in Mr. Avery's trailer is inconsistent with her being stabbed or otherwise having sustained a significant blood-letting injury in Mr. Avery's trailer."

But didn't Kratz have a comeback for that? Didn't Manitowoc County's special prosecutor speculate that perhaps the empty jugs of bleach around the Avery property proved Avery and Brendan teamed up to saturate the concrete surface of Avery's garage to get rid of all Teresa's blood and they were masters at it, leaving no blood behind?

"In my professional experiences, it is extremely difficult to clean blood stains with heavy applications of bleach and paint thinner," James said.

At Avery's murder trial, his defense was handicapped and severely undermined because his lawyers chose not to hire a bloodstain pattern expert. The effect was disastrous because, as a result, the defense wasn't able to put forth a compelling argument against the persuasive prosecutor.

"The prosecutor, Ken Kratz, argued that Ms. Halbach was thrown into the rear cargo area of the RAV4 and that her blood was in motion when it struck the interior panel of the cargo door. The cargo door of the RAV4 opens with hinges on the passenger side of the vehicle to create a ninety-degree

---

47. Affidavit of Stuart James, May 3, 2017

angle with the threshold of the cargo area," James said. "If the bloodstain pattern observed on the interior cargo door had been created when Ms. Halbach was thrown into the cargo area and while the cargo door was open, it would likely produce elongated stains that indicate a right-to-left direction of travel relative to the cargo door. No such pattern was observed on the interior of the cargo door. In fact, Stahlke accurately described the bloodstains on the rear cargo area as being 'circular or near-circular.'"

Additionally, there was something else striking about the blood on the cargo door. It was concentrated at the bottom in the left corner.

"The bottom of the cargo door is seventeen inches from the ground. The concentration of bloodstains in this area is not consistent with blood being deposited as a result of Ms. Halbach's body being thrown into the rear cargo area ... The pattern on the rear cargo door is consistent with a stationary blood source being struck with a bloodied object and creating a cast-off pattern where the blood droplets have traveled from left to right relative to the rear of the vehicle and onto the open cargo door. I have directed experiments where similar cast-off patterns were created using a hammer swung at a low angle to deposit blood onto the rear cargo door of a 1999 RAV4."

James carried out a first-of-its-kind scientific experiment relative to Teresa's slaying. Kratz didn't do one and neither did Avery's defense team of Strang and Buting.

"For one experiment," James said, "a mannequin was obtained to reenact the scenario presented to the jury by the prosecution. Weights were attached to the mannequin to achieve a weight of approximately 135 pounds to replicate Ms. Halbach at the time of her death."

James worked with staff members of Kathleen T. Zellner & Associates who participated in his series of blood spatter experiments. The mannequin's hair was soaked with EDTA preserved blood and the vehicle used for the experiment was

Zellner's 1999 Toyota RAV4. The volunteer participant was 5-foot-10, 185 pounds, and 36 years old. Avery was listed as being 5-foot-6, 218 pounds, and he was 43 years old.

"The goal of the experiment was to replicate the prosecution's version of events. First, one of the volunteers attempted to create a bloodstain pattern on the cargo door by flinging the mannequin, but he was not able to do so. Then two volunteers threw the mannequin into the cargo area. They could not create a bloodstain pattern similar to what was observed on the rear cargo door of Ms. Halbach's vehicle."

Finally, James had the volunteers bind the mannequin's hands and feet with rope "in an effort to replicate the scenario described by Brendan Dassey in his confession. The addition of the rope had no effect on the experiment. After I concluded that no blood was being deposited on the cargo door when the mannequin was being thrown into the cargo area, the weights were removed from the mannequin to see what, if any, pattern was created when the weight of the mannequin was reduced to a fraction of Ms. Halbach's body weight. Without the added weight, the mannequin weighed approximately 15 pounds. Even still, we were unable to create a bloodstain pattern that resembled the cast-off pattern observed on the interior of the cargo door."

Stuart James has determined the actual sequence of events of Teresa Halbach's attack.

Eventually, another blood-spatter experiment involved the RAV4 cargo door being kept wide open.

"When completely open, the cargo door sits perpendicular to the threshold of the cargo area. A volunteer from Kathleen T. Zellner & Associates created cast-off bloodstain patterns on the cargo door by wetting the head of a mason's hammer with EDTA preserved blood and swinging. Cast-off bloodstains are created when blood is flung from a bloodied object."

It was this blood experiment that left James certain as to how Teresa met her end.

"To a reasonable degree of scientific certainty, the bloodstain pattern observed on the rear cargo door of Ms. Halbach's RAV4 was a cast-off pattern created by a blunt instrument. This bloodstain was not consistent with a knife because the blood droplets cast off by the blade of a knife are usually smaller than those observed on the rear cargo door. This bloodstain was not consistent with a gunshot because droplets of blood resulting from a gunshot are smaller than those observed on the rear cargo door. The bloodstain patterns that were most similar to the pattern observed on Ms. Halbach's rear cargo door were consistent with when the victim's body was in a prone position on her back on the ground with her head near the driver's side of the rear bumper and the attacker was kneeling over her, striking her with a bloodied object, consistent with a hammer or mallet while the rear cargo door was open.

"It is my conclusion that the bloodstain pattern on the rear cargo door of Ms. Halbach's RAV4 was not created in the manner described by the prosecution and their experts at Mr. Avery's trial."

Avery's lawyers Buting and Strang theorized Lenk or Colborn doctored the vehicle with a Q-tip of blood once Pam Sturm found the car on Saturday, November 5. Kratz dismissed that scenario. For him, the blood was proof of Avery's guilt.

In July 2017, James offered up his analysis to the ignition stain.

"The prosecution told the jury that all of the blood deposited in the RAV4 was from the cut on the middle finger of Mr. Avery's right hand and that he was actively bleeding. However, there was no blood on the door handle, key, gearshift, interior hood release, hood latch, hood prop and battery cable. It is my opinion that Mr. Avery's blood in the RAV4 is consistent with being randomly distributed from a source because his blood is present in some locations but absent in some reasonably anticipated locations ... The absence of bloodstains in these locations: door handle, key, gearshift, interior hood release, hood latch, hood prop, and battery cable is inconsistent with an active bleeder."

The Avery blood droplets, James interprets, "are consistent with an explanation other than Mr. Avery being in the RAV4 and depositing his blood in those locations with his actively bleeding cut finger. Had Mr. Avery been actively bleeding in the RAV4, it is my opinion that his blood and bloody fingerprints would have been deposited elsewhere in the vehicle."

Once again, James conducted a series of rigorous scientific experiments inside the RAV4 to draw his conclusions. He utilized a pipette to drip blood on the front seats, on a CD case, and on the metal frame by the rear passenger door. Also of note, James used Avery's authentic bathroom sink. It was removed from his Wisconsin trailer and brought to Zellner's suburban Chicago law office about three hours away. Also of note, Zellner's 1999 RAV4 had similar upholstery fabric on the seats of her vehicle. This signified the steering wheel, gear shift, dashboard, and console were probably from the same material.

"An applicator was used to create the stain near the ignition," James said. "For this experiment, I used fresh blood to better represent the time it would take for blood shed by Mr. Avery in his bathroom sink to coagulate and dry.

Blood was drawn from a volunteer and was deposited on the bathroom sink from Mr. Avery's residence. The blood dried on the sink for approximately thirty minutes. Dried flakes of blood were then lifted from the sink using a scalpel."

At that point, James drew even more fresh blood from his volunteer.

"Using a pipette, blood was taken from the sink and transported to Ms. Zellner's 1999 RAV4. Blood was then dripped on the driver's seat, the passenger's seat, between the driver's seat and center console, on a CD case sitting on the passenger seat, and on the door jamb of the rear passenger door. An applicator was used to recreate the stain near the ignition. Depositing blood in this manner and at these locations took less than three minutes."

Moreover, they dripped blood on the carpet floor between the driver's seat and the center console. "The fresh blood absorbed into the carpet and did not form flakes."

In his final analysis, James categorized the blood drops on the driver's seat as a "passive drop." The blood on the passenger seat and CD case also were "passive drops." He classified the blood on the passenger's side door jamb as "passive drop with flow pattern."

The blood near the driver's ignition was produced "with an applicator."

"The stain near the ignition of Ms. Halbach's RAV4 was approximately 2.25 inches from the ignition," James said. "To a reasonable degree of scientific certainty, Mr. Avery would not have deposited blood at that location with his right middle finger while turning the key in the ignition."

It's hard to say whether Avery would have walked free had Strang and Buting directed their suspicions about the planted blood as coming from an alternative suspect instead of trying to blame Lenk and Colborn for any and all shady behavior.

"I told my trial defense lawyers that my blood in the RAV had been taken from my sink," Avery said. "I woke up at 6 a.m. and went into the bathroom to take a shower. I saw that most of the blood on my sink, which I had not cleaned up the previous night, was gone. It seemed to me that the blood had been cleaned up ... I tried to tell my trial defense attorneys about the blood in the sink. They did not listen to me and told the jury the blood came from a blood tube at the courthouse."[48]

If the killer methodically planted blood from Avery's sink, the job could be accomplished with a wet sponge and driving to the RAV4 hidden at the Old Dam along Highway 147 in barely five minutes. Dripping the blood inside the RAV4 would take sixty to ninety seconds. Besides a wet sponge, a rag or wet towels would work, James determined.

What does Zellner say about the performance of Buting and Strang regarding their unsuccessful attempt to blame Lenk and Colborn for planting the blood?

"Mr. Avery's trial defense counsel relied exclusively upon a frame-up theory of defense, correctly arguing that all evidence inculpating Mr. Avery was fabricated," Zellner said. "However, they incorrectly argued that Mr. Avery's blood found in Ms. Halbach's vehicle was planted by law enforcement and that it came from a 1996 blood vial held in the Manitowoc County Clerk of Courts Office. Trial defense counsel represented to the jury that the seal of the 1996 blood vial package had been broken and resealed with a strip of Scotch tape. Trial defense counsel would have been aware that this package was opened by members of the Wisconsin Innocence Project in 2002 to examine forensic evidence that could be tested. At that time, Mr. Avery's Wisconsin Innocence Project attorneys broke the seal of the 1996 blood vial package and resealed the enclosed box using only a strip of Scotch tape. There was no credible proof presented to the jury establishing that Lt. Lenk and Sgt. Colborn accessed

---

48. Affidavit of Steven Avery, November 23, 2016

the Clerk of Court's file to obtain Mr. Avery's blood to plant it in the RAV4."

Zellner has taken Buting and Strang to task for making it appear Lenk and Colborn had prior knowledge of the blood vial's existence in the courthouse vaults.

"However, trial defense counsel failed to present evidence that proved, in any matter, that Lt. Lenk had knowledge of the 1996 blood vial. Trial defense counsel relied on a transmittal form that showed that other evidence from Mr. Avery's 1985 case was sent to the (Wisconsin State Crime Lab) for testing. Simply stated, there is no evidence that Lt. Lenk ever had possession of or even knew about the 1996 blood vial of Mr. Avery's blood stored in the Clerk of Court's office. Despite knowing that there was no provable connection between Lt. Lenk and the 1996 blood vial, trial defense counsel represented to the jury that Lt. Lenk must have inadvertently found the 1996 blood vial in examining the file. This argument was totally lacking in credibility because there was no corroborative evidence to support it.

"Trial defense counsel's theory about the 1996 blood vial was carelessly constructed without corroboration. The blood vial theory was abandoned during the trial and it resulted in no viable theory being presented to the jury about trial defense counsel's claim that the blood in the RAV4 was planted. Trial defense counsel lost credibility with the jury when it was unable to present any evidence that Mr. Avery's blood in the RAV4 was planted.

"Current post-conviction counsel's blood spatter expert has been able to demonstrate that all of Mr. Avery's blood in the RAV4 was selectively planted and that the blood spatter on the rear cargo door was not the result of Ms. Halbach being thrown into the cargo area by her attacker as the State told the jury. The failure of trial defense counsel to have a viable theory supported by expert testimony explaining how Mr. Avery's blood was planted in Ms. Halbach's vehicle all but guaranteed his conviction and life sentence without parole."

DEC 1 2016 19:28:43

Stuart James is positive that blood was selectively planted into Halbach's auto by the killer, not the Manitowoc County Sheriff's Department, as Avery's original trial lawyers asserted.

***

On Friday, November 4, the Manitowoc County Sheriff's Office decided to revisit Avery. Jim Lenk and his apprentice, Detective Dave Remiker, rode together, arriving around 10:20 a.m. If it wasn't evident the night before, it was now apparent during the daylight hours that Avery Road and Steven Avery were under intense scrutiny. Remiker knocked on the door at Avery's but no one was home. Next, he walked next door to the gray trailer. "This is a residence adjacent to the residence belonging to Steven. I again did not receive any contact from anyone at the residence."

Before Lenk and Remiker went on their way, they saw a golf cart riding through the scrap yard. It was Avery and his mother Dolores. Remiker and Lenk introduced themselves and Avery did not hesitate to answer their questions.

"Steven stated he recalls on Monday, October 31, between 2 and 2:30 p.m., Teresa came to Avery Road and was taking photos of a maroon in color van parked near his residence. Steven stated he had very minimal conversations and contact with Teresa. 'It was just hi, how you doing.' Avery estimated Teresa was gone within five minutes. Steven stated Teresa has been on the Avery property numerous times in the past and occasionally comes to the property to take photos of vehicles to be sold."[49]

At that point, nobody had seen Teresa for four days, Remiker informed Avery. If Avery killed Teresa inside his trailer, would he let the two detectives inside to peek around? Remiker and Lenk decided to pose the question to see how Avery reacted. "I asked Steven if he would be willing to provide me with a verbal consent to search his residence for Teresa," Remiker stated. "Steven immediately provided verbal consent. He stated we could search the interior of his trailer home. I requested Steven to accompany Lt. Lenk and me to his residence to conduct the search. He seemed very surprised. I felt this was the first time that he had knowledge of or was informed that Teresa Halbach is missing."

Remiker searched the trailer. He opened several doors including the bedroom closets and other doorways and closets throughout the trailer. "I did not locate any signs of Teresa inside the residence. Prior to leaving, we thanked Steven for his cooperation."

By 10:38 a.m. the pair of Manitowoc County detectives drove off. If they expected incriminating clues to turn up at Avery's, Lenk and Remiker were both let down. They left empty handed but Avery was definitely not in the clear.

The continued presence of Manitowoc County Sheriff's detectives hovering around Avery Road only served to stoke the rumor mill of Avery's involvement. Several hours after Remiker and Lenk left, Avery made a disturbing observation.

---

49. Dave Remiker's summary, Manitowoc County Sheriff's Office report on Halbach Investigation

"I smelled cigarette smoke in my trailer on November 4," Avery said. "This was very strange because I did not smoke and Jodi, who lived with me, did not smoke. I thought that someone else had been in my trailer, and I said that in one of my interviews."[50]

Although Bobby does not smoke, Scott Tadych was a heavy cigarette smoker, Zellner observed.

Avery also found signs of forced entry. To document it, he made an entry inside his notebook, the one where he kept Teresa's phone number handy. In his notebook, Avery scribbled the words, "Back to Patio Door."

"Before I left for the family property in Crivitz on November 5, I opened the south door of my trailer and observed pry marks near the door latch."

Not long after the Avery family had cleared out of Avery Road and drove up north to their cottage in Marinette County early that Saturday morning, Teresa's RAV4 was discovered back on the Avery property.

However, just the day before that, on Friday afternoon, an older man, accustomed to minding his own business out in the country along Jambo Creek Road, saw something suspicious from out in his backyard.

What the man saw was central to the still-developing missing person probe of Teresa.

---

50. Steven Avery Affidavit, November 23, 2016

CHAPTER THIRTEEN

TWO CARS

Some Manitowoc County citizens prefer an easy simple way of life. One such person was Wilmer Siebert, now in his eighties. He lives on Jambo Creek Road near the massive Fred Radandt & Sons sand and gravel pits. He's a junk collector. His backyard is littered with cars and car batteries. His two-story white house has seen better days and looks like it would blow over in a strong windstorm.

A guy like Siebert never expected to be roped into Teresa's murder investigation, and he certainly never figured his wandering, watchful eyes would have a pivotal role in helping Avery's lawyer expose more police corruption than was initially suspected.

"On November 4, 2005, I became aware through the news media that Teresa Halbach was missing and that one of her last stops was at Avery's Auto Salvage. From the media coverage, I learned that Teresa Halbach drove a 1999 Toyota RAV-4 blue-green in color," Siebert said.[51]

On Saturday morning, November 5, the RAV4 turned up double-parked facing in a westerly direction; all the surrounding cars on the outer ridge of Avery Salvage faced east. The persons who decided to dump Teresa's RAV4 there also left it covered with broken tree branches, cardboard boxes, and a rusty car hood. But this was not done to conceal the car as many people who watched *Making a Murderer* mistakenly have said.

---

51. Affidavit of Wilmer Siebert, March 23, 2017

"The tree branches on the RAV show that it was planted by the cops," Zellner told the author. "The branches and random car hood were placed on the vehicle so Kratz could argue that the flyover would not pick up the RAV because it was covered. The other tell that the cops and not the killer planted the RAV is that the vehicle was locked. The killer would not waste time locking the vehicle."

To recap, the following events likely unfolded on Friday, November 4.

Sgt. Colborn was off work, but he would not reveal anything he did that day when asked to do so.

Colborn made a personal phone call into Manitowoc dispatch from a private phone line, reciting Teresa's license plates and seeking confirmation she owned a 1999 Toyota. And then there was the sighting by Wilmer Siebert off Jambo Creek Road.

Zellner said the mid-afternoon sighting by Siebert fits with the time frame of former Mishicot Kevin Rahmlow who maintains he spoke with Sheriff's Sgt. Andy Colborn at the Cenex gas station alerting Colborn to the turnabout on Highway 147 where Rahmlow had seen the abandoned vehicle.

"Sometime before Teresa Halbach's vehicle was discovered, I saw a similar vehicle matching in color, style, and size drive into the Fred Radandt Sons Inc. gravel pit on the access road that is just south of my house. I remember this vehicle had the same spare wheel and cover on the rear cargo door as Ms. Halbach's RAV-4," Siebert said.

But the RAV4 was not the only vehicle that pulled off Jambo Creek Road.

Two vehicles went in, but only one came out.

"I saw a white Jeep closely follow the other vehicle down the access road into the gravel pits. The Jeep looked like an older model and had paint chipping off of the hood," Siebert said.

Two vehicles had sneaked into the far edge of the Avery Salvage property. Siebert, the curious neighbor, watched from his yard. He knew something was up, some mischief.

"A short time after the two vehicles entered the gravel pits, the Jeep exited the gravel pits, again using the access road just south of my house," he said.

In 2007, Ken Kratz told the jury deciding Avery's guilt or innocence how, "Pam Sturm described it as divine intervention ... that it was the hand of God ... as to where we should look at the 4,000 cars that were on this property. Pam Sturm looked in that one place. She never would have gotten through all those cars."

***

Back in 2005, people following Teresa's murder investigation did not have the foggiest clue that the real murder investigation was taking place away from the Avery property.

This was kept hush-hush, a closely guarded secret for a number of reasons. For one, the search and recovery for noteworthy clues of Teresa's murder far away from Avery's red trailer only served to fuel doubts about his role in causing her to die. There was a general consensus within the ranks of Manitowoc County, Calumet County, and the Wisconsin DOJ that Avery needed to be dealt with, this was time to rewrite history and get rid of this persistent, ever-growing public perception problem around Manitowoc County that their local Wisconsin cops were dirty, no good, rotten scoundrels.

During the early stages of the case, the police leaned on Avery's adjoining landowner, Joshua Radandt, who owned and operated Fred C. Radandt Sons quarries. His quarry was directly west and south of Avery's forty-acre tract. Radandt, however, was not the only quarry in the immediate area. There also happened to be a quarry directly south of his land, owned by the government of Manitowoc County. Saturday, November 5, 2005, was a date Josh Radandt would never forget. And neither would people interested in Avery's plight. Late that morning, the SUV of Halbach, without its license plates, was located by volunteer searcher Pam Sturm.

"On November 5, 2005, I was with several friends at the hunting camp," Radandt said. "Law enforcement officers arrived at the hunting camp and asked us if we had seen or heard anything unusual about the Avery property recently … By this time, there was already news media coverage of Teresa Halbach's disappearance that included coverage of the Avery property."[52]

Thinking fast, Radandt remembered how someone at the Avery property was burning a fire a few days earlier. But from his perspective, this was not anything out of the ordinary or suspicious. It went on all the time.

"I told the officers that I saw a fire, orange in color, when I was driving from the Radandt sand and gravel pit to the hunting camp on October 31, 2005, at approximately 5 p.m. I told the officers that I saw the fire from the direction of the Avery property. Because it was dark, or getting dark, when I saw the fire, I was not sure where exactly the fire was located. I did not observe any smoke coming from the fire."

The fire was hardly roaring. There was no thick black smoke or awful stench, such as the foul smell of a young woman's body from being left outside in an open burn pit on a cool autumn night. In fact, there were probably dozens of bonfires set that night throughout Manitowoc and Calumet County out in the country. After all, it was Halloween night.

"The fire did not appear to be spread out and its flames appeared to be two and a half to three feet in height. These characteristics were consistent with my personal knowledge

---

52. Affidavit of Joshua Radandt, February 10, 2017

of burn barrel fires," Radandt said. "I assumed the fire was contained in a burn barrel. I did not see whether the fire was actually contained in a burn barrel."

Since the overzealous police out to get Avery were desperate for leads, after all, they lacked a body and any physical evidence, the idea of a fire sounded intriguing. The police made Radandt return to their command post headquarters along Avery Road that Saturday evening, hours after the RAV4 had turned up.

"Less than one week after I provided that written statement, two officers, who I believe were from the Wisconsin Department of Justice, met me at the hunting camp to discuss the fire I saw," Radandt said. "I remember them asking me if I was sure what I said I saw. It seemed to me that they weren't satisfied with my statement about the fire. Specifically, it seemed to me that they wanted me to change my story to include a larger fire. Because they were reluctant to accept my story as true, I eventually asked them what they wanted me to say. They told me that all they wanted was the truth. I advised them that I had been telling the truth."

The State investigators made what now appears to be a startling revelation.

"At that time, I was told by the Department of Justice agents that they believed Teresa Halbach's vehicle was driven to the Kuss Road cul-de-sac by driving west through an empty field, then south down the gravel road that ran northeast into the Avery property. They told me that they believed Teresa Halbach's vehicle turned northeast onto that gravel road and entered the Avery property at its southwest corner. It is my understanding that this theory was based on the work of scent tracking dogs," Radandt said.

If Avery killed Teresa, would he hide her vehicle off-site only to move it back onto his family's property knowing the police had the area under siege, thinking he was Teresa's abductor and killer?

Radandt furnished the police the keys to search his three deer camp trailers at his sand and gravel pit behind Avery Salvage. "Later that day, law enforcement called my cell phone again. They informed me that they completed the search of my trailers and that I could use them normally. During the course of this phone conversation, law enforcement informed me that they were going to collect the contents of the burn barrel at the hunting camp at a later time. When I returned to the hunting camp, I observed that they had cordoned off the area surrounding that burn barrel with yellow tape."

But why was one of Radandt's burn barrels at the heart of Teresa's murder mystery? He was never told by police, but he knew something was there.

"To the best of my knowledge, Wisconsin State Patrol assigned officers to watch the burn barrel day and night on a rotating basis until its contents were collected. I was not present when the contents of the burn barrel were collected."

Then Radandt made another observation during that first week of November while Teresa was still being considered a missing person.

He saw the cops on the move. They were far away from the Avery property and working under the cloak of darkness.

"A few days after November 2005, I remember seeing tower lights in the Manitowoc County sand and gravel pit to the south of Radandt's quarry. I remember the lights appeared to illuminate the entire Manitowoc County pit."

Was the real murder investigation taking place in secrecy, far away from Avery's red trailer and his ramshackle detached garage? Radandt began to wonder.

"I understand that there were suspected human pelvic bones recovered from a gravel pit property south of Avery's Auto Salvage. Upon reviewing a map showing the coordinates at which these bones were found, I believe they were found in the Manitowoc County sand and gravel pit."

Back in 2005, the large county-owned sand and gravel pit would have been the perfect place to burn up a body under the cover of darkness. The property along County Road Q was not being used at the time. The land was isolated, far from any immediate homes or commercial businesses. It spanned hundreds of acres.

If someone wanted to trespass at the county quarry or wander through Radandt's sand and gravel pits, back in 2005, it was fairly easy.

There were 'Private Property' trespassing signs posted around the perimeters of the Radandt sand and gravel pits, but that was about it.

"There were locking gates or cables at each access road, but they were rarely used," Radandt said.

During Avery's trial, Kratz did not want to put Joshua Radandt on the witness stand as a prosecution witness. And yet Kratz was keenly interested in learning what information Radandt knew, perhaps so he could spin a yarn for the jury that was simple and easy to follow.

"Approximately one or two months before the start of Mr. Avery's criminal trial in 2007, I was summoned to the courthouse," Radandt remembered. "At the courthouse, I was questioned again about my recollection of seeing a fire in the direction of the Avery property on October 31, 2005. I was not called as a witness to testify at Mr. Avery's criminal trial in 2007."

CHAPTER FOURTEEN

CANINE NOSES

It may have been a night for trick-or-treaters, but Travis Groelle remained steadfast at work for Radandt's gravel pit. He was working near County Highway Q where he was loading and feeding the rock crushing machines. He remembered at least one other employee was working there that night. As Groelle was hard at work, he noticed a strange smell. There was something blowing in the cool autumn breeze and it was unsetting.

"Regarding the smell, he said it was not tires. Said it was a smell that he hadn't experienced before so he could not say what was causing it. (Groelle) said the smell was still in the air when he left and it was coming from east, more towards the middle of the quarry. He did not see any fires."[53]

The surrounding area where Groelle was working is rural, rugged terrain just south of Highway 147. There are hundreds of tall, mature cedar trees planted along both sides of Q. The county gravel pit could be accessed by pulling off Q or by someone wandering in from Josh Radandt's adjacent quarries. To drive to the pits from Avery's takes only a couple minutes.

In November 2005, during the height of the quest to find Teresa, several of Wisconsin's all-around best tracking and cadaver dogs were utilized by law enforcement. The dogs were ushered throughout Avery's red trailer by their handlers and taken near his garage. But those were not the spots that drew the most intrigue. Instead, the action was coming away

---

53. Jim Kirby interview of Travis Groelle, August 8, 2016

from Avery's property, about a half-mile away, over toward the spooky stretch of Kuss Road. Kuss Road runs east-west. Avery's place was to the east of Kuss Road.

This was a small, secluded local road flanked by tall cedars on both sides of the street. Less than a dozen acres were nestled along Kuss Road off the woodlands. At the end of Kuss Road was a cul-de-sac overlooking Radandt's quarries; way off in the distance you can see the Avery Salvage Yard. At the cul-de-sac, however, was a winding little conveyor road. The dirt road led into the back of Radandt's deer hunting camp consisting of three mobile trailers.

Prosecutor Kratz theorized that Avery lured Halbach into his red trailer. In reality, the Wisconsin police were concentrating their criminal investigation along a lonely stretch of Kuss Road, about a half mile away.

Monday, November 7, marked the fifth consecutive day of a constant Manitowoc County law enforcement presence around Avery's property. But not everybody who showed up at Avery Road had a stake in the outcome of making sure that Avery went down hard for the crime, notably Kaukauna canine handler Sarah Fauske who showed up with her bloodhound Loof.

"Sheriff Pagel did have two pairs of shoes that belonged to Teresa Halbach. Both were bagged separately in plastic bags. I placed sterile gauze in the toes of all the shoes and removed the insole in a plastic bag with sterile gauze. The shoes were then secured in my personal vehicle," Fauske explained. "When Loof began her task of sniffing for Halbach's scent, it was around 1:30 p.m., 57 degrees, and there was a slight breeze, zero to five m.p.h. blowing from the northwest."[54]

"Find!" Fauske yelled to Loof.

Out near Avery's yard, Loof followed her nose over toward Barb Janda's maroon van where Teresa had snapped a few photos a week earlier.

Eventually, "Loof went up to the south door of the trailer home. The door having a small porch entrance and the door was white in color. K9 Loof wanted to enter the home. K9 Loof continued north along the trailer and went between some pine trees and a burning barrel. K9 Loof smelled a charred area showing some interest then continued west. K9 Loof went west in a picked cornfield. Directly to the south was a gravel pit and in between the two was an area of brush and trees."

The dog became preoccupied with the Kuss Road cul-de-sac.

"K9 Loof worked this area with indications of very strong scent. K9 Loof worked west coming out to a cul-de-sac that was taped off with crime scene tape and two deputies were not allowing access. K9 Loof crossed the tape on one occasion and then was told to not go any further. The

---

54. Exhibit 46, Scent and Cadaver Dog Reports, handler and officer Sarah Fauske

deputies phoned Sheriff Pagel to see if I could continue but were (sic) told to not allow anyone access at this time."

Interestingly, Loof's nose led the bloodhound directly to the same spot that, it just so happens, a small group of men from the Manitowoc County Sheriff's Office were already inspecting that morning. But these men were not about to let a pair of outsiders into their club. As a result, Fauske and Loof were off-limits because it appeared the local police did not want them seeing what they were up to. Was evidence being mishandled or manipulated off Kuss Road? Fauske and her bloodhound weren't allowed access to the closely guarded property, a half mile west from Avery's.

***

Loof was not the only highly specialized dog whose nose steered him away from Avery's. Bob and Julie Cramer of Great Lakes Search and Rescue Canine Group brought along Brutus and Trace, two of their top scent-tracking dogs. Over the weekend, the Cramers were out with the dogs in one of the quarries east of Avery Road, where the dogs alerted. However, when they returned to the gravel piles that Monday, November 7, Brutus and Trace did not alert at the flagged location or the same general area the second time around.

"We then proceeded to a location we were requested to check on Kuss Road where a potential burial site had been located. K9 Brutus checked the area and after passing the area upon entry in the wooded area, he gave a head check returning to the location and gave his bark alert. Alert #12 and seemed particularly interested in a shovel lying next to the disturbed earth."[55]

---

55. Exhibit 46, Scent and Cadaver Dog Reports submitted by Julie Cramer, training director Great Lakes Search and Rescue Canine, Inc.

According to the Cramers, "K9 Trace checked the wooded area first and did not alert, but did show interest, increased animation, and high head checks. Upon returning to the area a second time, K9 Brutus again barked and alerted near the area of disturbed earth."

Later on, the pair of dogs drew a new assignment closer to the Avery compound.

"At the exterior of the home, Brutus again barked at the door and scratched to enter the residence. K9 Trace also barked at the front door. Once inside the trailer, K9 Brutus proceeded to check the interior, alerting inside a bedroom at the bed and pile of clothing. He was very agitated, but no scent source was noticed."

That particular trailer, however, was not Avery's. It belonged to his older brother Chuck.

To reiterate, most of the police focus remained off-site away from Avery's.

"K9 Brutus was then sent to check the berm just west of Steven Avery's property. There was a report of a suspicious looking pile of disturbed earth. Brutus showed no interest in that pile, but did alert on a pile of brush and trash just west of the Avery residence and was very excited along the edge of the berm. This excitement continued as we proceeded south along this ridge and he carefully checked brushy areas west of the Avery yard and along the edge of the salvage yard. His behavior was noted by law enforcement personnel in the area, who indicated that man trailing bloodhounds had also been interested in the same area."

Back at the command post, Julie Cramer compared notes with the others.

"We met with the bloodhound handlers on scene, and it was noted that both live scent dogs and the human remains detection dogs had shown excessive interest in the ridge of land beginning behind Steven Avery's residence and running south to the corner of the salvage yard, where the gravel conveyor is located. This area seems to be of particular interest to the dogs although no scent source has been located in the area."

***

During Avery's trial, any mention of law enforcement's regular presence along Kuss Road during the early stages of the investigation was downplayed.

Kratz tried to avoid the sensitive subject. Just what was Manitowoc County's preoccupation with this area far removed from Avery's trailer? Why were police devoting their utmost time and careful attention to this area if it was of no relevance at all? The answer seems obvious. The police probably uncovered clues and signs of a violent crime. Therefore, they needed to be very secretive and clandestine. Little was written about the efforts to mine the quarry properties for physical evidence related to Teresa's violent death. Along those lines, the police statements that were written down and entered into the official case file were strange.

Some police reports divulge that Calumet Investigator Mark Wiegert had contacted colleague John Dedering at 10:35 a.m. on Monday, November 7.

"He requested that an investigator go to the east end of Kuss Road. I did respond to the area and spoke with retired Deputy Inspector Michael Bushman, Manitowoc County Sheriff's Office. Bushman was leading a team of searchers in the area. It should be noted that the end of Kuss Road is approximately one half mile away from the western edge of the Avery property.

"I arrived at the east end of Kuss Road approximately 10:45 a.m. and spoke with former Deputy Inspector Bushman. He indicated he had found a possible excavation site and did take us to the site. The area was then taped off with crime scene tape and the area was frozen. No one was allowed in or out."[56]

Roughly six hours of time was spent on Kuss Road, the very same spot where the dogs kept finding Teresa's scent. And yet Dedering's report made the following declaration, "At 4:51 p.m., I was notified the excavation area was not pertinent to this case."

The mere fact that Bushman showed up to work Teresa's investigation and then had a leading role in the biggest event of November 7 warrants further scrutiny. Mike Bushman's name is mentioned in only three paragraphs in the entire Calumet County investigative file, which consists of 1,116 pages. Bushman was not even active law enforcement anymore. He was retired, and retired from Manitowoc County, the tarnished agency that already had a direct conflict of interest in spearheading the evidence-gathering efforts against Avery. But Bushman's role in the case went much deeper. As mentioned in Chapter Two, Bushman had a direct role in carrying out the biggest miscarriage of justice in northeastern Wisconsin. Bushman, along with then-Sgt. Kenny Petersen, had implicit orders to arrest Avery for the vicious attack and rape of the candy store owner along the sandy shorelines of Lake Michigan. Now, two decades later, Bushman sprang out of retirement to fulfill another important task, which marked the eighth day of Teresa's disappearance.

As mentioned earlier, much of the preoccupation at Avery's trial by Strang and Buting surrounded evidence planting suppositions, but at that time, a decade ago, nobody was giving much credence to an alternative scenario.

If the sheriff's higher ups at Manitowoc County had no concerns about using fake evidence to nail a guilty suspect or frame somebody they loathed, wouldn't they be just as

---

56. Information Developed Regarding Possible Items of Interest on Kuss Road, Inv. Dedering Report, Nov. 7, 2005

devious about making legitimate evidence and legitimate crime scenes go away or disappear, to seem as if they never existed in the first place?

If that were so, such an assignment was highly sensitive, incredibly covert, and could only be carried out by someone up to the task. A logical candidate would be someone experienced at covering up crime scenes or staging an incident to divert attention away from a criminal suspect to someone else. That person would need to be dependable and someone who would never squeal.

Aside from Teresa's killing, the biggest mystery case at the Manitowoc County Sheriff's Office during the past twenty years concerns the long-suspected police cover-up of the gruesome death of a local teenager, Ricky Hochstetler. He died on a snowy January night in 1999, just six years before Teresa was slain.

The lead investigator assigned to that case by Petersen and Kocourek was a fiercely loyal traffic lieutenant named Mike Bushman.

Under Bushman's direction, the culprit responsible for the Ricky Hochstetler tragedy was never identified, and scores of locals suspect the case remained intentionally unsolved. Other key Manitowoc sheriff's officials assigned to work on that case included Andy Colborn, James Lenk, Dave Remiker, and Jason Jost.

CHAPTER FIFTEEN

COVER UP

The winter of 1998 marked a contentious time for the husband and wife who rented the two-story farmhouse on the far southern outskirts of Manitowoc. Once that winter, the Manitowoc County Sheriff's Office responded for a domestic violence call. The couple was in the midst of a bitter divorce. They had three children, the oldest being a teenage boy named Ricky. He had a part-time job at the Manitowoc Hardees and liked to hang out with fellow teenagers. On Ricky's last night alive, he was dropped off at a house in Manitowoc.

"He was going for a pizza party and movies with his friends," his mother recalled. "On that particular night, I was surprised that he didn't call for a ride home. If he felt that it was too cold or too nasty out, he would always call, 'Mom, can you come and get me?'"[57]

When Debi Hochstetler dropped her son off around 5 p.m. that Saturday, the snow was starting to fall. As the night wore on, a blowing snowstorm kicked up. Winds became nasty and the snow was drifting. It was not a safe night to be out driving, especially for anyone who had consumed too much alcohol at one of the Manitowoc area watering holes.

"When their movies were done, Ricky walked a friend Jennifer home, and then he proceeded to walk home. He was

---

57. 2016 interview with John Ferak for special report published in USA TODAY NETWORK Wisconsin newspapers.

a little past his curfew, so that's probably why he didn't call me. He didn't want to wake me up," his mother said.

Ricky's walk home was about three miles.

Trudging through the snow, Ricky was bundled up in his warm green winter jacket. He began his journey home between 1 and 1:30 a.m.

"He was walking, with traffic, along the edge of the road, three feet off the edge of the road. And they said they could see the vehicle tracks were in and out, in and off the road. Then the vehicle hit Ricky, and he was on the hood of the vehicle and he was dropped down and dragged. And they said that the person made no attempts to stop," his mother said.

Manitowoc County Highway CR is a dark, desolate road out in the country. The posted speed limit is fifty m.p.h. Ricky endured a brutal, agonizing death. He was struck from behind by an intoxicated motorist right around bar closing time.

His broken and battered body separated from the car in the middle of the road.

The drunk driver kept heading south on CR for another two miles until he reached the T-intersection for Newton Road. The hit-and-run motorist had a chance to hop on the interchange for Interstate 43, where heading south goes to Milwaukee and going north ends up in Green Bay.

The fleeing motorist chose to stay on the off-the-beaten-path country roads.

Keep in mind, these were extremely local roads. Only someone who regularly traveled the back roads of southern Manitowoc County would be driving these roads at such a late hour on a weekend after having too much to drink.

There just so happened to be a late-night drinking establishment barely a quarter-mile up the road from where Ricky was run over. The Bil-Mar supper club had been a popular banquet hall and bar for many years around Manitowoc County. Manitowoc's movers and shakers and politically connected wined and dined there. Among them, Manitowoc Sheriff Tom Kocourek had his wedding reception there. There were also a couple of large gatherings at the Bil-Mar that particular Saturday night. One was held for employees and guests of the Manitowoc Ice company and the other affiliated with the Copps Grocery Store. The bar was also open to the general public. A few of the stragglers stayed until the wee hours of the morning, and they pulled out of the parking around the time Ricky was trudging through the drifting snow along the dark road, just minutes away from making it home.

The hit-and-run driver who plowed into Ricky and continued driving was already outside of Manitowoc's city limits, making it highly unlikely the inebriated motorist lived in Manitowoc. Three very small communities were in the general vicinity of the drunken motorist's path, the town of Newton, the village of Cleveland, and the village of Kiel. Based on the travel route, a number of other small Manitowoc County communities such as St. Nazianz, Valders, Whitelaw, and Reedsville were virtually out of the question.

This is known because a Newton resident spotted several broken car parts scattered in the snow the next morning on his way to church. The debris was found one mile to the west of County CR, at the rural intersection of Newton and Center Roads. That intersection was in the middle of nowhere, three or four miles south of the city of Manitowoc, which had a population 35,000.

"I wholeheartedly believe this was an accident," Ricky's mother said. "I know this person didn't mean to do it. But this person also needs to take responsibility, come forward, and help the family."

That Saturday night, Mike Bushman patrolled Manitowoc County's roads as the overnight shift commander. He even saw Ricky's fresh footprints in the snow as he made the rounds along County Highway CR. Five years later, when the Wisconsin Department of Justice opened an investigation into a suspected police cover-up, a state investigator made this notation concerning Bushman: "He was going to check on the condition of the person to make sure they were OK considering the snowstorm. Deputy Inspector Bushman decided to get gas first before following the footprints in the snow."

Bushman's decision to fill up his squad car rather than check on the wandering pedestrian walking home in the fierce snowstorm possibly cost Ricky his life. The seventeen-year-old high school student was hit by a car and his body came to a rest in the road only fifty yards away from his front door.

Around 2:25 a.m., a newspaper delivery driver made the gruesome discovery.

She called 911 and Bushman, Manitowoc County's night patrol commander, learned about the collision as he was filling his tank at the county gas pumps about a half mile away. He made it to the scene at 2:28 a.m.

Around 4 a.m., Bushman and the county coroner Deb Kakatsch knocked on the front door of the Hochstetler white farmhouse. Debi Hochstetler was then rustled out of bed and notified that her only son, the oldest of her three children, was dead in the middle of the road. He had suffered a fractured skull resulting in brain trauma, as well as spinal cord injuries, a fractured neck, internal injuries, and leg injuries.

Many people suspect the cover-up was activated soon after the crime. Off-duty Lt. Rob Hermann, who was working at the time as the Manitowoc County juvenile jail administrator, managed to rush out to the scene.

It's been long suspected by fellow Manitowoc County sheriff's deputies that Rob's younger brother, Todd Hermann, may have been the hit-and-run driver and that Rob showed up at the scene to cover up the crime to ensure the culprit was never identified. The Hermann brothers were untouchable in the sheriff's office, thanks to their father. As a result, Sheriff Kocourek and Undersheriff Kenny Petersen were not about to launch a criminal investigation against one of the Hermann brothers. That would never happen, and Bushman would be tapped to run the investigation to make sure of that.

Even though the banquet hall parking lot was a quarter mile up the road from the hit-and-run tragedy, Undersheriff Petersen told the Manitowoc newspaper within days of the hit-and-run fatality that the Club Bil-Mar was not being probed because "I don't know if the person could have gotten up to a speed that would have caused that kind of injury to the victim or damage to the vehicle," Petersen was quoted as saying to the Manitowoc newspaper in January 1999.

Sheriff Kocourek was also content to let the homicide go cold. He did not want any help from the Wisconsin State Patrol's technical crash reconstruction experts. And he also did not want the Wisconsin Division of Criminal Investigation meddling in the vehicular homicide investigation, either.

Before an autopsy was even done, the local news media was duped by the Manitowoc County Sheriff's Office into believing that Rob Hermann single-handedly had figured out the hit-and-run driver's vehicle. The whole thing was a set up to divert attention away from the real hit-and-run vehicle.

"I determined the vehicle would have to have a gray, painted grill, being a model year from 1985 to 1988," Rob Hermann's reports state. "This vehicle would include Chevrolet pickups, Chevrolet K5 Blazer, and Chevrolet Suburban."

Weeks later, to add to the confusion, Bushman and Rob Hermann alerted the gullible local news media that the broken grill parts may also belong to a 1988 to 1991 full-sized van.

They summoned Manitowoc County Sheriff's deputy Jason Jost to pose for a newspaper photo-op, standing with his back up against a big blue van. The photo, in turn, was seen by thousands of avid newspaper readers in the Manitowoc County area. It served its purpose. It gave the locals the impression that a big full-sized van ran over Ricky Hochstetler, when that was never the case at all.

In fact, no van, no truck, no Suburban, and no Blazer were ever found.

As for Bushman, a dear friend of Kocourek and the Hermann family, who owed both of them for his career in law enforcement after working as a school bus driver, his ambitions of climbing the administrative ladder inside the Manitowoc County Sheriff's Office were also riding on his performance running the hit-and-run probe.

Would he prove himself worthy to Kocourek and Kenny Petersen? That's what this case was about.

As time marched on, though, Bushman recognized that whispers of a police cover-up under his watch were growing louder and louder around Manitowoc County. He decided to take decisive action. He hauled in the father of the hit-and-run victim to the police station for a face-to-face interview.

"I decided to question him about a statement he made reference the opinion that the police may have been involved in the accident and are attempting to cover it up. I wished to catch what type of reaction this would bring," Bushman's reports indicated. "I stated to him that there are over 300 complaints that I worked on and many turned to be just rumors just like the one, for example, that the police were somehow involved in the incident and were intentionally covering it up."

Bushman's decision to confront the victim's poor father by putting the man on the spot had a successful result. "The desired response was received and the redness in his face indicating he was embarrassed at that point indicated he, himself, had been the source of that type of rumor."

Nobody was arrested that year, in 1999, for the vehicular homicide.

Kocourek announced his retirement the following year, enabling Petersen to take over the reins. But it remained to be seen who Petersen would appoint to fill the void inside the culture of corruption at the Manitowoc Sheriff's Office. Because of another retirement and his own promotion to sheriff, Petersen now had to fill the two other top administrative openings at the sheriff's office, both the undersheriff and deputy inspector.

Petersen chose the two men within his ranks who were at the center of the cover-up allegations.

In 2000, Rob Hermann got promoted to undersheriff and Bushman got promoted to deputy inspector. This made Bushman in charge of the entire traffic patrol unit as well as the entire detective bureau even though he had no prior detective experience.

As third-in-command of the entire agency, Bushman decided to hand the sensitive hit-and-run homicide off to someone he trusted, Detective James Lenk, who would not disappoint him. Under Lenk, no progress was made in terms of identifying the killer and the sheriff's office was doing nothing to keep the case in the public spotlight. In 2002, the third anniversary, The Associated Press in Milwaukee tracked down Sheriff Petersen for an interview. He assured reporters that the hit-and-run homicide was not about to be solved.

"What it's going to take to solve the thing would just be luck at this point. I doubt if the truck exists anymore, especially in any kind of evidentiary form," Petersen was quoted as saying.

But why was Sheriff Petersen such a proud pessimist?

Several employees within the Manitowoc County, the ones who had integrity and held their heads high with dignity, suspected their administration had been infiltrated by a number of rats. They believed Ricky's case was a shoddy investigation that arose from incompetence, flat out corruption, or a combination of both.

Bushman and Rob Hermann, the two key promotions given by Petersen, were both responsible for compromising physical evidence, broken vehicle debris found at the snowy scene during the early morning hours of January 10, 1999. Regardless of their motive, their conduct jeopardized any future attempts at prosecuting the culprit.

Even though this was a high-profile vehicular homicide involving the death of a local teenager, the two men at the sheriff's office had not properly tagged, logged, and photographed the broken vehicle parts discovered at the hit and run scene. Most disturbingly, Bushman gave Hermann permission to scoop up the vehicle debris from the scene and to drive around unsupervised with the precious crime scene evidence during the wee hours of the night. Many Manitowoc County residents strongly suspect that the car that hit Ricky Hochstetler ended up at the Hermann family's Cleveland Auto Salvage where it was either repaired or stripped. Cleveland Auto, the family-owned business, was also a perfect place to swap out the evidence.

Considering there was strong sentiment within the local law enforcement community suspecting that Ricky Hochstetler's hit-and-run death was a cover-up, one has to realize the police reports submitted by Rob Hermann may not be reliable. If he was attempting to cover up a crime involving a close family member, there's no telling what was true and what was false. Hermann's overnight report states that he drove around to several Manitowoc area closed auto dealerships and closed businesses during the wee hours of the morning – in his personal vehicle - with the broken grill pieces from the scene of the crime in his possession. There is also no way to verify that anything he wrote actually happened since he did not take photos of any of the businesses and auto dealerships he allegedly visited. Furthermore, nobody else was with him.

"You can get fired for that stuff. That piece of evidence might as well not exist. You have made that evidence have less value or no value at all," noted Brent Turvey, forensic scientist at Forensic Solutions in Alaska.[58]

In Turvey's mind, given Manitowoc County's reputation, there's a strong chance that the police tampered with or swapped out the pieces of evidence from the scene, if they were attempting to cover up the crime for a fellow officer.

"It's all reputation and if Manitowoc County had a good reputation, you don't have to defend it. Because of their bad reputation and continually bad decisions, it's a lifestyle. It's not a mistake. It's who they are."

Before the Teresa Halbach case came along, there were already strong suspicions that the Manitowoc County Sheriff's Office covered up the hit-and-run homicide of Ricky Hochstetler, 17.

---

58. September 2016 Interview with USA TODAY NETWORK-Wisconsin for three-part series on the Ricky Hochstetler hit and run homicide case of Manitowoc County.

Bushman has said he was under the impression that Rob Hermann took the broken vehicle parts scattered along CR back to his family's "boneyard" in Cleveland, which was about five miles down the road. The Cleveland Auto Sales & Salvage was just a few blocks away from the home of Todd and Shelby Hermann.

Both Rob and Todd Hermann had substantial expertise as auto body technicians and mechanics at Cleveland Auto Sales & Salvage, a rival business of Avery Salvage.

"You don't take parts from a crime scene home with you because you don't know who's going to potentially become a suspect," Turvey added.

At no point during his tenure did Bushman ever once investigate Todd Hermann or Rob Hermann as suspects or co-conspirators in the evidence-mishandling escapade. To this day the question lingers, why did Robby Hermann, the off-duty juvenile jail administrator, respond to the scene of the crime, take charge, and convince everyone to announce later that same morning that the hit-and-run vehicle was a truck, van, or sports utility vehicle - before the autopsy was even done to examine the victim's body and leg injuries?

What motive did Bushman and Rob Hermann have to feed this information to the press, strongly desiring to have it consumed by the public?

In 2004, the Wisconsin Division of Criminal Investigation showed up in Manitowoc to investigate Undersheriff Rob Hermann as the hit-and-run suspect. The DCI agent's reports indicate the victim's mother suspected Bushman "might fear some type of reprisal or professional retaliation from Rob Hermann if the matter was taken seriously."

In August 2004, Wisconsin DCI Agent Eric Szatkowski "informed Hermann that his name had been associated with rumors in the Manitowoc area that he might be involved in the hit-and-run death of Richard Hochstetler. Inspector Hermann said he was called in to work on the case by Deputy

Michael Bushman possibly because Inspector Hermann was experienced in accident reconstruction."[(59)]

During that same interview, Hermann insisted he was not the hit-and-run driver because he drove his 1998 Chevrolet truck to the scene. "Inspector Hermann stated that he never owned a vehicle matching the description of the suspect vehicle, specifically a Chevrolet truck or van manufactured between 1985 and 1988."

As one might expect, the DCI investigation left more questions than answers. Why didn't the agent probe Todd Hermann, when the same special agent's own reports indicated he heard Todd Hermann was mentioned as a possible suspect?

Foremost, why did the special agent take it at face value that the hit-and-run vehicle was a mid-1980s truck, van, or Blazer given that conclusion was based solely on the word of Rob Hermann, the same sheriff's official under a dark cloud of suspicion for either being the culprit or the ringleader of the cover-up?

In 2006, after being elected sheriff of Manitowoc, one of Rob Hermann's first actions was to appoint his younger brother Todd Hermann to Bushman's former job as third-in-command of the entire Manitowoc Sheriff's Office.

In 2016, I worked as a Wisconsin investigative newspaper reporter re-examining the Ricky Hochstetler case, I tracked down the work cell phone number for Todd Hermann. I called and asked a number of questions about him being a suspect in Ricky's death. Todd Hermann was on vacation that week so I caught him off guard when he answered my call. After I asked my first question, there was a long pause before he responded by saying no comment. He continued to say no comment, suggesting I contact the sheriff, who was his older brother, for any comment pertaining to the case.

---

59. DCI report compiled by Szatkowski from 2004 summarizing his interview of Rob Hermann

At the time of our conversation, Todd Hermann was deputy inspector of operations. He oversaw the entire detective bureau including the lieutenant of his agency's detectives, Andy Colborn.

Despite the best efforts of the Hermann family to keep Ricky's case out of the Wisconsin press and off anybody's radar, the case remains like a smoldering fire which keeps burning. It's an eternal flame for the community around Manitowoc. People in town are mad and frustrated that Ricky's family never got justice and they're more outraged by the belief that the Manitowoc County culture of corruption was responsible for the case going unsolved.

Back in July 2009, five years after closing its initial corruption investigation into the Manitowoc County Sheriff, the Wisconsin DCI revived Ricky's case while Rob Hermann was sheriff and Todd Hermann was third-in-command of the sheriff's office. The decision to reopen the matter came from the top: Craig Klyve, the DCI's director of the bureau for investigative services, noted, "The caller wanted to remain anonymous and would provide no information on the source of the allegations other than the individuals who provided the information were high school friends of the suspect that did not want to get involved in the investigation and did not know the caller was providing information to authorities."

Three months later, a different special agent traveled to Two Rivers to interview the former live-in girlfriend of Rob Hermann, also the mother of his child. She maintained she could not remember if he was actually awakened by a phone call to their house around 3 a.m. back in January 1999. It had been more than ten years since the tragedy. She later urged the DCI to check with the Bil-Mar Club to see if they had any records to verify whether or not Rob Hermann patronized the banquet hall party club that night.

By the time the DCI tracked down the club, the social hall informed the state of Wisconsin investigators that too much time had passed to be of any help.

The Bil-Mar no longer had any records pertaining to the names of their guests on January 9-10, 1999, the night of Ricky's horrible death.

In October 2009, the DCI probe reached a dead end, now a second time.

That same month, the fifty-two-year-old Klyve turned up dead inside his car on a Friday night in Madison at a parking garage. His wife, an assistant attorney general in the Wisconsin Department of Justice, found his body. The *Wisconsin State Journal* reported Klyve had committed suicide using his service weapon.

"Craig Klyve, our beloved son, brother, husband, father, uncle, and friend, who is cherished by all who knew him, died far too early when he unexpectedly took his life on Friday, October 23, 2009," his obituary notes.

CHAPTER SIXTEEN

NOTHING THERE

If the Manitowoc County Sheriff's Office was never supposed to be investigating Avery because of conflicts of interest, then why was a man in his fifties who was directly involved in Avery's false arrest in 1985, coming out of retirement on the fifth day of Teresa's missing persons case?

That man, designated a team leader for the day, was responsible for the only two events of magnitude that day.

Sign-in logs indicate Mike Bushman, who was at the center of the Ricky Hochstetler hit-and-run cover-up suspicions involving the Manitowoc County's Sheriff's Office, had no prior involvement in the nearly week-old investigation of Teresa. But there he was, showing up on the Avery property, bright and early, around 7:30 a.m. Monday, November 7. He signed in to the command post at the same time as Lt. Todd Hermann, the same man many suspect was responsible for Ricky Hochstetler's death, from six years earlier. Bushman and Todd Hermann signed the command center log at 7:38 a.m.

They were soon joined by fellow deputies Dave Siders, Sgt. Jason Jost, and Sgt. Scott Senglaub. That day, the Manitowoc County Sheriff's group would achieve the most success in turning up previously undiscovered physical evidence as well as mysterious evidence that strongly suggested Teresa had met her gruesome demise about a half mile away from the Avery property.

"The group I was put in was Group A, and the team leader was Deputy M. Bushman," Siders said. "The property which we were assigned to search was a wooded area on White Cedar Road west of Avery's Auto Salvage, in addition to the property north of Steven Avery's residence."[60]

The key word is "assigned." It was a specific assignment and Bushman was brought out of retirement to oversee the very delicate task.

Little was documented in writing by Manitowoc County Sheriff's personnel about the mysterious site on Kuss Road including any interactions between Bushman and Wiegert prior to Bushman heading out to the off-the-beaten-path location. Bushman, the designated Group A team leader, chose not to memorialize any of his activities for that entire day.

Logs show he checked in to the Avery Road command center at 7:38 a.m. There is a second log entry of Bushman re-entering the command post at 4:14 p.m. along with Jason Jost. At 5:33 p.m., Bushman, Jost, and Siders all signed the log showing they were done for the day.

But Bushman's presence during the investigation of the Avery case only begs more questions. By Monday, November 7, Kocourek was just days away from being hauled in to a room full of hostile lawyers ready to grill their co-defendant in Avery's $36 million wrongful conviction lawsuit. Was Bushman someone who was supposed to drop into Teresa's investigation for one day, set the table, and quickly fade into the background before anybody would even notice he was there?

***

In Ricky Hochstetler's horrific hit-and-run death, Bushman's legacy was not bringing the intoxicated and callous hit-and-run driver to justice. Several hours after

60. Manitowoc County Sheriff's summary report Halbach investigation, Deputy Siders, Nov. 7, 2005

Ricky's death, after the sun came up, Manitowoc County resident Robert Jeffery saw several broken vehicle parts in the fresh snow at the rural intersection of Center and Newton Roads, the main intersection that led to Cleveland, Wisconsin. This was the same road that led toward Cleveland Auto Sales & Salvage as well as Todd Hermann's house.

Bushman showed up at the intersection, yet did not take any photos or measurements of the vehicle debris. He also did not bring along any trained evidence technicians even though this was a felony vehicular homicide, a serious crime that would have meant prison time for the culprit. Instead, he used a snow shovel to scoop the broken auto parts out of the snow banks and chose not to pursue the fleeing motorist's direction of travel. Bushman was in no mood to pursue the probability that the hit-and-run motorist lived just a few miles down the road around Cleveland. He wrote in his report that the Newton driver "was unable to tell me which direction the suspect vehicle may have went (sic) after the pieces fell off."

It was almost as if the car parts discovered at the seldom-traveled rural intersection never existed. Once Bushman showed up to retrieve them, that intersection became an afterthought as Bushman took enormous measures to steer the case away from Cleveland, Wisconsin.

Bushman had a knack, the record reflects, for making sure critical evidence, which could have aided in finding Ricky's killer, became irrelevant. By the time Ricky's relatives and friends visited the family home on County Road CR, around the date of the funeral services, the large snowbanks started to thaw, thanks to the sunshine. When one of the mourners pulled into the victim's family's driveway, the woman made a startling discovery. She saw numerous broken car parts protruding from the snow. Keep in mind that Ricky was struck just yards up the road and the hit-and-run driver heading south would have passed the house. The damage in the fresh snow included a section of headlight lamp with letters and numbers from the manufacturer. The mourners knew the damage surely came from the vehicle that killed Ricky. The witnesses phoned their local sheriff's office, but this would turn into a major letdown once Deputy Jason Jost arrived to investigate.

Besides recovering the main headlight lamp, "I also observed three other pieces of plastic lying just around the corner." In total there were four broken vehicle parts that appeared to be from a newer style car, Jost stated in his reports.

There were no other violent wrecks or collisions reported in front of the Hochstetler rural country farmhouse that winter. Yet the identification of car damage was very problematic for sheriff's officials because, less than seven hours after the crash occurred, Rob Hermann already informed his agency's dispatchers to contact the Wisconsin Department of Transportation to obtain a five-county listing of older model GMC trucks. This was a classic case of misdirection. Hermann wanted to keep the rest of the sheriff's office preoccupied with a never ending pile of busy work over the next several months. More importantly, Hermann's coworkers never got hot on the trail of catching the true villain.

Anyway, Deputy Jost returned to the sheriff's office and, in the days ahead, he huddled with Bushman and the two discussed the fresh car parts found in the snow in front of Ricky's house.

Jost wanted to climb the ladder at the sheriff's office. He was tight with the Hermann brothers. In the end, Jost submitted the following report, "I checked with Lt. Bushman and due to the fact the pieces looked newer, he did not believe they belong to the suspect vehicle on the hit-and-run fatality. At this time, no further follow-up will need to be done."

At no point over the years did Manitowoc County explore the possibility that a car was the type of vehicle that struck Ricky. As far as framing Avery for the crime, that was not possible since Avery remained in prison at that time, still serving out his unjust thirty-two-year prison sentence for Gregory Allen's brutal rape.

In 2004, when the DCI came to Manitowoc asking questions about a cover-up, Bushman responded by saying the state of Wisconsin's registry contained about 25,000 vehicles matching the description of the striking vehicle and Bushman claimed that all 25,000 vehicles were cleared. Overall, the DCI special agent was troubled by Bushman's performance, as noted in his 2004 investigation, but he seemed to view the case more from the angle of incompetence, rather than outright police misconduct on Bushman's part.

"In reviewing the reports, many of the vehicles that were reported do not have detailed descriptions of how they were cleared. This review assumes that every officer did a physical inspection of every vehicle, looking closely for signs of repair/replaced parts in areas that were damaged or could have been damaged. If each officer for each vehicle inspected did not follow that procedure, there is a possibility the striking vehicle was missed."[61]

But how do you pull off a successful police cover-up? Misdirection is critical.

The hit-and-run driver's path of travel home at bar closing time on a Saturday night made it obvious the culprit was headed into far southern Manitowoc County, a largely rural and isolated area. But rather than pursue the most obvious angles, Bushman instructed others, such as Andy Colborn, David Remiker, and James Lenk, to waste precious on-duty time running down worthless leads. Assignments given to a number of patrol deputies put them on the road far away in places including Appleton, Fond

---

61. DCI field report written by special agent Eric Szatkwoski in 2004

du Lac, Green Bay, Kaukauna, Menasha, Neenah, Oconto, Shawano, and Waupaca. Around the one-year anniversary, Sheriff Kocourek informed the local newspaper that he was shipping off the broken grill pieces to the FBI laboratory for analysis. It was unclear why he waited an entire year to do so. Additionally, the FBI was never given access to the broken headlight parts that surfaced in the melting snow near Debi Hochstetler's driveway.

In reviewing the case files, it was obvious Kocourek controlled the investigation and Bushman was there to obey his orders. Under no circumstances were the Hermann brothers, Rob and Todd, to be treated as criminal suspects in the crime or the cover-up. Other members of the sheriff's office have said that Bushman and Kocourek were in agreement, they would prefer to let Ricky's case go cold rather than conduct a rigorous investigation that would lead to one or two outcomes: either clear the brothers of wrongdoing or find evidence showing the brothers had culpability in the crime and or the cover-up.

As it stands, the facts remain the same: Ricky Hochstetler was dragged to his death by a fast car at bar-closing time while walking home. Vehicle parts were located about four miles southwest of the crash scene, at the rural intersection that was the main road toward Cleveland, Wisconsin, home of Cleveland Auto Sales & Salvage. Nobody was ever charged in connection with the gruesome hit-and-run death. What is known is that Mike Bushman spearheaded a sloppy, high-profile homicide investigation that got off to a suspiciously disastrous start and the case floundered from there. Crucial crime scene evidence was mishandled and other noteworthy clues were allowed to fade into oblivion, all thanks to Bushman.

So it stands to reason, in the 2005 disappearance of the *Auto Trader* photographer, had someone in Manitowoc County called Bushman out of retirement realizing they were at a crossroads and an experienced problem-solver was needed to put the Kuss Road intrigue to a final rest?

That morning, November 7, 2005 only a select number of key law enforcement got to the police command post on Avery Road before Bushman, notably Mark Wiegert at 6:32 a.m., and Bushman's replacement, Deputy Inspector Gregg Schetter, who was a dear friend of the Hermann brothers, at 6:53 a.m., John Dedering at 7:01 a.m., Tom Fassbender at 7:09 a.m., Jim Lenk at 7:15 a.m., and Andy Colborn and Dennis Jacobs at 7:16 a.m. as well as Calumet Sheriff Jerry Pagel and several other Calumet Sheriff's deputies and investigators.

But with no arrests and every day moving closer toward retired Sheriff Tom Kocourek's unsettling federal lawsuit deposition, the discovery of a genuine burial site off Kuss Road was not conducive to an Avery-is-a-guilty-bloodthirsty-psychopathic-killing-machine narrative that Manitowoc Sheriff Kenny Petersen wanted to gin up around the community.

That Monday morning, after Manitowoc County sent a large contingent of loyalists and minions of Sheriff Petersen back to Avery Road, two major events occurred, both involving Manitowoc County's personnel in the search group associated with Bushman.

"While searching land north of Steven Avery's residence, a corn field, I came across a burning barrel which was in my section of area to search. The burning barrel was located out in front of Steven's residence next to the cornfield. I approached the burning barrel and looked inside. I observed a metal vehicle rim and laid it outside the burning barrel. Once I lifted the metal rim, I observed some burnt, melted plastic items ... it appeared to me to be a cell phone. I took a closer look at the cell phone and noted there was an 'M' emblem on the front of it. It appeared to be the emblem for a Motorola brand cell phone," Deputy Siders said.

"Deputy Bushman came over and observed the remains of what appeared to be a cell phone. He then contacted the (officer in charge) and informed him that we had some items which needed to be looked at by detectives."

Later that same morning, Bushman was directly involved in the second major incident, arguably the biggest event of the day. As mentioned earlier, Bushman did not document any of his activities that day, including why he was even involved, given that he was already retired, given that he worked for Manitowoc County, and given that he was involved in the 1985 false arrest of Avery.

Calumet County's John Dedering summarized the day-long events at Kuss Road in five short paragraphs. He chose to put few, if any details, in his report. At 10:35 a.m., Wiegert "requested that an investigator go to the east end of Kuss Road. I did respond and spoke with retired deputy inspector Michael Bushman, Manitowoc County Sheriff's Department. Bushman was leading a team of searchers in the area. It should be noted that the end of Kuss Road is approximately one-half mile away from the western edge of the Avery property."

Here's what Sgt. Bill Tyson, one of Dedering's colleagues, wrote in his report. "I received a phone call indicating we needed to leave Barbara Janda's residence and respond to Kuss Road for a suspicious incident. Lt. Lenk, Sgt. Colborn, and I left Barbara Janda's residence at 10:58 a.m. After clearing from the suspicious incident, we did go back to Barbara Janda's residence to finish collecting firearms from the residence."

Tyson added that "search volunteers … had located an area approximately three feet by three feet that appeared to be disturbed soil."

Dedering got to the dead-end road at 10:45 a.m. where he huddled with Bushman, who "indicated he had found a possible excavation site and did take us to the site." What Dedering's report did not point out was the enormous lag time in contacting state forensic scientist John Ertl and his three-person unit from the Wisconsin State Crime Lab that were being used that week to exclusively process a potential crime scene in Teresa's disappearance.

Wiegert and Fassbender may not have wanted the state crime lab intimately involved in overseeing the evidence collection efforts, probably because, if evidence was being planted, shifted, or collected to go away, Ertl's unit was likely to blow the lid and unmask somebody's cover. Having a whistleblower as a constant presence could have been disastrous for Manitowoc and Calumet Counties' all-out efforts targeting Avery for Teresa's killing.

Several top-trained police dogs detected Teresa Halbach's scent at the end of Kuss Road, raising the likelihood that she met her demise off-the-beaten path, away from Steven Avery's trailer.

***

Despite the red alert on Kuss Road, Ertl's team remained jettisoned forty-five miles away, toiling away inside an enclosed garage at the Calumet Sheriff's Office. The discovery on Kuss Road remained tight-lipped within the inner circle of Wiegert, Dedering, and Bushman who then chose to notify Colborn, Lenk, and Tyson. At no point that Monday morning was Ertl's three-man crew summoned to Kuss Road to investigate the suspicious possible burial site, near where the bloodhounds and tracking dogs also located Teresa's scent.

While the Manitowoc County-led group huddled and plotted strategy regarding Kuss Road, Ertl's team began combing through four burning barrels that were confiscated the previous day by Lenk, Colborn, Remiker, and Dan Kucharski from the Bobby Dassey property. For reasons never explained, the four deputies had inexplicably chosen to ignore the lone burn barrel of Avery even though it was out in plain view in the front of his yard, and he was their prime suspect. Another twenty-four hours would pass before Deputy Dave Siders, a member of Bushman's Group A, would follow his intuition and not only peer into the Avery barrel, but reach inside and then start pulling out the contents.

"We set up the sifting equipment in the garage and began examining the contents of the barrels beginning with the two of interest to the dog," Ertl said. "These contained a lot of partially burned food and game animal material including chicken, fish, and deer.

"Some hair, metal items, (and) as many unassociated bones as possible were recovered. The first barrel was finished and the second begun."[62]

After a busy morning, Ertl and his crew took a noon lunch break. Back in neighboring Manitowoc County, where the action was heating up, Dedering and Bushman, two men

62. John Ertl's Wisconsin State Crime Lab report of November 7, 2005

about the same age, remained in conversation on Kuss Road. A total of ninety minutes had passed since Dedering learned of the suspicious possible burial site, but there was still no phone call to alert Ertl's team from the state crime lab to the mysterious find.

Ertl's team finished lunch at 12:30 p.m. and resumed their work in the sheriff's office garage. By the time Ertl's crew got to Kuss Road, shortly before 2 p.m., more than three hours had passed since Bushman notified his long-time confidants at neighboring Calumet County about his Kuss Road discovery. The lag time only deepens suspicions about whether incriminating evidence of a crime scene was being hauled away.

In any event, when Ertl's unit arrived at Kuss Road, he saw "white plastic sheeting (that) protruded from the ground on either side of an area 3 feet in diameter, devoid of plants, apparent decomposed wood, or peat-like material. Some moss lay nearby, uprooted, however, there was no sign that soil had been excavated and replaced."

Now that Ertl's group had been called to the scene, there was apparently nothing incriminating there.

"The area devoid of plants appeared to be peat moss and the plastic sheet, the remnants of a peat moss bag as per the label on the underside. Beneath the bag were the decomposing remains of a wooden pallet ... The area was excavated further and no disturbance to the soil layering was evident."

By mid-afternoon, the team of Lenk, Colborn, and Tyson was also summoned back to Kuss Road for a second time. "After the photography by the Wisconsin State Crime Lab was completed, Lt. Lenk, Sgt. Colborn, and I began digging up the area and quickly found out this was not a possible grave or burial site. Upon reporting those findings to Investigator Dedering, the crime scene tape had been removed and the area was reopened," Tyson said.[63]

Ertl's group, summoned to the highly suspicious scene three hours late, finished their assignment at 5:45 p.m. and then returned to the garage in Chilton to continue to process Bobby's four burning barrels. But now another one had been delivered to the sheriff's garage.

"A fifth barrel, reportedly containing remnants of a Motorola cellular phone, had also been transported to the Sheriff's Office in Chilton," Ertl noted.

Between 7:30 and 9:30 p.m., Ertl's crew continued processing Bobby's burn barrels.

"We finished with the second barrel, cleaned up the work area, and departed the sheriff's office. We proceeded to the Best Western motel in Chilton, ate dinner, and retired."

As far as the investigation's paper trail was concerned, the incident at the cul-de-sac off Kuss Road was a big nothing.

"The possible excavation area was processed by Wisconsin State Crime Lab personnel and at 4:51 p.m., I was notified the excavation area was not pertinent to this case," Dedering wrote.

As for Bushman, he faded into the sunset. He never wrote a single report concerning any of his activities on Kuss Road even though he was made a search team leader, he was indirectly involved in the recovery of the charred phone at the bottom of Avery's burn barrel, and he was directly responsible for the events that made Kuss Road a day-long police circus.

Had Bushman stumbled upon something on Kuss Road that he should not have? The absence of paperwork only widens the mystery concerning why one of Sheriff Kocourek's most loyal henchmen was suddenly tapped to

---

63. Supplemental report, Sgt. Bill Tyson, November 7, 2005

come out of retirement to help for only one day on the Avery case.

In the end, the police maintained a constant presence on Avery Road for five more days, through Saturday, November 12, 2005. But Bushman's role in the case was now over.

He had done well.

CHAPTER SEVENTEEN

EVIDENCE PILE

On the same day as the Kuss Road controversy, a team of three, two from Manitowoc County and one from Calumet, got the green light to roam the Avery Salvage Yard. They could wander the vast rows of junked and wrecked automobiles, a golden opportunity for one of them to plant evidence, particularly in proximity to Avery's trailer. One man on the assignment seemed less likely to be engaged in planting evidence, though; Sgt. Bill Tyson of Calumet County.

"Upon returning to the crime scene on Monday, November 7, 2005, I was informed that my duty for the morning would be to work with Lt. Lenk and Sgt. Andrew Colborn," Tyson said. "I was informed they did wish for us to open the trunks on all remaining vehicles on the property and after that was completed, enter all the residences and collect all firearms."

Unlike Tyson, Lt. Lenk and Sgt. Andrew Colborn chose not to write any reports to memorialize their activities rechecking the cars around the Avery property that morning.

By the time their day ended, Kuss Road was now off the grid. That following morning, Tuesday, November 8, the generals had realigned their troops squarely back to Avery Road. Wiegert and Fassbender assembled another huge contingent of Wisconsin State Patrol troopers, volunteer firefighters, and area police officers to conduct another all-out blitz canvassing the wrecked vehicles around Avery Salvage. The assignment seemed redundant, considering how the same cars were the subject of a fruitless daylong search two days earlier, on Sunday, November 6.

But this second full-blown search, now called upon the day after Colborn and Lenk went wandering around the salvage yard premises, was sure to bear ripe fruit.

"On Tuesday morning, November 8, 2005, shortly after 9 a.m., we were advised by a trooper that he and his fireman partner had located Teresa's auto license plates along the north border of the salvage yard," Calumet Lt. Kelly Sippel said. "This station wagon would have been parked between the fenced-in compound to the east and an old trailer to the west."[64]

A month later, Wiegert interviewed Brillion firefighter William Brandes Jr. to learn how his evidence harvest was made at 9:15 a.m. "According to William, while searching a car, he noticed some license plates that had been folded twice and were lying on the folded down backseat of an older station wagon ... William reached through the driver's side rear window and picked up the license plates. He indicated he was wearing gloves at that time. William unfolded them so he could read the number on the plate. William stated the registration we were looking for matched the plates he had found."

That same morning of the license plate find, Lenk, Colborn, and Dan Kucharski meandered over to Avery's little red trailer, for the umpteenth time.

"Sgt. Colborn searched the desk area as well as a small cabinet next to the desk for pornographic materials," Lenk said. "I took a three-ring binder from the cabinet which was filled with news clippings of Steven Avery since being released from prison. There were no pornographic materials in the binder. Sgt. Colborn even tipped the cabinet to its side,

---

64. Supplemental Report of Lt. Kelly Sippel

away from the desk, to be sure that no photographs or other materials had fallen between the desk and the cabinet."[65]

Unlike Lenk, Colborn's incident report for his duties that day completely avoided any mention of his activities in Avery's bedroom. He left that up to Lenk.

"When Sgt. Colborn and I were putting magazines and papers back into the cabinet, we were pushing into the cabinet, striking the back of the cabinet as we pushed them in. When I replaced the three-ring binder into the cabinet, I met with some resistance. I pushed it two to three times before it finally went into the cabinet."

At that point, Lenk notified the two others he needed to walk out of the room to make a call to the command post. Then he walked back into the bedroom.

"When I reached the bedroom, I observed a single key laying on the floor," Lenk said. "The key and the key (fob) were laying on the floor just in front of a pair of slippers next to the rear corner of the cabinet ... I informed Deputy Kucharski and Sgt. Colborn that there was a key here and it was not here before.

"We all looked at the key. It appeared to be a key from a Toyota brand vehicle due to the emblem ... We all believe the key was dislodged from the back of the cabinet as we were tipping and banging the magazines and binder in and out of the cabinet."

The license plates and spare key which had surfaced were scooped up that morning. Then in the middle of the afternoon, Manitowoc County Sgt. Jason Jost, the same deputy who worked closely with Bushman on the Ricky Hochstetler hit-and-run case, acted upon his instincts and walked the grounds of Avery's burn pile pit between 1:40 and 2 p.m.

---

65. Manitowoc County Sheriff's Office summary from Lt. Jim Lenk for November 8, 2005.

"Upon returning to the command post, I made contact with Calumet County Sheriff's Office Lt. Kelly Sippel," Jost said. "He responded to the property with me. Without disturbing the area, we walked close to the burn pit to take a further look.

"As we were looking at the ashes laying in the area, it was evident that someone used some type of front end loader to remove ground from this particular location ... as we looked at the ash pile, we observed that there was a bone laying near the south side of the pile, on the east side. Without disturbing the bone, I looked at it as closely as I could. It appeared as though it may have been a vertebrae bone. I could see another bone in the pile."[66]

Jost would also mention that "one piece appeared to be in the shape of a part of a skull."

No forensic anthropologists were summoned to the scene. The Manitowoc County Coroner Deb Kakatsch was kept away from the property. She was not even notified of the bone fragments. Also, the police at the scene, Manitowoc, Calumet, and the Wisconsin DCI, evidently came to a unilateral agreement that photographs and videotaping would not be done showing the bones and where they had been located in Avery's yard.

It was the recovery of the bones on the fourth full day of searching Avery's property that changed the dynamics of the case to Manitowoc County's great satisfaction. One day earlier, the authorities were focused intently on Mike Bushman's find on Kuss Road where the dogs also drew heightened excitement. But law enforcement's three amazing hunches all paid off on Tuesday, November 8. The decision to reprocess all the cars inside the salvage yard now turned up the license plates belonging to Teresa. The return to Avery's bedroom produced Teresa's spare key. The third,

66. Manitowoc County Sheriff's report of Jason Jost's activities of November 8, 2005

the decision to give more scrutiny to the burn pile pit behind Avery's red trailer, turned up charred bones that were later linked to Teresa.

The sudden trove of evidence caused a dramatic shift in the case, just in the nick of time. After all, former Sheriff Tom Kocourek was only two days away from being forced to raise his right hand and give a contentious videotaped sworn statement in Avery's $36 million lawsuit for running a crooked police department. But the work of his former disciples, people who deeply admired him, Lt. Lenk, Sgt. Colborn, and Sgt. Jason Jost, and of course, Mike Bushman, forever put the skids on Avery's federal lawsuit against their former leader.

On November 9, Avery would lose his freedom for good. The scheduled depositions for Kocourek on November 10 and former Avery prosecutor Dennis Vogel, set for November 15, would never happen.

But what would happen is that the tandem of lead investigators, Wiegert and Fassbender, would decide that their top priority on November 9, once they captured Avery, was to drive him to the local Manitowoc hospital to obtain more DNA samples from Avery, even though this was quite unnecessary.

But to them, maybe it was necessary. Perhaps additional clues would be needed down the road, to ensure Avery's guilt.

CHAPTER EIGHTEEN

HOSPITAL STOP

If the murder case brought against Avery was based on fabricated evidence harvested by the cops, then it had to be rock-solid, irrefutable evidence that stood up court. The best evidence to plant nowadays involves DNA, which is risky but rewarding for those who manage to bet away on their wicked misdeeds. Unfortunately for the police profession, there have been a number of crooked cops and CSIs have had their careers implode because they got exposed planting DNA against someone later proven to be innocent. A former friend of mine, the director of the Douglas County Sheriff's Office's crime lab in Omaha, Nebraska, the subject of my first true-crime book, Bloody Lies, was one such cop. In his public corruption case, which was investigated by the Omaha division of the FBI and successfully prosecuted, David Kofoed's downfall that led to his eventual imprisonment concerned his ability to gain access to additional blood swabs and blood that he and his CSI team collected from the crimes of at least two high-profile murder cases.

One happened in a garage and another inside a farmhouse. In the first case, the psychopathic killer was guilty and confessed on many occasions to his crime, but although there lacked a body, there was a trail of blood of the killer's murder victim, his 4-year-old son.

In the second case, Kofoed's CSI team collected several extra swabs of blood stains from two middle-aged farmers who were murdered in the middle of the night while they slept in their upstairs bedroom. Kofoed also went into one of the evidence bags and re-examined the bloody shirt of the farmer.

The special prosecutor was able to convict Kofoed by providing that he would plant evidence in cases where his fellow police detectives needed a boost, where they were a wee bit short on having enough solid physical evidence to make an arrest or ensure a guilty verdict. In the first case with the dead little boy, Kofoed dodged a bullet, because the crazed killer pleaded guilty to the crime and did not challenge the strange evidence finds that turned up against him, including blood that was supposedly found inside the bowels of a dirty commercial Dumpster some five months after the boy's body was said to have been put there.

Then, three years later, Kofoed met his downfall because of the brutal farmhouse killings. In that crime, he had fabricated swabs of DNA blood evidence to use against a pair of Nebraska cousins after they were incarcerated by the local police. He mistakenly assumed the small-town police force had arrested the true perpetrators, but he was badly mistaken and ruined his career, making himself into a criminal.

It's safe to say that nobody overseeing Teresa's murder case wanted to have another scenario involving Avery beating the rap. The second time around, in 2005, Sheriff Petersen wanted Avery found guilty and sent away for the rest of his life, punishment for bringing shame and humiliation to himself and other old-timers from the Kocourek administration who were part of Avery's 1985 rape arrest. The sheriff's office endured two years of non-stop embarrassment and ridicule between 2003 and 2005. Avery's arrest for first-degree murder was meant to bring an end to this innocence project wave that so many people and politicians in Wisconsin were beginning to champion.

So on November 9, 2005, the first order of business for Wiegert and Fassbender included a visit to the Aurora Medical Center in Manitowoc with Avery. The two investigators had already made arrangements with a local nurse they trusted to help with their mission. It was around 1:20 p.m. when Wiegert and Fassbender escorted prisoner Avery into an examination room at the hospital.

What was entirely odd about the incident is that Avery was not even under arrest for murder. He was being taken into custody on a gun charge, for having possession of a shotgun that he was not supposed to have as a convicted felon. One of the crimes that Avery was convicted of stemmed from the January 1985 incident where Avery stood along the road and pointed an unloaded shotgun at the wife of the sheriff's deputy because Avery believed the woman was spreading false rumors about him in the community. One of Avery's other crimes during his twenties concerned a 1981 burglary at a local bar where he and a friend stole a couple cases of beer and some sandwiches.

And yet there they were, Fassbender and Wiegert, taking a man being charged with a gun crime over to the local hospital to collect additional samples of his DNA.

"Towards the end of the examination, Nurse Fritsch took two swabs of Mr. Avery's groin area in direct contravention of the search warrant, which specifically restricted that DNA samples were to be taken from Mr. Avery's saliva and blood," Zellner said. "There was no reference to groin swabs in the search warrant. Significantly, Nurse Fritsch's documentation of taking swabs from Mr. Avery excludes any mention of taking groin swabs. A well-qualified nurse following acceptable standards of charting would never fail to document taking the groin swabs unless she were instructed not to document taking the groin swabs by Agent Fassbender or Investigator Wiegert.[67]

"Agent Fassbender and Investigator Wiegert's explanation that they did not realize that the search warrant did not call for taking groin swabs is not credible."

---

67. Zellner motion for post-conviction relief, June 7, 2017

Agent Fassbender's report claims that Nurse Fritsch disposed of the groin swabs.

"Agent Fassbender's report is not credible because Nurse Fritsch never mentions in her charting disposing of the groin swabs. Agent Fassbender's report directly contradicts Mr. Avery's account of his examination as described in his affidavit."

The most reliable witness account of the strange events taking place at the hospital appears to come from Avery himself.

"As Mr. Avery followed Agent Fassbender and Nurse Fritsch out of the examination room, Mr. Avery heard Investigator Wiegert tell Nurse Fritsch to give him the groin swabs, and Mr. Avery observed Investigator Wiegert walk to the examination receptacle as if to discard the groin swabs. Mr. Avery observed that Investigator Wiegert did not drop the groin swabs into the receptacle."[68]

But if Wiegert had pulled a fast one, a well-planned devious scheme to fabricate more evidence against Avery, a golden opportunity presented itself four months into the murder case against Avery.

By February 27, 2006, Wiegert and Fassbender realized the dynamics of Wisconsin's biggest murder case had changed. Avery now had major league criminal defense lawyers, having just hired Strang and Buting. At that point, it appears a decision was made to take out Avery's main alibi witness, Brendan Dassey, and force him to implicate himself and his uncle under a wildly sensational murder plot that had Avery committing premeditated murder inside his back bedroom only to be distracted in the middle of his savagery by the knocking and ringing of his doorbell by his developmentally slow nephew. This distraction apparently caused Avery to take a break from his bedroom rape and torture of Teresa to walk down the hallway to see who might

---

68. Motion for Post-Conviction Relief, June 7, 2017

be at the door. Then, upon realizing it was not his mom or dad, or brothers Earl and Chuck, or his sister Barb, he invited young Brendan to step inside his lair to participate in the evilness.

"It was not until four months after Ms. Halbach's RAV4 was analyzed by the Wisconsin State Crime Lab in Madison that investigators became interested in the hood latch," Zellner said. "The hood latch was first introduced by Agent Fassbender and Investigator Wiegert during their March 1, 2006, interrogation of Brendan."

Here are some questions posed by Wiegert and Fassbender during their interviews with Avery's learning-disabled sixteen-year-old nephew, who ultimately went along with their wishes and implicated himself as the co-conspirator in Teresa's murder.

Fassbender: "OK. Did he go and look at the engine? Did he raise the hood at all or anything like that? To do something to that car?"[69]

Brendan: "Yeah."

Wiegert: "What did he do, Brendan? It's OK. What did he do?"

Fassbender: "What did he do under the hood, if that's what he did?"

Brendan: "I don't know what he did, but I know he went under."

Fassbender: "He did raise the hood?"

Brendan nodded in the affirmative, trying to please his captors.

Fassbender: "You remember that?"

Brendan: "Yeah."

Wiegert: "While he was raising the hood, did you take the license plates off?"

---

69. Interviews of Brendan Dassey by Tom Fassbender and Mark Wiegert, contained in Calumet County investigative reports of Halbach murder case.

Brendan: "No. He did. He took them off. He had them in his house but I don't know after where he put them."

Wiegert: "Where was the knife that he used, you used? Where'd that knife go?"

Brendan: "He left it in the Jeep."

Wiegert: "It's not in the Jeep now. Where do you think it might be?"

Brendan: "I'm sure it was."

Wiegert: "Did you see it in the Jeep?"

Brendan: "Yeah, cuz he set it on the floor, in the middle of the seats."

Wiegert: "Anytime during this, did he get injured?"

Brendan: "Just that scratch, that's all I know; on his finger. It was bleeding a little bit."

Wiegert: "How'd he get that scratch?"

Brendan: "Probably when he was under the hood."

Since Halloween was on a school night, Brendan remembered how his mother Barb called him, reminding him that he needed to be home by 10 p.m.

Wiegert: "When did you clean the place up?"

Brendan: "Like at 9:50. He took the bed sheets outside, and he burnt them."

Fassbender: "Was there blood on the bed sheets?"

Brendan: "Yeah."

Wiegert: "What else did he do?"

Brendan: "That's when he hid the key in the dresser."

Fassbender: "So you and Steven do what at 9:50 p.m. then?"

Brendan: "We cleaned that up and then he told me to throw that on the fire, the clothes, that's full of the blood that was like cleaned up."

When Wiegert asked Brendan to remember the clothes, he drew a blank stare.

Wiegert: "What about the shirt, what color was the shirt?"

Brendan: "Black."

Wiegert: "What about … did you have her bra and panties too? Where were those?"

Brendan: "I don't know."

Wiegert: "So you took it outside and threw it on the fire?"

Brendan: "Yeah."

Wiegert: "Now the shirt, earlier you told us the shirt had blood on it, had a hole in it, was that not true then?"

Brendan: "No."

Wiegert: "Was Steven bleeding?"

Brendan: "On his finger, that's it."

Wiegert: "What did Steven say he was going to do with her car?"

Brendan: "That he was going to crush it."

Wiegert: "Did he say when he was going to try and do that?"

Brendan: "No. He said he would of (sic), actually the sooner, he said, the sooner the better."

Overall, Brendan was doing a terrific job of repeating and regurgitating what Wiegert and Fassbender wanted him to say. In the back of their minds, deep down, these two veteran cops knew his life was over. They were pleased. After all, they wanted to make sure Brendan never saw the daylight outside of a Wisconsin penal institution, at least during their lifetime.

In order to decimate Avery's criminal defense, Fassbender and Wiegert wanted Brendan thinking of them as his father figures, upstanding men Brendan could trust. Under no circumstances was Brendan going to be shown their dark side, their devious side.

Fassbender: "You need a break, any soda or something? I got water here."

Wiegert: "We can get you a soda if you want one. Would you like one?"

Brendan: "Coke."

Since this was going to be Brendan's last day of freedom and the two interrogators knew this, they wanted him to go out with a nice last meal.

Fassbender: "We got some food here, sandwich or anything?"

Brendan shook his head no.

Fassbender: "Are you sure?"

Brendan nodded his head yes.

Fassbender: "Bathroom?"

Brendan shook his head no.

Fassbender: "Just a soda?"

Brendan nodded his head yes.

"All right, Bud, hang in there," Fassbender responded.

A few minutes later, Fassbender returned with the soda for his sixteen-year-old captive.

"Here you go bud."

"Thank you."

"Would you like to have a sandwich or anything?"

Brendan shook his head no.

Fassbender: "You sure?"

Brendan: "Not hungry."

As Brendan was enjoying his refreshing can of Coke, Fassbender remained fixated on Teresa's RAV4.

Perhaps this was because Fassbender knew that a major piece of DNA evidence was still available for evidence planting purposes.

***

March 2, 2006, marked the infamous Ken Kratz press conference where the following ghoulish assertions were not backed up by the facts.

"Sheriff Pagel and I will be releasing to the media the specifics of this case. I will be filing, as I mentioned tomorrow, a criminal complaint by 2 p.m. that will be available for release to all of you.

"We have now determined what occurred sometime between 3:45 p.m. and 10 or 11 p.m. on the 31st of October. Sixteen-year-old Brendan Dassey, who lives next door to Steven Avery's trailer, returned home on the bus from school about 3:45 p.m. He retrieved the mail and noticed one of the letters was for his uncle Steven Avery. As Brendan approaches the trailer, as he actually gets several hundred feet away from the trailer, a long way from the trailer, Brendan already starts to hear the screams.

"As Brendan approaches the trailer, he hears louder screams for help, recognizes it to be of a female individual, and he knocks on Steven Avery's trailer door. Brendan says he knocks at least three times and has to wait until a person he knows as his uncle, who is partially dressed, who is full of sweat, opens the door and greets his sixteen-year-old nephew. Brendan accompanies his sweaty, forty-three-year-old uncle down the hallway to Steven Avery's bedroom, and there they find Teresa Halbach completely naked and shackled to the bed. Teresa Halbach is begging Brendan for her life … The evidence that we've uncovered establishes that Steven Avery at this point invites his sixteen-year-old nephew to sexually assault this woman that he's had bound to the bed. During the rape, Teresa's begging for help, begging sixteen-year-old Brendan stop, that you can stop this. Sixteen-year-old Brendan, under the instruction of Steven Avery, cuts Teresa Halbach's throat; but she still doesn't die."

Fast forward a month.

Kratz began to realize his twisted sexual fantasy involving a bloody butcher knife, a naked young woman chained to the bed, and two bloodthirsty monsters named Brendan and Avery was not corroborated by any physical evidence. This was not good.

Deep down, Kratz realized this could be troublesome as the biggest criminal case in the state of Wisconsin moved closer toward trial with Strang and Buting now on the case fighting for Avery. Kratz was no longer up against a couple of country bumpkins from the Manitowoc County Public Defender's Office, who were there to get paid to go through the motions of putting forth a defense.

Many people now suspect that Ken Kratz's wild and outrageous press conference claiming that a naked Teresa Halbach was shackled to Steven Avery's bedposts, begging and screaming for her life, was actually a fantasy Kratz came up with based on his own real-life experiences of treating women as his sex slaves, during his time as the Calumet County District Attorney.

"In an effort to corroborate Brendan's confession taken on March 1, Agent Fassbender and Investigator Wiegert ordered that the hood latch be swabbed for DNA evidence," Zellner said. "On April 3, 2006, Agent Fassbender and Investigator Wiegert specifically directed Deputy Jeremy Hawkins and Sgt. Tyson to go into the storage shed where the RAV4 was located to swab the hood latch, battery cables, and interior and exterior door handles."

Actually, how the follow-up search went down only raises more red flags about the dark cloud dangling over the heads of Wiegert and Fassbender.

"The instructions Agent Fassbender and Investigator Fassbender gave Deputy Hawkins and Sgt. Tyson are inconsistent with a good faith effort to recover forensic evidence. If they really thought Mr. Avery had opened the hood and wanted to collect any possible DNA of his from the RAV4, they should have also instructed Sgt. Tyson and Deputy Hawkins to swab the interior hood release lever and hood prop, which, by necessity, Mr. Avery would have handled when opening the hood to disconnect the battery cable," Zellner said.

On the evening of the special task, Tyson gave the hood latch swabs to Hawkins. Hawkins put them into Calumet County's evidence storage. Then the next day, April 4, they were taken out and moved.

"Investigator Wiegert transferred custody of the swab to Wisconsin State Crime Lab personnel, purportedly delivering the swab collected from the hood latch for analysis. However on … custody transmittal documents Deputy Hawkins' name is typed as the submitting officer. Additionally, Deputy Hawkins' name is printed by hand as the submitting officer on the Wisconsin Department of Justice transmittal form … There is no evidence that Deputy Hawkins submitted swabs to the Wisconsin State Crime Lab and all of the evidence establishes that it was Investigator Wiegert who delivered the hood latch swab and printed Deputy Hawkins' name on the transmittal form. It is therefore reasonable to conclude that Investigator Wiegert printed Deputy Hawkins' name by hand in direct violation of all established chain of custody standards and protocols," Zellner said.

During a 2017 NBC *Dateline* exclusive, Fassbender was reminded how Avery once said, "These guys had it out for me. The whole department was angry at me. This was the perfect opportunity for them to have access to my trailer, plant the key."

"I never actually saw that; never, never saw that from anyone in Manitowoc County," Fassbender told viewers. "I could go on and on about the planting defense and how absurd it is with the multiple agencies we had in there."

At the time of the NBC *Dateline* interview, however, Fassbender got a free pass. He was not asked whether he had knowledge or a direct role in fabricating evidence or falsifying police reports against Avery. He also was not asked to give an accounting for his appearance in the hospital examination room when the mysterious groin swabs were taken from Avery when they were not supposed to.

As for Wiegert, he remained in the shadows. He did not participate in any on-camera interviews with the NBC anchor. That seems to be his M.O., preferring to lurk in the background. He's the ultimate puppet master, just like he was at Avery Road.

"According to Agent Fassbender's report, the groin swabs taken of Mr. Avery at Aurora Medical Center were discarded … it is a reasonable probability that they intended to plant DNA from the groin swabs and conceal, from the official medical report, that groin swabs were taken. Investigator Wiegert clearly fabricated the chain of custody form given to Wisconsin State Crime Lab. In light of the new scientific testing done on the hood latch, Investigator Wiegert submitted the groin swabs for the hood latch swabs collected by Sgt. Tyson," Zellner said.

But how would Wiegert have carried this out?

CHAPTER NINETEEN

SECOND TRY

One of the most highly suspicious evidence finds to turn up in the Avery murder case did not result when the independent team of highly trained forensic examiners from the Wisconsin State Crime Laboratory in Madison had their opportunity to inspect, from top to bottom, the interior and exterior of the RAV4. At that period, the car was kept within the confines of their indoor garage, away from any outside interference or skullduggery.

But the Calumet County Sheriff's Office was itching to regain control of Teresa's motor vehicle. Sheriff Jerry Pagel and Investigator Mark Wiegert wanted her SUV back in their property, under their safeguard, sooner rather than later.

Only two days after Avery's arrest, Calumet Corporal Chris Wendorf and Lt. John Byrnes were sent to retrieve a pair of vehicles from Madison. The two summoned Bryan Roehrig and Dan Bangart, who operated Scott's Towing and Dan's Towing, both in Chilton. The two vehicles retrieved on November 11, 2005, were described in police reports as a blue four-door Toyota RAV4 and a 1993 Pontiac Grand Am. "The Toyota RAV4 was loaded on the Scott's Towing flatbed along with the hood of the Rambler strapped to the flatbed underneath the Toyota RAV4.[70]

"Also given to me by (Lucy) Meier was a key the Wisconsin State Crime Lab had made in order to enter the Toyota RAV4 vehicle as the original vehicle key had not been

---

70. Transport of Toyota RAV4 and Pontiac Grand Am, Corporal Chris Wendorf, report Nov. 11, 2005

located at the time they had received the vehicle," Wendorf said. "Also ... I had delivered an envelope addressed to the Wisconsin State Crime Lab that had been given to me by Deputy (Jeremy) Hawkins that did contain evidence with a buccal swab from Steven Avery and palm and print cards from Charles Avery, Earl Avery, and Bobby Dassey."

The police entourage left Madison at 1:30 p.m. and made it back to Chilton, their little county seat, at 3:40 p.m. The RAV4 was moved into unit 7 of the Chilton storage units off Mary Avenue.

"I then did tape the vehicle doors with evidence tape, and initial, date, and time stamp such evidence tape," Wendorf said. "The unit was then closed and locked with a fresh, brand new Master Lock key lock that had been removed from its packaging. Evidence bags and property tags, along with evidence, were deposited in Locker 1 of the storage area to wait the property custodian for proper logging."

***

No credible evidence surfaced that Avery ever threw away his bed mattress and box springs, which were surely drenched and saturated with Teresa's blood if the gory killing happened the way Kratz described her death during his wild press conference on March 2, 2006.

But on April 3, 2006, Calumet evidence custodian Jeremy Hawkins and Sgt. Bill Tyson were summoned by their superiors who pulled the strings to refocus on the murder defendant's bedroom material.

"Both Sgt. Tyson and I checked the mattress for any red in color stains on the mattress. The mattress was also checked with ultraviolet light for any stains on the mattress. Presumptive stains were collected and tested. All presumptives on the mattress were negative," Hawkins said.[71]

Nothing of note was found on the headboard, either.

Then, three hours later, for reasons that were never explained in the police reports, Tyson and Hawkins were now being dispatched to the Chilton storage units, the facility housing the RAV4 that was already analyzed by the state crime lab.

But unlike before, the victim's auto was back under the watchful eye of Kratz, Calumet, and Manitowoc Counties. Theoretically, it was now far easier to perpetrate evidence tampering. So, just hours after an inspection upon the bed mattress found no signs of a bloody attack, as Kratz had already declared to the world as fact, Tyson and Hawkins were given new marching orders.

"At 7:25 p.m., Sgt. Tyson and I went to the storage units located at Ann and Frontier Streets. We went to storage unit 7 where the victim Teresa Halbach's RAV4, was located."

Had the time arrived for another improper evidence harvest? Hawkins had specific instructions to start taking DNA swabs inside the car that drew the preoccupation of Fassbender and Wiegert during their interrogation of Brendan.

"At approximately 7:41 p.m., I took a photograph of the hood latch of the Toyota RAV4. At approximately 7:45 p.m., I took a photograph of the left battery cable ... At approximately 7:47 p.m., I took a photograph of the right side battery cable ... After I photographed the right and left battery cable and hood latch, and Sgt. Tyson took DNA swabs of these locations, the storage unit containing the Toyota RAV4 was secured."

Unlike the Hawkins report, Sgt. Tyson made sure to include a noteworthy observation that called into question

71. Processing of evidence, April 3, 2006, Deputy Jeremy Hawkins report

prosecutor Kratz's wild tale about Teresa supposedly being shackled to Avery's bed, fighting for her life.

"It shall be noted that when we analyzed the headboard, we could not see any striations around the spindles of the headboard consistent with that of having handcuffs or leg irons secured to the spindles of the headboard."

When it came time to remove Avery's bed mattress and place it in the evidence training room around 4:30 p.m., "Deputy Hawkins and myself did look at the mattress and did observe numerous stains on the mattress. Deputy Hawkins did numerous presumptive tests on those stains, all of which turned up negative for the presence of blood. The mattress was then returned to the evidence room."

From there, Sgt. Tyson called his boss. "I did place a telephone call to Investigator Wiegert and did inform him of our findings."

Three hours would pass. Wiegert and Fassbender had put their heads together and would have remembered how they were present when the extra pair of unnecessary groin swabs was taken from Avery's body by Manitowoc nurse Faye Fritsch, back on November 9, 2005. These were the swabs Avery said he saw Wiegert pretend to put into the garbage can, but apparently didn't. Had the time finally come to deploy one of these extra Avery DNA specimens?

"Investigator Wiegert and Special Agent Tom Fassbender had informed us they wished for us to do DNA swabs on the interior and exterior of the door handles of Teresa Halbach's vehicle. They also requested DNA swabs done on the hood latch as well as battery cables for the vehicle," Tyson said.

Tyson faithfully carried out the assignment at the storage shed in Chilton. "After the DNA swabs had been collected, the door to the storage locker was secured. Deputy Hawkins and I transported the swabs that were collected to the sheriff's department and the swabs were secured in the Calumet County Sheriff's Office evidence room."

But it was not for long.

Out of nowhere, six months after the car was processed in Madison, Wiegert decided the extra DNA samples were suddenly important to the case. Rather than have the items placed into a sealed FedEx container as is customary for many police agencies, Wiegert assigned himself to personally drive the DNA samples to Madison. He appeared to want to do this alone, without any interference. The records seem to reflect he did not want anybody else looking over his shoulder.

By April 2006, Wiegert's behavior was becoming more bizarre and cryptic. It was as if he were becoming paranoid and obsessive about all of Avery's DNA samples.

Wiegert, the head of the investigation, even authored a strange police report that has no date on it, and yet Wiegert made a point to send a copy of the memo to his friend, and long-time professional colleague, Ken Kratz.

"I had spoken with Detective Remiker in the middle part of April," Wiegert said. "My reason for speaking with Detective Remiker was to request his assistance in determining whether they had any DNA samples, including but not limited to buccal swabs and or blood samples, in their custody from Steven Avery. It should be noted on May 4, 2006, I did receive a copy of Detective Remiker's report detailing any type of DNA evidence, which they have no file."[72]

***

Most people forget, or perhaps they don't realize, but when Avery was arrested by Wiegert and Fassbender on November 9, 2005, his private criminal defense lawyers Dean Strang and Jerry Buting were not yet in the picture.

---

72. Receipt of DNA information from Manitowoc County Sheriff's Department, Inv. Mark Wiegert report

It was not until February 2006, the fourth month of Avery's murder prosecution, that Avery severed ties with the Manitowoc County Public Defender's Office as his legal representation. The Wisconsin Department of Justice and the Manitowoc County Sheriff's Office personnel were surely alarmed and intimidated by the announcement of the new legal team coming on board to represent Avery. After all, Avery continued to insist, over and over, that he was being framed and had nothing to do with Teresa's death.

If the RAV4 was strategically put onto Avery's property to ensure his arrest, and if the spare ignition was strategically dropped onto Avery's bedroom floor on the sixth day of the investigation by a member of the Manitowoc County sheriff's department, you have to step back and ask yourself the following question: Would it be more likely or less likely that the police leading this investigation had another bag of tricks in mind?

The RAV4 was under the control of Wiegert, who put the car into a local police impound lot where he and his cohorts had easy access.

Wiegert, of course, had easy access to the evidence trove taken from the Avery property, as well as to the numerous samples of DNA collected from the bedroom and bathroom of Teresa.

The day after Teresa's RAV4 was found, Wiegert tasked Deputy Craig Wendling with going over to Halbach's house. "Investigator Wiegert wanted me to pick up evidence that would contain Teresa Halbach's DNA in case it would be needed for further identification … Investigator Wiegert told me a toothbrush, lip Chap Stick, and possibly a vibrator that was located in a dresser would be good items to collect."[73]

---

73. Supplemental report Deputy Craig Wendling, November 6, 2005

Sure enough, all the objects Wiegert had vividly remembered as being inside of Teresa's place, were all still there.

"I did find Teresa's toothbrush ... and some Chap Stick ... Those items were placed into a plastic bag and sealed."

The deputy also collected "another lip moisturizer that had some hair stuck to it and a hairbrush ..." And then in Teresa's first floor bedroom, the deputy carrying out Wiegert's tasks found a cardboard box "containing a reddish maroon case with a zipper. Once I opened that case, I did locate a vibrator or a sexual device. I re-zipped the case, placed it into a plastic bag and sealed it ... Investigator Wiegert was notified that the items were obtained and placed into evidence."

Wiegert, of course, was present when the highly questionable two extra DNA samples were collected from Avery, groin swabs that were not necessary, a prisoner who was supposedly being taken into custody on a gun charge, not a first-degree murder charge.

If you believe these cops were crooked and hell-bent on putting Avery in prison to never to come out alive, you have to realize it would only be logical that they would carry out additional dirty tricks in a win-at-all costs mentality, now that Avery had hired Strang and Buting to attempt to prove his innocence.

On the other hand, it's also possible that some of these cops had overestimated the strength and power of Buting and Strang.

CHAPTER TWENTY

GARAGE

Because timing is everything, about a week after Strang and Buting joined the case and championed Avery's defense, people who worked at the Manitowoc County and Calumet County Sheriff's Offices came to a not-so-surprising decision. Sure enough, a follow-up search was needed to go back through Avery's garage.

Why?

There was a feeling in the air that this follow-up garage search, just like the search of Avery's tiny bedroom when the spare key emerged, would not be a failure.

The following line of questioning was posed by Strang to Remiker during Avery's murder trial:

"The search of the garage on November 6, I think that's the first time you actually searched the garage rather than simply sweeping through it to look for Ms. Halbach?"

"Correct."

"You folks found some empty shell casings, looked like .22 caliber rounds?"

"Yes. I think eleven."

"Were you looking for bullets?"

"We were looking for everything."

"Found no bullets in the search on November 6 of the garage?"

"Correct."

"Found no bullets any other time in Steven Avery's garage anytime in November of 2005?"

"Correct."

"It was March 2, 2006, and you were present when bullets or bullet fragments were found in that garage?"

"On March 2, yes, one bullet fragment."

"One bullet fragment?"

"Yes."

During Lenk's testimony, Strang asked the following questions.

"Had Steven Avery actually been sitting there during your deposition?"

"He came in after I had started giving my deposition. Yes, sir."

"And without you telling Mr. Fassbender, and Mr. Wiegert, Sheriff Pagel about the deposition, there's really no way they would have known about it, would they have?"

"No, sir."

"So that's not information they could consider in deciding whether to accept your offer to volunteer to search Mr. Avery's trailer?"

"They didn't have that information, sir."

"Because you didn't give it to them?"

"No, sir, I did not."

"And before you went rummaging through Steven Avery's bedroom once, twice, three times, whatever it was, for hours, would it have been fairer to Steven Avery if someone other than a person who had been deposed in his lawsuit had done that search?"

"No, sir, I don't think it would have been."

"You came back to Mr. Avery's four months later? Not quite four months later?"

"Yes."

"March 1st and March 2nd of 2006?"

"That's correct, sir."

"Much smaller search this time, wasn't it?"

"Yes, sir. I believe it was just the garage."

"A search was going on in the garage?"

"That's correct."

"You came back?"

"Yes, sir."

"Did you participate in that search?"

"No, sir, I did not."

"Why were you back?"

"I came back to see if they needed any, uh, food, any assistance with supplies, see if I could help out. I believe I was there both days, I'm not sure."

During the trial, Calumet County investigator Gary Steier testified he, too, had a critical role in the recovery of the mysterious bullet fragments that turned up in Avery's garage.

"Day 1 of the search warrant, a bullet fragment was located. The item was located by Agent (Kevin) Heimerl and was collected by myself," Steier told the court. "Day 2 of the search warrant, a second bullet fragment was also located by Agent Heimerl and was collected by Detective Remiker."

At the trial, Kratz represented to the jury that the bullet fragments found in the March 2006 garage search were indeed bullet fragments that passed through Teresa's skull.

Fast forward the case a decade.

On May 23, 2017, Christopher Palenik of Microtrace, the company's senior research microscopist, began his analysis upon the questionable bullet fragments used to convict Avery. Microtrace formed in 1992, specializing in the identification of tiny unknown substances and small particles, through chemistry, geology, biology, and materials science. The company became intimately involved in some of the world's most high-profile crimes and disasters including The Unabomber, Oklahoma City Bombing, the Green River serial murders, JonBenét Ramsey case, Atlanta child murders, the Ivan the Terrible war crimes trial in Jerusalem, and the murder of DEA special agent "Kiki" Camerena in Mexico.

Now, Microtrace had gotten involved in the Avery case.

But first, before conducting any full-blown scientific experiments relative to Teresa's murder trial, four exemplar bullets were fired through bone at the Microtrace laboratory by Lucien Haag, who has authored more than two hundred scientific papers dealing with ballistics. Haag's expertise involves reconstructing shooting scenes and shooting incidents.

Scientist Christopher Palenik works at Microtrace, which is regarded as one of the world's top companies for analyzing trace evidence.

Dr. Lucien Haag of Arizona is regarded as one of the world's top ballistics experts.

Haag's four test bullets all displayed "white translucent particles consistent with the appearance of bone, on the surface of or embedded in each of the four exemplar bullets."

At that point, the test bullets were packaged and sent to the Independent Forensics Laboratory in Lombard, Illinois, where supervisor Liz Kopitke put the four damaged bullets into separate test tubes. She submerged them into what's known as a buffer fluid.

"Ms. Kopitke then shook the test tubes in her hand. The post-extraction exemplar bullets were again examined and photo-documented ... this examination showed that white, translucent particles, morphologically consistent with bone, remained on and embedded in each of the four exemplar bullets."[74]

In other words, the DNA extraction performed by Independent Forensics Laboratory "did not cause the white, translucent particles consistent with bone to fall or become dislodged from the exemplar bullet."

It was now time for the big moment, May 23, 2017.

The Avery case bullet known as evidence tag number #FL was hand-delivered to Microtrace, in Elgin, Illinois, by Wisconsin DOJ Special Agent Jeff Wisch.

After analyzing this bullet under one of the most high-powered microscopes available, Palenik made the following determinations: "There is no evidence to indicate that the bullet passed through bone. In fact, the particulate evidence that is present strongly suggests an alternate hypothesis which is that the trajectory of the fired bullet took it into a wooden object, possibly a manufactured wood product. Furthermore, the presence of red droplets deposited on the bullet suggests that the bullet had picked up additional contamination from its environment at some point after coming to a rest. Based upon these findings, it is our understanding that an investigator was sent by the Zellner

---

74. Affidavit of Dr. Christopher Palenik May 31, 2017

Law Office to the Avery garage to review the area for possible sources of the particulate types described above."

According to Microtrace, two possible sources were recovered around Avery's property. One was particle board in the garage with apparent bullet holes and red painted surfaces including the red painted garage. The other was a ladder in the condemned man's garage.

"Each of the above-listed materials observed on the bullet could be identified specifically if their actual identity is of importance to the investigation. This may provide further constraints or refinement of the hypotheses I have advanced," Palenik said.

Additionally, the law firm of Kathleen Zellner & Associates sought out the expertise of Dr. Lucien "Luke" Haag, a distinguished independent forensic consultant who owns Forensic Science Services Inc. in Carefree, Arizona. Haag has been utilized as an expert witness on firearms identification and firearms evidence across the country.

"The damaged bullet recovered from Steven Avery's garage and purported to yield a full DNA profile of Teresa Halbach shows no evidence of having been shot through Ms. Halbach's skull," Haag said. "The bullet, which was identified as a .22 long rifle bullet, was comprised of such soft metal that there would be detectable bone fragments embedded in the damaged bullet if it had been fired through Ms. Halbach's skull. Because no bone fragments have been identified in the damaged bullet, Item FL, over the course of its examination, including DNA and firearms/tool marks analysis at the Wisconsin State Crime Lab, it is my opinion, to a reasonable degree of certainty in the field of ballistics, that Item FL was not fired through Ms. Halbach's skull."[75]

Haag further explains how he performed a rigorous battery of ballistics testing to illustrate for the court how

75. Affidavit of Dr. Lucien Haag, May 26, 2017

bone fragments would become embedded within .22 long-rifle bullets when fired through human bone.

"I fired two copper-plated lead CCI MiniMag .22 long rifle bullets through one layer of approximately two-millimeter-thick flat bone, then through five inches of soft tissue simulant as a means of recovering the bullet. Bone particles, embedded in the soft lead, were readily visible under a stereo-microscope for both the bullets fired through one thickness of bone and two thicknesses of bone."

Back at Avery's trial, William Newhouse of the Wisconsin State Crime Lab, a firearms examiner, testified as a prosecution witness used by Kratz. "According to Mr. Newhouse's bullet worksheet, Mr. Newhouse identified no trace evidence on the damaged bullet. If there were bone fragments embedded in the damaged bullet, I would expect a reasonably competent firearms examiner to have identified them during their microscopical examination," Haag said.

"Because Mr. Newhouse did not note or describe any bone or bone-like particles embedded in Item FL during his microscopical examination of this damaged bullet, it is my opinion, to a reasonable degree of certainty in the field of forensic ballistics that Item FL was not fired through Ms. Halbach's skull."

Haag's biography notes he is a former criminalist and technical director of the Phoenix Crime Laboratory with more than fifty years of experience in the field as well as having done forensic firearms examinations. He authored the first edition book called *Shooting Incident Reconstruction*. Haag was born in 1940 in Springfield, Illinois.

***

Because Avery's jury trial was heralded as Wisconsin's biggest trial since serial killer cannibal Jeffery Dahmer, it made perfect sense for a sly and unsavory prosecutor to represent wild assertions and stories as fact. Most people around the country fail to understand that court trials, notably murder trials, often don't get to the heart of the actual truth, but are often more about the theatrics and drama. The actors, the winners and the losers, are the lawyers. It's about presentation. It's about style. It's about pizazz. Ken Kratz recognized this, and he excelled at it.

Around the time of Avery's trial, Kratz also had a cozy relationship with several members of the Wisconsin press. They were not about to question him about how he came up with his wild stories of Teresa's murder. For them, he was a reliable and trustworthy source for their story tips, even though he was one of the most untrustworthy public office holders in northeastern Wisconsin.

"At trial it was claimed that the defendant's DNA on the listed item of evidence was deposited from sweaty fingers. This is, of course, pure speculation as there is no forensic test for the presence of sweat. Nonetheless, the DNA that generated the profile came from somewhere," Zellner said.

Enter Dr. Karl Reich. He was enlisted to conduct a series of fact-finding experiments surrounding the mysterious so-called hood latch DNA specimen. That item was the late-to-the-game damning piece of DNA evidence used by the special prosecutor to stick the nail in the coffin at Avery's murder trial.

Dr. Reich runs Independent Forensics in Lombard, Illinois. His company in DuPage County focuses on forensic DNA, molecular biology, protein biochemistry, microbial and human functional genomics, and protein purification. A highly distinguished scientist, Dr. Reich has eight years of post-graduate and fifteen years of experience in the pharmaceutical and biotechnology industries.

The chief scientific officer at Independent Forensics since 2002, Reich is a court-qualified expert witness on forensic DNA, forensic biology, and forensic biology and statistics. As of June 2017, Dr. Reich had given court testimony and sworn pretrial depositions in more than eighty cases in state, federal, and international courts for both civil and criminal matters.

Now he needed to determine, once and for all, was the infamous hood latch DNA specimen used to convict Avery legitimate?

"Volunteers were enlisted to open the car hood of this surrogate vehicle using the engine compartment hood latch, the current and identical method used by the Wisconsin State Forensic DNA Laboratory, Madison," Reich said. "This experimental test was repeated fifteen times. The hood latch was, of course, cleaned after each round of hood opening and subsequent swabbing."[76]

Here were his results.

"In eleven of the fifteen replicates, no detectable DNA was recovered from the hood latch ... In other words, in almost three-quarters of the hood opening trials no measurable DNA was left behind by the individual who opened the hood. Put another way, even when DNA was left on the hood latch after opening the hood, the amount of DNA recovered was between twenty and thirty-five times less than that recovered from the item identified as M05-2467.

"To put it yet another way, the Madison laboratory recovered from six to seven times more DNA than all of the DNA recovered from all of the fifteen hood openings combined."

But how could such a phenomenon occur?

"Given the experimental results, both the body fluid detection data and the DNA recovery data from the hood latch opening trials, the question of what sample M05-2467 #ID really might be, becomes a subject for investigation," Dr. Reich said.

---

76. Affidavit of Dr. Karl Reich, June 6, 2017

Dr. Karl Reich now knows why there was an extraordinary amount of Steven Avery's DNA recovered from the hood latch swab and the spare key on Avery's bedroom floor.

In addition to scrutinizing the dubious hood latch DNA sample, Reich also performed a similar experiment related to the highly questionable spare key. This was the key that surfaced on Avery's bedroom carpet, recovered by Lenk and Colborn, to give Manitowoc County its lone item of evidence to tie Teresa's disappearance to the inside of Avery's trailer.

"Similar to the experimental work to replicate the hood latch results an experiment was done to try to replicate the results from the ignition key of the victim's automobile. An exemplar key, reportedly held by Mr. Avery as if to start a car, gripped by ungloved fingers for twelve minutes, was subject to DNA quantification. It was determined that 0.017 nanograms per microliter was recovered. This result was ten times less DNA than reported by the Wisconsin Department of Justice State Crime Laboratory-Madison on the key they analyzed, item M05-2467 #C."

In both instances, Dr. Reich found the DNA experiments quite startling. "An order of magnitude difference is a significant finding," he said.

Regarding the supposed hood latch DNA, Dr. Reich opined "it is an oft-repeated fear heard from many defendants that the evidence in their case has been enhanced, manufactured, or otherwise manipulated to their disadvantage. There is no doubt that evidence tampering occurs, though there is little to support the contention that this is a widespread practice."

But why would some lawmen, people such as Wiegert, Fassbender, Colborn, Lenk, and possibly others, become tempted to take matters into their own hands?

"It is often assumed that creating an item of evidence de novo or enhancing an item of evidence is an effective method of evidence tampering; however, simply relabeling an errant known standard/reference swab as a questioned item/exhibit accomplishes the goal of identifying the defendant far more efficiently. There is sufficient evidence to hypothesize that this approach to evidence tampering occurred for sample M05-2467 #ID, which was the hood-latch swab," Dr. Reich said.

When Avery went on trial, his lawyers portrayed Colborn and Lenk as the prime evidence planters.

Attorney Zellner's research does not completely abandon Lenk and Colborn as being intimately involved in planting evidence, but her investigators strongly suspect Fassbender and Wiegert were involved in facilitating some of the extraordinary evidence harvests.

If you go back and study the many questionable evidence finds, they often happen after Wiegert and Fassbender give one of their underlings a specific assignment or task that comes at an odd or strange time in the case.

In Omaha, Nebraska, CSI Director David Kofoed ruined his career and went to prison after he got exposed for planting blood swabs as a method to shore up a high-profile double murder case. Kofoed believed the case lacked sufficient physical evidence to move forward with a successful criminal prosecution against the jailed suspects.

Suspects that he was under the erroneous impression were guilty. Kofoed fabricated a perfect DNA sample containing the murder victim's blood to make it look like the jailed suspects had transferred blood from the shotgun killings to their supposed getaway car.

Kofoed waited to plant the blood swab only after he had been assured by one of the misguided lead detectives that the pair of codefendants had to be involved in the farmhouse killings of Wayne and Sharmon Stock in Murdock, Nebraska. The badly mistaken detective, however, had obtained a false confession from the murder victim's mentally impaired nephew. That relative, who had no prior criminal history and had been in special education classes throughout his schooling, ultimately broke down under pressure and threats of being hanged from a tall tree and being put in a gas chamber from his two police interrogators.

The mentally impaired man, in his late twenties, had an IQ in the high sixties.

The nephew of the murder victims agreed to implicate himself as the killer and he named another cousin as his accomplice.

Here's an excerpt from his false confession. The questions were being asked by one of the lead detectives on the double murder case.

"And you fired a shot to shut her up? Isn't that right? I need you to say it out loud, buddy?"

"Yes, sir. Yeah, I think I got him in the head."

The detective then asked if Matthew Livers shot his uncle in a part of his body where it would be hard to walk.

"The knee," Livers confessed. "So he is trying to crawl to the office and then (aunt) Sharmon was woke up screaming of course I believe."

After a brief pause, Livers collected his thoughts and blurted out, "Then I just pulled that trigger and shot her and then she screamed more and then I just ..."

"You just what, buddy?" asked Detective Earl Schenck Jr., a legacy police officer whose father was a long-time sheriff in western Nebraska.

"Put the gun to her face and blew her away," Livers claimed. "Then, then as I headed out, I just stuck it to him and blew him away."

About two weeks later, not a shred of physical evidence existed to tie Livers and his cousin Nick Sampson to the farmhouse murders of their relatives. That was when Kofoed decided to save the day. He produced a perfect DNA sample of murder victim Wayne Stock's blood. He claimed he found the blood when he went back inside the impounded car belonging to the codefendants, a vehicle being kept under police safekeeping at Kofoed's sheriff's office in Omaha, Nebraska. He claimed to have found the blood underneath the dashboard, suggesting to others that this was an area of the car that they forgot to check during the initial eight-hour search that he had supervised about a week or so earlier.

Then, months later, overwhelming evidence showed the real getaway vehicle was a red Dodge Ram truck, stolen in Wisconsin, by the real killers, a teenage boyfriend and girlfriend who were psychopathic goths with an itch to kill.

Livers and Sampson were later proven to be innocent. They had been victims of a sloppy small-town police investigation that led to their unjust incarcerations for a double murder they did not commit. Many months later, the righteous Prosecutor Nathan Cox set them free. The fabricated DNA swabs later put CSI commander Dave Kofoed in prison, but only after the Omaha branch of the FBI got involved.

***

Although most people believe the spare key found on Avery's bedroom carpet was put there by Lenk and Colborn,

Avery's original trial lawyers never developed a strong theory to explain why their client's DNA was on that key.

Strang and Buting also could have devoted more research into the hood latch DNA swab touted by Kratz. Even though they knew the evidence was likely phony, Strang and Buting did not have a strong argument or an expert witness to refute this damning piece of unorthodox forensic evidence when it came time for their client's trial.

The lawyers for Avery also didn't spend enough time following up on the two highly irregular groin swabs Wiegert and Fassbender collected from their client at the time of his arrest when Avery was just being arrested on a weapons violation charge.

According to Dr. Reich, "The chain of custody and disposition of two groin swabs taken from the defendant during his arrest is neither complete, accurate, nor transparent. Such a sample, relabeled as taken from the hood latch of the victim's vehicle, would satisfy all of the observed facts: lack of body fluid, sufficient amount of DNA for a profile, and would link the defendant to the victim without all of the messy and complicated effort to actually deposit DNA on a grease and engine grimed engine compartment metal latch.

"But this hypothesis is a better fit to the data, experimental trials, and needs of the investigators for clear and convincing evidence of a link between the defendant and the victim's vehicle. A swab truly taken from the engine compartment hood latch should have been covered in black engine grime and grease as anyone who has ever had to open the hood of a high mileage car can attest. The swab batting in question was merely very lightly discolored; another fact that does not fit with the claimed origin of this sample."

Another major event in Avery's prosecution occurred on the first and second of March, 2006, when the Manitowoc and Calumet County deputies returned back to the Avery property. Kratz called it the "thorough search" of Avery's detached garage.

But the search warrant also afforded police another opportunity to wander back inside Avery's bedroom. Calumet Deputy Rick Riemer, working closely with Investigator Wendy Baldwin, also confiscated evidence item 8359 which was "a left foot slipper near the east wall in the south bedroom" and item 8360 "A right foot slipper."

But why, four months into the murder case, were authorities, all of a sudden removing Avery's slippers from his bedroom?

Dr. Reich wanted to examine whether the police were attempting to extract DNA from Avery's slippers to have it handy against the despised murder defendant.

"Our lab conducted an experiment to examine whether the bedroom slippers recovered from Mr. Avery's residence could have been the source of his DNA detected on the Toyota ignition key, M05-2467 #C, allegedly recovered from Mr. Avery's bedroom. This hypothesis was tested by creating a pair of worn slippers, sockless, nine hours a day for five days and using this worn item as a source of DNA on an exemplar ignition key. The procedure was to prepare the slippers, rub the key, and then measure the DNA that was transferred ... This approach yielded 0.0393 nanograms per microliter, well below the concentration of DNA reported by the Wisconsin Department of Justice State Crime Laboratory-Madison for the key they analyzed ... at 0.17 nanograms per microliter.

"These data do not support the hypothesis that the DNA identified on the Toyota ignition key came from contact with the slippers photographed in and recovered from Mr. Avery's bedroom. If the Toyota ignition key was indeed enhanced, then it is likely that some other personal item of Mr. Avery's was used for this purpose, some possible examples might include a toothbrush or a cigarette butt."[77]

---

77. Karl Reich, affidavit, June 6, 2017

Of course, simple logic dictates that if Wiegert and Fassbender gathered up two perfect DNA samples from Avery's groin, and they were holding on to them for devious purposes, one groin swab may have been substituted as the hood-latch DNA specimen. The other likely got used for the spare key DNA sample.

"It is hypothesized that a rubbed groin swab taken from the defendant was relabeled and thus became evidence from a hood latch," Reich said. "This hypothesis has not been proven, but it fully explains all of the known facts regarding this item. Taken in context with other facts and allegations in the case of *Wisconsin v. Avery*, this hypothesis deserves careful consideration from the trier of fact."

CHAPTER TWENTY-ONE

HEROES OR GOATS?

In the 2018 Super Bowl, backup quarterback Nick Foles led the Philadelphia Eagles to defeat Tom Brady and the New England Patriots. But after the game, you didn't see crazed football fans storming the field hoisting Brady on their shoulders, giving him a hero's victory celebration. Of course not.

In Avery's murder case, his lawyers Jerry Buting and Dean Strang had engineered an unsuccessful defense and their client got convicted and continues to serve a life prison sentence. And yet the world could not get enough of them. They capitalized on the worldwide notoriety that came from the *Making a Murderer* documentary series, and became like a couple of rock stars. They were booked for countless European media tours to talk about their role on the Avery case. They were the darlings of national television shows including Dr. Phil.

"Mr. Avery holds Buting and Strang partly responsible for his guilty verdict despite the Brady violations of the prosecutors," Zellner said.

Those Brady violations have nothing to do with Tom Brady the losing quarterback in the Super Bowl. Rather, it deals with a federal case law decided by the U.S. Supreme Court that forbids prosecutors and police from hiding and concealing what's known as mitigating evidence, evidence that would be helpful or advantageous to the defendant. Under federal law, prosecutors are expected to provide all information in their possession to the criminal defense's counsel for review as part of the pretrial discovery process.

Here's what Zellner has to say about the overall performance of Buting and Strang. "Strang and Buting had a couple of stellar moments in the courtroom but unfortunately those moments were not nearly enough to win Mr. Avery's case," Zellner said.

"They failed to hire the necessary experts in blood spatter, ballistics, fire forensics, pathology, trace and DNA to combat the avalanche of testimony by the State's fourteen experts. They got hopelessly bogged down and sidetracked by the blood vial theory which was easily refuted by the State. They talked a big game about the cops planting evidence but in the end, they were unable to deliver anything but their own speculative theories."

Based on Zellner's real-life practical experience inside the courtroom, "it is always fatal with a jury to promise something and then fail to deliver on the promise. They failed to carefully review the State's discovery disclosures for impeachment evidence to use against the State's witnesses. Their biggest failure, in that regard, was in failing to call Bryan Dassey to impeach his brother Bobby's testimony that Ms. Halbach never left the Avery property. Bobby would have been discredited and the State's case would have collapsed. After *Making a Murderer* aired, Buting and Strang launched a worldwide tour, as if they had won, rather than lost."

During their pretrial preparation, Buting and Strang overlooked the actual swabs that may have been tampered with by police in order to produce the perfect DNA specimens that came from the spare key in Avery's bedroom and the highly dubious hood latch DNA search, another six months later.

"There is compelling evidence, as we have explained in our pleadings, that Wiegert was involved in switching the hood latch swabs with the groin swabs," Zellner said. "A careful examination of the chain of custody forms for the hood latch swabs demonstrates that Wiegert delivered the so-called hood latch swabs to the Wisconsin Crime Lab but identified another officer as having done so."

Zellner contends that Buting and Strang missed a golden opportunity to destroy the credibility of Colborn's trial testimony about his discovery of the spare key to Teresa Halbach's vehicle. The spare key had suddenly turned up on the carpet near Avery's bed on what marked the sixth time that Manitowoc County Sheriff's officials went into Avery's tiny bedroom. The key gave Manitowoc County a noteworthy clue to finally tie their murder suspect to the Auto Trader photographer's mysterious disappearance.

"We tried many times to duplicate Colborn's story about manhandling the bookcase, and we could not get the key and lanyard to fall out of the back of the bookcase and land where it did. Also, all of the items on top of the bookcase fell on the floor during our experiments. Another great failing of Buting and Strang was in not subpoenaing the bookcase for trial and requesting Colborn, during his cross examination, to come off the stand and demonstrate this miraculous event with the actual key, lanyard, and bookcase for the jury. Colborn could have never replicated what he told the jury happened."

Zellner has unbelievably high standards in terms of taking new clients. Her law firm has a rigid screening process when it comes to accepting condemned prisoners who insist that they were wrongfully convicted.

"I took the Avery case because I thought if I could demonstrate all of the forensic evidence was planted, it would be a wakeup call to law enforcement, juries, judges, and lawyers that they must start demanding the replication of the forensic evidence before they rely upon it in seeking a conviction," Zellner said. "We have challenged anyone to attempt to replicate the State's forensic evidence used to convict Mr. Avery and absolutely no one has been able to do so."

***

During Avery's trial, Strang and Buting put up a valiant effort at one point when they tried to put forth an alternative theory regarding the actual crime scene.

But they were up against the mischievous and cocky Ken Kratz, who wanted to make sure that his salacious story about a bedroom sex-crime murder stuck with the jury's minds. Though there were charred pelvic bones that turned up inside the Manitowoc County quarry several hundred yards south of the Avery property, it appears that Kratz did not want to take the risk that these bones were Teresa's, and possibly neither did Wiegert and Fassbender, so they seem to have reached a consensus, that particular item of evidence would simply be classified as bones of undermined origin and that was that.

That tactical move left defense attorney Dean Strang swimming upstream when he had a chance to cross-examine the prosecution's bone expert, Dr. Leslie Eisenberg of the Wisconsin State Historical Society, during the murder trial.

"Now, you found in the material from the quarry pile two fragments that appeared to you, in your experience, to be pelvic bone, is that right?"[78]

"That's correct.

"There were some cuts, appeared to be some cuts on those pelvic bone fragments?"

"Yes."

"But you weren't able to conclude, 100 percent certain, that these were human pelvic bone fragments; do I understand that correctly?"

78. Dr. Leslie Eisenberg, forensic anthropologist, February 28-March 1, 2007 Avery trial testimony

"That's correct."

Eisenberg was also asked about the cut marks to the pelvic bones.

"It was a long, linear cut, on either side of those two bones that were still in proximity. They were essentially a slicing cut on one side and a sharp slicing cut on the other side."

"Did it appear to your eyes that these cuts were, if you could draw any conclusion at all, that the cuts on these pelvic bones were from a smooth edged instrument or a toothed instrument?"

"I cannot answer your question … because of the burning and charring of the bone itself, it was difficult to make any additional observations beyond that … If I could place those two adjoining fragments in anatomical position, which I was able to do, as part of the right pelvic structure, those cuts were made on either side, in what I would call a north/south direction, an up and down direction."

When Strang asked if evidence tag 8675 contained multiple burned bone fragments, Eisenberg answered, "That is correct, sir."

Then he asked her if there were separate sites where charred bones, all suspected human bones, shared the same charring and calcination.

"That is correct."

"All of them were fragmented, similarly, from the three sites, again, human bone?"

"That's correct."

"You would certainly agree that it would be very strange weather conditions, indeed, that would transport human bone fragments from the Avery garage area into burn barrel number two on the Janda property?"

"In fact, I would submit there would be no weather conditions that could make that happen."

"You would rule that out?"

"I would."

"Likewise, the quarry pile?"

"Yes, sir … some bone fragments identified as human had been moved, that's correct."

"Now you have no evidence that human bone fragments actually were burned at more than one site, do you?"

"I do not know that."

"But the burnt bone fragments that you saw from the three sites, again, all were roughly similar in their burning, charring, and calcining?"

"That is correct."

When Strang finished, the prosecution had another chance to sweep away the defense theory about the suspicious pelvic bones being those of Teresa.

Assistant Attorney General Tom Fallon, Kratz's trial sidekick, asked their side's witness, "As you sit here today, you cannot tell us that those bones, to a reasonable degree of anthropological or scientific certainty, are human, can you?"

"I cannot."

***

Dr. Steven Symes has a Doctorate Degree in physical anthropology and he worked as a forensic anthropologist at the Department of the Mississippi State Medical Examiner's Office. In 2008-2009, Symes was honored with the 15th T. Dale Stewart Award, a lifetime achievement given by the American Academy of Forensic Sciences for anthropology, recognizing him for his career, scholarship, and remarkable productivity. He served on the board of directors for the American Board of Forensic Anthropology from 2003 through 2009.

His resume also noted that he is presently on call as the outside forensic anthropology consultant for Summit County, Ohio, Singapore Medical Examiner's Office, Detroit Medical Examiner's Office, Polk County Medical

Examiner's Office in Des Moines, Iowa, and the Will County Medical Examiner's office for its disaster plan.

One of the country's leading forensic pathologists, Dr. Steven Symes of Mississippi has concluded the burning of Teresa Halbach's body did not occur at Avery's property.

"I have testified extensively in forensic trauma to bone and surrounding tissues. The principal topic of my research and experience has been trauma injuries to the skeleton, including ballistic, blunt, burning, healing bone with specific focus on sharp force trauma."[79]

Dr. Symes was retained by Zellner to examine whether Eisenberg had sold out her soul to help the prosecution at Avery's murder trial in a win-at-all-costs scenario. Dr. Symes reviewed all known photographs taken of evidence tag 8675 – the suspected human pelvic bones examined by Dr. Leslie Eisenberg. Then he reviewed all the trial testimony

---

79. Affidavit of Dr. Steven Symes, April 19, 2007

regarding the supposed attempts to identify the pelvic bones that were found at the Manitowoc County gravel pit.

"A microscopic examination of the suspected human pelvic bone, performed in 2005, would have determined to a high percentage of accuracy, whether the pelvic bones were human, and histological slides, made in 2005 from the suspected human pelvic bones, would have determined to a high percentage of accuracy whether the pelvic bones in evidence tag number 8675 were human," Dr. Symes concluded.

But did Dr. Eisenberg sell out her soul, her ethics, and her integrity, to make sure the state of Wisconsin achieved a murder conviction against Avery? After all, she knew how critical her testimony was to the success of the prosecution's case.

"It is certainly below the standard of practice for a reasonably well-qualified and competent forensic anthropologist, at this current time and place, to not perform microscopic and histological examinations of the possible human pelvic bones, and it may have been below the standard of practice in 2005 for a reasonably well-qualified and competent forensic anthropologist to not have performed microscopic and histological examinations of the possible human pelvic bones in evidence tag number 8675," Dr. Symes said.

But there was more in his damning assessment of Dr. Eisenberg's performance.

"It was below the standard of practice for a reasonably well-qualified and competent forensic anthropologist to have relied exclusively upon photographs of the pelvic bones to complete the forensic examination."

Third, "it may be below the standard of practice in 2005 for a reasonably well-qualified and competent forensic anthropologist to have performed an examination and interpretation of bone trauma without microscopic assistance."

Besides Symes, Dr. John DeHaan, one of the world's leading fire and burn experts, also examined the entire Avery case files. DeHaan has worked as a forensic scientist and criminalist since 1970. DeHaan served with the Alameda County Sheriff's Office, the California Department of Justice Bureau of Forensic Services, and the U.S. Treasury Department Bureau of Alcohol, Tobacco and Firearms. He also served as president of Fire-Ex Forensics Inc., since it formed in 1999.

"I have been involved with various aspects of fire and explosion investigation since 1971. In the past twelve years, I have testified as an expert witness in over fifty cases," DeHaan said.[80]

Dr. John DeHaan has conducted dozens of scientific experiments burning the bodies of cadavers under different temperature scenarios as well as indoor and outdoor settings.

In 2017, he was retained by Kathleen T. Zellner & Associates to study everything from the trial testimony, police reports, maps, photos, animated reconstructions, and forensic anthropology reports surrounding the discovery of Teresa's skeletal remains around the Avery property.

For DeHaan, studying the lay of the land was critical. Avery's forty-acre square property was rural, surrounded

80. John D. DeHaan affidavit, May 25, 2017

by forests and farms. Their land is south of State Highway 147, about five miles east of Interstate 43, less than ten miles northwest of Two Rivers and about twenty-five miles southeast of Green Bay. The northeast corner of the Avery property had four business buildings including an office, garages, and storage spaces. The residence of Al and Dolores Avery was in the northeast corner. A dirt lane led into the salvage yard where the wrecked cars were left. Another dirt lane, to the south, was where Chuck Avery lived. A third dirt lane ran due west of Avery Road and this lane featured two trailers about sixty-five yards apart, each with a detached garage. Steven Avery lived in the northeast corner trailer and his sister Barb lived in the other trailer with her four sons.

"In the southwest corner of the Avery property there was a dirt lane that ran immediately adjacent to an old gravel conveyor. This lane connected the Avery property to the gravel pits to the south. Within the car pit area, there were numerous dirt lanes separating rows of wrecked vehicles," Dr. DeHaan said.

There were also seven burn barrels spread out across the entire Avery parcel. Steven Avery kept one about forty yards northeast of his trailer. Four more burn barrels were clustered just south of his sister Barb's trailer. The parents, Allan and Delores Avery, had a burn barrel west of their residence. The seventh barrel was west of Chuck's domicile. All seven barrels were regularly used to burn common garbage from the kitchen and bathrooms. Steven Avery's burn pit behind his detached garage burned "household and automotive discards, trash, and animal remains," DeHaan said.

Then, to the south and to the west, the Avery land was bordered by active gravel pits owned by Radandt and Manitowoc County.

One important distinction DeHaan made was that "The Manitowoc County pit did not border the Avery property."

During Avery's trial, Kratz speculated that Teresa's body was incinerated outside under the dark skies of Halloween.

The circular area consisted of a mound of gravel, about one to two feet high. The entire mound of gravel was about thirty feet in diameter. The burn area was rectangular, about six feet long. "On November 8, 2005, Sgt. Jason Jost of the Manitowoc County Sheriff's Office observed what he suspected may be a vertebrae on the grass outside the south edge of the burn pit ... The burned remains of vehicle tires, unburned tires, various hand tools, and a vehicle's bench seat were recovered in the vicinity of the burn pit."[81]

Because the Manitowoc County Sheriff's Office had a reputation for sloppy and incompetent work, no examination was ever done on the wire rings from the tires, an unburned tire, a rubber mallet, a fire-damaged claw hammer, a gravel shovel, the burned vehicle seat, and burned/charred metal scraper with a wooden handle.

"Apparently no examination was performed to establish if any trace evidence linked these items to the death of Ms. Halbach or the burning of her body," DeHaan states.

Here's what else the world-famous fire expert noticed:

The burned debris developed a hard crust, perhaps from the heavy rains between Saturday, November 5, and Monday, November 7.

No forensic anthropologist was present during the November 8 police excavation that began around 3 p.m.

"Crime lab personnel, untrained in anthropology, visually examined potential skeletal fragments to determine their evidentiary value. There was no effort to document from where in the burn pit certain bones were recovered or otherwise document the order with which bones were situated in the burn pit. The crime lab personnel excavating the burn pit placed items of potential evidentiary value in a single box and sent it to Dr. Leslie Eisenberg for off-site examination."

81. DeHaan affidavit: Discovery of Bones in Steven Avery's burn pit

Puzzlingly, a decision was made by the leadership team of Wiegert and Fassbender to do no further excavation at the Avery burn pit on November 9. That day came and went without any additional digging. Then on November 10, after Avery was jailed, the Wisconsin Department of Justice was summoned to resume the excavation. "Again there was no forensic anthropologist called to the scene to conduct this secondary excavation. The burn pit was first excavated by hand then dug out using Bobcat-type front-loading tractors," Dr. Symes said.

The bone fragments examined by Dr. Eisenberg led her to conclude the bones came from a woman younger than thirty to thirty-five, shot in the head. "She also concluded that a number of bone fragments showed evidence of crushing or cutting with a tool."

Keep in mind that only a portion of the skeletal remains were recovered. The remains Eisenberg examined were only forty to sixty percent of the total mass of someone Teresa's size. In other words, most of Teresa's bones remain hidden. Perhaps they remain hidden underground, buried somewhere around Manitowoc County's maze of quarries and conveyor roads.

"Dr. Eisenberg identified that two bones recovered from the Manitowoc County gravel pit were still articulated, that is, they had maintained anatomical continuity," Dr. Symes said.

Looking back, the manner in which processing of the burn pits was conducted in such a high-profile murder case was an embarrassment to those involved in the effort: people supposedly proficient at their jobs, people employed by the Wisconsin Department of Justice, the Manitowoc County Sheriff's Office, and Calumet County.

"In this case, the minimal photographs taken before the excavation revealed very little useful information as there were few close-up photos taken before or during the recovery/excavation process ... In the few photographs of the burn pit, there appeared to be numerous dried leaves that obscured nearly all identifiable detail of the material below. From Sgt. (Jason) Jost and Wisconsin DOJ Special Agent (Tom) Sturdivant's descriptions, it appeared that the remains showed no anatomical relationship to each other. Some remains were found outside the burn pit and no large bones more resistant to fire were visible at all," Dr. John DeHaan said.

From that point forward, Kratz took it from there.

According to John De Haan, "There was no assessment of fuels associated with the fire other than describing the remains of the steel belts and beading of burned vehicle tires."

Unlike the operation that dug up Avery's property, "I have had the opportunity to see some fifty or more unembalmed adult, human cadavers exposed to a variety of real-world fires," DeHaan said. "These range from accidental kitchen fires, to whole room, post-flashover structure fires, to trench and roadside body disposals, to vehicle fires, to dumpster and burn barrel disposals."

In fact, DeHaan works closely with two of the country's foremost forensic anthropologists, Dr. Allison Galloway from the University of California Santa Cruz and Dr. Elayne Pope from the Virginia State Medical Examiner's Office. "We all assist in the preparation of the demonstration fires set as practical exercises for the students, observe the fires, and document the results."

In his 2012 book he co-authored, *Kirk's Fire Investigation*, 7th edition, DeHaan explains the human body's destruction during a fire is progressive. At first, "the skin shrinks, chars, and splits, exposing the subcutaneous fat. The fat renders out to support a flaming fire adjacent to the body. The muscle tissues dehydrate, char, and burn reluctantly ... Extreme exposure to fire results in loss of mechanical strength. Calcined bones are usually white, blue-white, or light gray in color and are brittle and are easily broken or shattered by contact or pressure."

The bone fragments in Dr. Eisenberg's photographs "appear to be coated with a yellow or tan soil or dust. Dr. Eisenberg reported that she rinsed some of the recovered bone fragments to allow detailed examination."

Most of the bone fragments she studied were one to four centimeters in length. "Many were completely calcinated with no charring of organic tissue visible," DeHaan said. "Others bore charred residues of organic material in the cancellous or spongy structure within."

What does this mean?

"Such damage can be induced by exposure to an open-air fire of ordinary combustibles for six to eight hours or for shorter times - three to four hours in a well-ventilated fire in a metal enclosure such as a burn barrel or automobile trunk."

DeHaan further explained that there is a huge distinction between fires set inside a metal enclosure and those set outside.

"In open-air field cremations, exposure to the flames is not uniform, there is minimal additional radiant heat, and charred masses of soft tissue will survive even a prolonged fire, particularly around the head or lower torso."

Of particular interest, the heat output generated by a human body is not substantial. It's on par with an office wastebasket fire, according to DeHaan.

"If a body is allowed to burn undisturbed to completion in either an enclosure or a well-fueled and ventilated fire, the large bones will retain their relative anatomical position, head, neck, shoulders, upper arms, spine, hips upper legs The process of stoking a fire with additional lumber or stirring with an implement during its active burning will cause the mechanical destruction of the bones as they are calcined by the flames and often, considerable displacement."

So what was John DeHaan's analysis of the bones in Teresa's slaying?

"The appearance, size, and type of bone fragments documented in Dr. Eisenberg's forensic anthropology reports and photographs exactly mirror the fragments recovered after burn-barrel cremations involving frequent stirring and stoking observed by this author. Such destruction was observed in wood-fueled burn barrel cremations in as short as three and a half hours."

In another recent criminal case where his expert analysis was sought, the accused killer described stoking a large wood-fueled pyre with several adult human bodies over the course of fifteen hours, DeHaan pointed out.

Later, Dr. DeHaan asserted, most of the bones were crushed with rocks and wood clubs. From there, the larger identifiable body parts that survived the fire were transported to a river for disposal.

"The hundreds of small fragments that were recovered from the burn site were very similar in size, shape and condition to the fragments in Dr. Eisenberg's forensic anthropology photos in this case. Note this involved no confinement except for the wood fuel and was accomplished over a span of 15 hours in an open-air burning pit."

Generally, the destruction of a human body in an open pit fire takes at least six hours, probably longer. The burning of a body thrown into a fifty-five-gallon steel drum with wood fuel can be accomplished in "as little as three and one half hours."

DeHaan is willing to put his name and reputation on the line on behalf of Steven Avery. He signed a sworn court affidavit attesting "it is further my opinion that the body was not burned in the burn pit. This is based on the reported lack of anatomical continuity of the remains, the findings of similarly charred/calcined fragments in burn barrels and other locations on the property and the absence of the more massive fragments that normally resist such exposure.

"I disagree with Dr. Eisenberg's opinion that the main destruction of the body took place in that pit based merely on the amounts of remains recovered from the pit compared to the small fragments found elsewhere in two locations, one being a burn barrel from behind Barb Janda's residence and the other, a burn site in the Manitowoc County gravel pit."

Even more noteworthy, "the reported lack of anatomical continuity of the human bones recovered from Steven Avery's burn pit indicates that Teresa Halbach's body was not burned there. Therefore, it is my opinion that someone transferred Teresa Halbach's bones to Steven Avery's burn pit."

DeHaan said the recovery of the victim's bones inside Bobby Dassey's burn barrel ties everything together.

"The finding of human bone fragments with similar degrees of fire damage in numerous other areas including burn barrels on site is also consistent with the dumping of burned remains into the pit, with some rolling away.

"It should be noted that there were numerous steel vessels on the salvage yard and surrounding properties that could have been used to burn a human body. These were not examined. The wood-fueled boiler and smelter were examined … and no residues were detected there."

But now for the true test: was DeHaan, a nationally recognized fire expert, willing to put his professional reputation on the line and go against the conventional wisdom, to speak out against the Wisconsin police and prosecution team that assembled a successful jury verdict against Avery based on their speculation Avery's open backyard burn pit was the scene of the dismemberment?

"The State represented to the jury that Ms. Halbach's body was burned in an open air burn pit behind Steven Avery's garage from around 7 p.m. to 11 p.m. on October 31, 2005, a period of only four hours. Based upon my review of the descriptions and photographs of the bone fragments analyzed by Dr. Eisenberg, the State's theory is not supported by the physical evidence … burning a body in an open-air burn pit takes six to hour eight hours to accomplish thermal destruction to the degree I observed in Dr. Eisenberg's reports and photos. It is my opinion that the burned bones found in Steven Avery's burn pit could not have been burned to the degree I observed after four hours of burning in an open-air pit like the one behind Steven Avery's garage."

Moreover, DeHaan adds, "the State's theory was also incorrect in its assertion that the burned vehicle bench seat was used to fuel the burning of Ms. Halbach's body. The burned remains of the bench seat were not found in the burn pit, but near it. Its involvement as an external fuel to aid the combustion of a body in a burn pit is speculative and unsupported by any documents I have reviewed.

"The State represented to the jury that the bones were fused with the metal belts in a manner that suggested that the tires from which the steel belts came were burned with the body in Mr. Avery's burn pit. Based upon my review of photographs taken on November 8, 2005, and November 10, 2005, on the occasion of the second excavation of Steven Avery's burn pit, the bone fragments appear to simply be mixed among the metal belts."

DeHaan, president of Fire-Ex Forensics Inc., in Vallejo, California, has expert knowledge of steel-belted car tires involved in fires with human bodies.

"During fire exposure, the steel multi-strand wires degrade, break, and fray to form bristles that readily trap any material coming into contact with them, during or after the fire. Small calcined bone fragments are especially easy to trap. This has been observed in test fires where the fires were under or alongside a burned body as well as on tap."

At Avery's trial, Wisconsin Special Agent Tom Sturdivant noted how Avery's guard dog Bear was on a lead "sufficiently long to give him access to at least some of the burn pit. A quantity of the tire wires/belting was observed to be tangled in the dog's lead at one point ... Dragging the tire remains across the burned debris fragments after the fire would result in the accumulation of fragments in the wire.

The burn pit may have been used previously to dispose of tires so there was no evidence that the entrapment of the debris occurred during the fire that consumed the remains. From my review of these photographs and reports generated by law enforcement at the scene and Dr. Eisenberg in later examination, there is nothing to suggest that the tires were, in fact, burned with the human bones recovered in Steven Avery's burn pit in the manner described by the State," Dr. DeHaan concluded.

Would Avery's murder trial have turned out differently if Buting and Strang had hired a highly regarded fire expert? That's entirely possible. In fact, Buting and Strang had DeHaan on their mind, court files show. They contemplated hiring him, but they didn't carry through with it.

"I personally went through the files of Mr. Avery's trial defense counsel, Dean Strang and Jerry Buting, which they gave to our firm when we announced we were taking on Mr. Avery's case. As I went through the files, I noticed a folder marked 'John DeHaan.' This name stuck out to me because Ms. Zellner had consulted with Dr. John DeHaan, a forensic fire expert, in this case," said Lauren Hawthorne, a law clerk for Kathleen T. Zellner & Associates.[82]

"Inside the folder was the curriculum vitae of Dr. DeHaan. There were no other documents in this file folder. Dr. DeHaan did not testify at Mr. Avery's trial. I checked the curriculum vitae of Dr. DeHaan from the trial defense counsel's box against the curriculum vitae provided to our office from Dr. DeHaan in 2017. I determined that the curriculum vitae of Dr. DeHaan in the trial defense counsel's box belonged to the same Dr. DeHaan that Ms. Zellner consulted."

---

82. Affidavit Lauren Hawthorne May 4, 2017

If Avery incinerated Halbach's body in the outdoor burn pit directly behind Avery's garage, the entire building would have gone up in flames, Dr. DeHaan noted.

CHAPTER TWENTY-TWO

THE CRIME

The same Manitowoc sheriff's officials involved in Ricky Hochstetler's hit-and-run vehicular homicide in 1999 never came up with an obvious motive for pinning Avery with the *Auto Trader* photographer's homicide. But these cops knew, collectively, that Avery needed to pay, and pay hard, for his sins of bringing shame and embarrassment to their Manitowoc County Sheriff's Office.

"Because the State did not need to establish motive, it did not spend any time trying to figure out why Ms. Halbach was murdered," Zellner said. "Both Mr. Avery and Ms. Halbach are victims of a justice system whose success depends upon the integrity, competence, and devotion of judges, law enforcement, prosecutors, and defense attorneys.

"Both Ms. Halbach and Mr. Avery have yet to receive justice. Ms. Halbach has been all but forgotten in the rush to judgment to convict and maintain the conviction of Mr. Avery. Mr. Avery has not been forgotten but buried alive because those individuals who were supposed to save him from a second wrongful conviction failed."[83]

Before his prosecutorial career went down in flames and he moved far away from Wisconsin's Fox Valley area in shame, Kratz was able to spin a courtroom tale suggesting that Avery, after raping and killing Teresa with the help of sixteen-year-old Brendan, got behind the wheel of her Toyota RAV4 and then drove to the far back perimeter of the

---

83. Notice of Motion and Motion for Post-Conviction Relief, Kathleen T. Zellner, June 7, 2017

salvage yard, squatting down to remove the license plates, disconnect the battery cable, then place large pieces of wood and a hood from another wrecked automobile on the RAV4.

"Mr. Kratz's theory of Ms. Halbach's murder is one of the most preposterous tales ever spun in an American courtroom. If Mr. Kratz's theory were true, then Mr. Avery is a true idiot-savant," Zellner said.

"Mr. Kratz, in a barrage of plot errors, creates an incongruent tale in which Mr. Avery, the savant, without wearing gloves, manages to not leave a single fingerprint in Ms. Halbach's RAV4, while Mr. Avery, the idiot, deposits six drops of his blood on the front seats, by the ignition, and on the rear door jamb. Mr. Avery, the savant, trying to save the day, manages not to leave a single drop of blood on the RAV4 door handle, key, and lanyard, hood prop, gear shift, steering wheel, or battery cables."

A total of eight latent fingerprints were recovered by the Wisconsin State Crime Lab from the doors and windows of Teresa's RAV4. However, Wiegert and Fassbender, with input from Kratz, only wanted those fingerprints compared to a small number of potential suspects. They were let down when they learned that Avery's fingerprints were not a match. None of Avery's fingerprints were recovered from the victim's vehicle. What was the significance of the unidentified latent fingerprints? It heightened the possibility that someone other than Avery was involved in the murder or in moving Teresa's RAV4 to the edge of Avery's property on the night of Friday, November 4, 2005.

"To absolutely ensure that his DNA is linked to the vehicle, Mr. Avery, the idiot, locks the car and opens the hood latch so that his 'sweat DNA' will be found on the latch, just in case the jury is smart enough to figure out that his blood in the RAV4 was planted," Zellner said sarcastically.

"Mr. Avery, the savant, burned the body in his burn pit in world-record time of three to four hours to a point where 60 percent of the bones completely disappeared and all but two teeth evaporated. Mr. Avery, the idiot, picked out some of the larger bones and moved them to his sister's burn barrel and the Manitowoc gravel pit."

"As Albert Einstein once said, 'The difference between stupidity and genius is that genius has its limits.' One would never imagine being convicted on such an idiotic theory, but Mr. Avery was. To understand how this happened, one must examine the other side of the coin: the performance of Mr. Avery's trial defense counsel. The State relied upon the following items of forensic evidence that allegedly linked Mr. Avery to the crime: Mr. Avery's blood in the RAV4, Mr. Avery's DNA on the hood latch, the electronic components, camera, palm pilot, and cell phone in Mr. Avery's burn barrel, the bones and remnants of Ms. Halbach's clothing in Mr. Avery's burn pit, the Toyota key in Mr. Avery's bedroom with Mr. Avery's DNA, and Ms. Halbach's DNA on the damaged bullet found in Mr. Avery's garage."

Zellner also realized that Avery's trial lawyers could have been much better prepared for the trial than they were.

"The State convicted Mr. Avery on this ludicrous theory because trial defense counsel only had two experts to combat the State's 14 experts. One of the trial defense counsel's experts performed at a substandard level and the other was not as qualified as the State's expert. Trial defense counsel claimed evidence was planted but failed miserably in proving that assertion by lacking experts in bloodstain pattern analysis, DNA, ballistics, forensic fire, trace, forensic pathology, and police procedure and investigation. Additionally, trial defense counsel failed to conduct a thorough investigation of the victim's background, deleted cell phone calls, potential third party suspects, or to construct an accurate timeline of Ms. Halbach and Mr. Avery's activities on October 31, 2005," Zellner said.

In 2017, Zellner uncovered an egregious potential Brady violation committed by Kratz. It concerned the behavior of

Manitowoc County Sheriff's Detective Dennis Jacobs, who worked closely with Lenk.

Jacobs was instrumental in retrieving the voice-mail message from the house of George and Jolene Zipperer, the property on County Highway B that may have been where Teresa was headed at the time of her death.

The voice mail, however, no longer exists and, quite suspiciously, it was never furnished by Kratz to Buting and Strang for their review as part of the discovery process at the time of Avery's 2007 murder trial.

"Trial defense counsel, by not carefully reviewing the discovery and not having the appropriate experts, failed to realize ... Mr. Avery's groin swab had been substituted for the hood latch swab by law enforcement; the key discovered in Mr. Avery's bedroom was a sub-key and was planted by Lt. Lenk and Sgt. Colborn immediately before its discovery... Ms. Halbach's last appointment was at the Zipperer's, not the Avery's, and the CD of her voicemail left on the Zipperer's answering machine was concealed and or destroyed by the State to mislead the jury into believing Ms. Halbach's last stop was Mr. Avery's," Zellner said.

"Current post-conviction counsel has retained ten experts and two investigators who have developed strong evidence that undermines confidence in Mr. Avery's verdict."

***

And those suspicions point directly to Bobby Dassey and his violent and abusive stepfather, Scott Tadych. "Current post-conviction counsel is providing this court with new evidence which establishes that Ms. Halbach and her vehicle left the Avery property; that Bobby Dassey gave false testimony about Ms. Halbach and her vehicle not leaving the Avery property; that Bobby Dassey and Scott Tadych gave false testimony establishing each other's alibi; that the

Dassey computer contains images of Ms. Halbach, violent pornography and dead bodies of young females viewed by Bobby Dassey at relevant time periods before and after the murder of Ms. Halbach ..."[84]

The two men gave themselves alibis at the time of Teresa's disappearance because they had alibied one another.

During his interview with police, Bobby told the police he was driving along State Highway 147, a highway with a fifty-five m.p.h. speed limit, but he somehow remembered seeing Scott Tadych driving the opposite way.

But at the time of Bobby's first police interview with Dedering, Bobby only drew up blanks. He failed to offer up any details of this strange highway encounter which had supposedly occurred just five days earlier. For instance, Bobby could not say precisely when and where on the road he and Tadych saw each other. This raises the likelihood the story was concocted by Tadych.

"Bobby indicated that as he was traveling on State Highway 147 towards the property he hunts deer on, he did observe an individual known to him as Scott Tadych. Bobby indicated that Scott would be able to verify precisely what time he had seen Bobby."[85]

The work of Zellner's investigators, however, has turned up several questions about their possible involvement in the murder and dismemberment.

"At 2:41 p.m., Ms. Halbach forwarded a call from her cell phone to voicemail, indicating she was preoccupied or distracted by another matter. Her cell phone was deactivated after this point in time, leading to the reasonable inference

---

84. Defendant Steven Avery's Motion for Reconsideration Oct. 23, 2017

85. Interview of Bobby Dassey, November 5, 2005, Investigator John Dedering report

that she was assaulted and murdered at approximately 2:45 p.m.[86]

"Further evidentiary support for Ms. Halbach being assaulted and murdered at the cul-de-sac on Kuss Road is that the scent and cadaver dogs detected a suspected burial site immediately south of the Kuss Road cul-de-sac."

In 2007, Avery's lawyers made the decision to keep their client off the witness stand and not let him to testify in his own defense even though he always professed his innocence in the crime.

Steven Avery has always remains steadfast that he is innocent and had no involvement whatsoever in the kidnapping and killing of Teresa Halbach.

"On October 31, 2005, I remember that I called Ms. Halbach once before she got to the Avery property," Avery said. "I called a second time at 2:35 p.m., but hung up immediately because I saw her at the van, photographing it. I have had the opportunity to review my phone records to refresh my memory. Based upon my recent review of my phone records, I know that Ms. Halbach began photographing Barb's van at 2:35 p.m.

---

86. Kathleen Zellner Motion for Reconsideration, October 23, 2017

"It did not take Ms. Halbach longer than a minute to complete the shooting of Barb's van. When I saw her drive up and park, I was looking out my front window. When I went outside to pay Ms. Halbach, I noticed that Bobby's Blazer was parked in a space between my sister's trailer and garage. By the time I got to my sister's van, Ms. Halbach had already finished taking the picture of the van. I handed her $40 for the listing and she walked to her vehicle and got in. She asked if I needed a receipt and I told her that I didn't. She handed me an *Auto Trader* magazine and I thanked her."

Avery said he returned to his trailer and put the magazine down on his computer "and walked back outside to go and visit my nephew Bobby. I walked to the middle of my driveway and saw Ms. Halbach's vehicle turning left on Highway 147, headed west," Avery said. "I looked to my right and noticed that Bobby's Blazer was gone. Bobby did not leave before Ms. Halbach because I observed his Blazer parked by Barb's residence when I was outside with Ms. Halbach. If Bobby left a few seconds behind Ms. Halbach, I would have seen his Blazer when I saw Ms. Halbach's vehicle leaving the property.

"I believe that Bobby left about left thirty seconds after Ms. Halbach because I could not see his vehicle. If he left thirty seconds after Ms. Halbach, he would have been near the intersection of the gravel drive, which leads to my and Barb's trailers, and Avery Road. It was not possible to see Bobby's Blazer at that location because there was a dip and a bend in the gravel drive as it approached Avery Road and there were buildings that blocked my view. If Bobby had left thirty seconds after Ms. Halbach, his Blazer would have been in a position where I would not have been able to see it."[87]

---

87. Steven Avery supplemental affidavit, November 14, 2017

These days, Avery's lawyer has also gained access to Bobby's cell phone records from around the time of the crime.

"Bobby stated that he would hunt on the property behind Tadych's house at 12764 State Highway 147 which was east of the Salvage Yard. At 3:02 p.m. on October 31, 2005, Bobby hit off Tower 363X, 5.47 miles west of the Dassey residence. Bobby's hunting spot was only 1.5 miles from Tower 370X. If Bobby was hunting where he claimed to be hunting east of the Avery property, there would be no reason that his call at 3:02 p.m. would have bounced off of Tower 363X, west of the Avery property, instead of 370X," Zellner said.[88]

Back in 2007, Kratz duped people into thinking that Brendan Dassey's blue jeans had been bleached as part of a conniving plot by Avery and Brendan to literally clean every single droplet and speck of blood from Avery's garage. But this was a way for Kratz to divert attention away from the behavior of his two deeply troubled witnesses who he needed to help make his case, Bobby and Tadych.

On March 2, 2006, Lisa Novachek, an employee at the Wisconsin Aluminum Foundry, told police "that on the date of Teresa Halbach's homicide, Scott Tadych did not show up for work. She said she did hear him say that he was going to see his mother in the hospital. Lisa said around the time of Steven Avery's arrest, another girl that works with her, by the name of Chris Graff, had taken a phone call from a hysterical young teenage kid asking for Scott Tadych. Scott was paged, took the phone call and left shortly after that. Scott Tadych's foreman, Keith Schaefer, informed Lisa that he was a nervous wreck when he left."

According to fellow Wisconsin Foundry workers, "he had made a comment that there was some blood on one of

---

88. Motion to Supplement Previously Filed Motion for Post-Conviction Relief, July 6,2018

the boy's clothes and that it had gotten mixed up with his laundry."[89]

The identity of the hysterical teenager who called Tadych at the Wisconsin Aluminum Foundry was never pursued by the police perhaps because they realized it may expose their arrest of Avery as a sham.

One thing is clear. The caller would not have been sixteen-year-old Brendan. He and Tadych didn't even associate with one another. The idea of Brendan having Tadych's phone number and then calling for him at work is preposterous.

Older brother Bobby, on the other hand, had a close relationship with Tadych.

Back in 2005, law enforcement from Manitowoc and Calumet Counties agreed that they would not attempt to obtain a search warrant to obtain any DNA specimens from Scott Tadych in connection with Teresa's disappearance.

A decision was also made not to compare Tadych's fingerprints with any of the fingerprints left on Teresa's RAV4, after the damaged vehicle turned up at Avery's property.

In 2018, Zellner laid out for Wisconsin's judicial system "the evidence supporting that Bobby was a viable third-party suspect and had a realistic ability to engineer the crime."

She also reminded the court that, "Mr. Avery does not have to prove that Bobby committed the crime as long as his theory is based on evidence beyond a possible ground of suspicion."

For the first time, she introduced for the court how Bobby had an unhealthy and dangerous obsession with Teresa.

Like many sadistic psychopathic killers, Bobby's unhealthy obsession with violent pornography was taking over his life. Court documents reveal he was spending more

89.   Interview of Lisa Novachek, March 2, 2006, by Investigator Wendy Baldwin

and more time on his personal computer when the rest of his family was not around.

Bobby did not have any girlfriends but he was falling into lust with young attractive women who bore the same general characteristics to Teresa.

Whenever Teresa showed up to do her *Auto Trader* assignments at Avery Salvage, Bobby seemed to know about her presence.

"Bobby had developed an obsession with Ms. Halbach and on a number of occasions, watched her from the window. The following day after her visits, Bobby commented about her, indicating that he was watching her. Because of Bobby's obsessive and compulsive preoccupation with viewing violent pornography of women who resembled Ms. Halbach, he developed violent sexual fantasies about her."[(90)]

Zellner suspects that Bobby Dassey tricked Teresa Halbach into stopping her vehicle along Kuss Road under the pretense of doing a hustle shot of his vehicle.

In March of 2006, Kratz held his infamous press conference advising minors not to listen to what he was about to reveal. Although Kratz sustained a murder conviction,

90. Defendant's Reply to the State's Response to Supplement Previously Filed Motion, August 3, 2018

most people agree the murder could not possibly have happened the way Kratz described the crime. The scientific evidence does not support his story.

After devoting more than two and a half years to reinvestigating the case, Zellner offered her own theory on how Teresa died to the Manitowoc County Circuit Court in her thirty-page motion for post-conviction relief filed August 3, 2018.

Here it is:

"Upon Ms. Halbach's arrival on October 31, 2005, Bobby watched her from his window, as he had in the past, but denied to the police that he was aware that she was coming to the property. As Ms. Halbach left the property, Bobby followed. Ms. Halbach was persuaded to pull over in the Kuss Road cul-de-sac area and open her rear cargo door to obtain her camera for a photograph. Advances were made, a struggle ensued, and Ms. Halbach was knocked to the ground and hit by a rock, causing blood spatter to land on the inside of the rear cargo door of her RAV4.

"Ms. Halbach was lifted into the rear of the RAV4 and driven to the area of the suspected burial site, assaulted, and then driven back to the Avery property. The hair bloodstain patterns on the inside panel of the rear cargo area of the RAV4 were created by Ms. Halbach's injured head as the car was driven back to the Avery Salvage Yard. The RAV4 was pulled into the Dassey garage and Ms. Halbach was shot twice in the head. The Dassey garage was never luminoled or checked for forensic evidence of any type; blood found between the Dassey garage and residence was never tested."

Another suspicious lead, pointing toward Tadych's possible involvement in Teresa's murder, went by the wayside by the Calumet County Sheriff's Office. On March 31, 2006, Jay Mathes, an employee at the Wisconsin Aluminum Foundry in Manitowoc, told investigator Wendy Baldwin "he has known Scott Tadych for approximately eight years ... He said he had been interested in buying a .22

for his kid and had told Scott about it because he was on a forklift and could find out if anyone had a gun for sale. Jay said about a week ago, Scott said he had a .22 Savage for sale that belonged to one of Barbara's kids … they agreed on a price of $100. Jay said it had a scope on it and figured it was a rifle and not a pistol.

"Scott approached him and told him he could go out to his truck and look at it. Jay told Scott he was not interested in looking at the gun that particular day and told him he was going to wait until the weekend."

Then, when Mathes inquired about the gun later, Tadych acted weird.

"Scott told him he never had the gun and the kid wanted to keep it now and it was not for sale. Jay described Scott as 'not being hooked up right' and has seen him fly off the handle at everyone at work.'"[91]

Zellner believes Teresa Halbach was attacked on Kuss Road and rendered unconscious with a heavy object after being struck in the head near the back of her RAV4.

***

91. Interview of Jay Mathes, Investigator Wendy Baldwin report, March 31, 2006

Truth be known, Tadych was a familiar name and face around law enforcement circles at the Manitowoc County Sheriff's Office and in Two Rivers, where he grew up. Without any doubt, his propensity toward violence was tenfold compared to Steven Avery. In fact, Tadych's temper makes Avery look like a little lamb. Yet Manitowoc County deputies who knew both men, Tadych and Avery, gave Tadych a free pass when it came to his version of events and his claims of an alibi, but they chose to disregard and not believe Avery in his repeated denials of guilt when it came to Teresa's disappearance.

On December 27, 1997, Tadych, then twenty-nine, had one of his many violent dustups, this one involving his mother, Patricia Tadych. Police who handled that call on Cottage Lane in Two Rivers Township included Manitowoc County Deputy Gregg Schetter, Sgt. James Lenk, and two other county deputies.

"The complainant … is informed by the reports of Deputy Schetter that upon speaking with Patricia Tadych … her son Scott Tadych came to the residence through the front door without knocking or receiving any type of permission. Patricia stated Scott informed her that he came to pick up his fishing equipment … Patricia stated Scott immediately noticed some of the fishing items had been moved and became angry about this. When Scott questioned her about this, Patricia stated she informed Scott that she needed to remove some of the fishing items due to the fact it was blocking a doorway and she needed to get through the door. Scott became very angry that some of his fishing equipment was missing and (began) yelling obscenities such as "Fucker," "Bitch," "A Cunt," and "A Loser" towards (his mother) Patricia …

"When she asked him to calm down, Scott told her he did not have to calm down … Scott came up to her and shoved his weight into the left side of her body which caused her to almost fall. Patricia stated she did have some trouble breathing and did have minor pain to her left side and shoulder area.[92]

"Patricia stated at this time she became extremely upset and continued to be scared that Scott would cause more injury to her ..."

At that point, she asked her other son, William, to come over.

"Get the Hell out of here!" William barked at his brother.

"I'm not leaving all my stuff," Scott Tadych snapped.

A physical altercation ensued.

William pushed his brother, causing Scott Tadych to fall into the pick-up truck parked in the driveway.

When Scott tried to get up, William pushed Scott again. The cowardly brother who had verbally demeaned and attacked his own mother now wanted to get out of Dodge.

"Scott then entered his vehicle and left the area. William stated Scott attempted to push back and fight back during the altercation but he did not injure William in any way."

For that offense, Scott Tadych was charged by Manitowoc County in January 1998 with unlawfully entering the dwelling of another without their consent.

Four years prior, on July 17, 1994, Tadych was charged with unlawfully entering the dwelling of another without their consent and with unlawfully and intentionally causing bodily harm to another. The Two Rivers Police Department criminal complaint states that Tadych struck and injured Martin LeClair.

A Two Rivers Police officer was summoned to the residence of Constance Welnetz on Jackson Street at 3:05 a.m. She told police that "at approximately 3 a.m. she was asleep with Martin LeClair when she heard a hard knock on their bedroom window. Constance stated she believed it was Scott Tadych as he had done this in the past."

---

92. State of Wisconsin vs. Scott Tadych, criminal complaint filed January 12, 1998

Later, she heard another loud knock. It was at the back door.

"Constance stated that Martin decided to go outside to speak with Scott to tell him to stop harassing her. Constance stated she told Martin not to go outside and she was going to call the police. Constance stated she heard some banging and shouting outside and as she was trying to see she lost the connection with the police. Constance stated at this time Scott walked into her residence without her permission and stated, "You will die for this, bitch."[93]

Constance ran outside. She found Martin LeClair laying in the driveway. He had endured a savage beating.

"He was covered in blood and had a cut on his head. Officer Mark Scheld spoke with Martin LeClair who stated at approximately 3:15 a.m. someone was pounding on the bedroom window and then knocking on the door and they believed it was Scott Tadych. Martin stated he got dressed and went outside to confront Scott. Martin stated they began to argue and were pushing each other and Scott swung at Martin and struck him on the left side of the face with a closed fist and Scott struck him with an unidentified object in his head and he believes he was unconscious for a brief time, but he can't remember until he was in the house and the police were there. At no time did he give anyone permission to strike him or cause him injury."

Scott Tadych's rage and his threats of violence did not slow down as he grew older. In January 2001, four years before Teresa vanished, he was the respondent of a restraining order, filed at the Manitowoc County Courthouse. The document reflects that on January 4, 2001, Tadych "called me at work seven times within a twenty-five-minute period. Threatened to 'kick my ass' and turn me over to

---

93. State of Wisconsin versus Scott Tadych, criminal complaint filed August 9, 1994

social services and just plain make my life miserable. Called me a 'Fucking Cunt Bitch.'"

Tadych had summoned a friend named Scotty to call the woman "and ask when I was going to pay him the $42 that I owed him. I told Scotty to stop calling me and not to follow in Scott Tadych's footsteps ... December 30, 2000, Scott Tadych started calling my house at 10:10 a.m. He called five times within a twenty minute period. I kept hanging up on him."[94]

The previous day, December 30, 2000, "I was getting ready to go out and at about 7 p.m. my phone rang. I answered it. It was Scott again. At that time, someone knocked on my back door. Scott asked what I was doing. I said answering the door stop calling here and hung up. I opened the back door. It was Scott and he pushed his way into my house. I told him to leave, he would not and started screaming and yelling and moving about my house, calling me a "Cunt, Slut, Bitch." Finally, I picked up (the) phone and said if he didn't leave, I would call police. He left slamming my back door knocking off the wreath. I then witnessed and heard him beating on my vehicle and saw him try all the doors to get into the vehicle. Then he spit on my vehicle."

Terrified, the woman sneaked over to the gas station, thinking this was a safe place to hide out.

"Scott followed me there and kept driving by all the while I was in Kwik Trip. When I was done, I went to leave. I backed out of the parking space and Scott blocked me from leaving for about two minutes. After he moved, I went directly to Two Rivers Police Department to report what Scott had been doing."

Even while the woman was giving her statement to the police, Tadych continued to call her. "After I was done with police, I went out. Scott started calling my cell phone from

---

94. Restraining order of Constance A. Welnetz versus Scott Tadych, dated January 4, 2001

a number belonging to Joanne LaRose. I answered and Scott said that if I didn't talk to him and give him another chance, he would ruin my life because I was a worthless piece (of) shit and he would hurt me. I hung up ..."

On June 24, 2002, Tadych was charged with causing a disturbance with Constance Welnetz. That May 14, a Two Rivers officer was dispatched to the Tadych house for a disorderly incident. The victim told police she had "just gotten into a verbal and physical altercation with her ex-boyfriend, Scott Tadych ... she tried to kick Tadych out of her residence because he yelled at her son, Ryan, for getting up late for school. According to Welnetz, Tadych then threatened to make their lives a living hell.

"She further stated that Tadych had shoved her up against the wall and struggled with her to take the phone away."[95]

The woman got her son and daughter out of the house and drove them to school. "Welnetz further stated that Tadych returned to the residence and was threatening to kill her and himself. According to Welnetz, Tadych took her keys and threw his watch and keys at her. When Welnetz called 911, Tadych left the residence."

When Two Rivers Police responded, they saw the woman's wrist was cut and a bathroom door yanked off the hinge.

"Welnetz stated that it was the wrist that Tadych was struggling to get the phone from. She also stated that she was punched twice by Tadych in the right shoulder and that he had used a closed fist."

According to court records, here's a summary of Tadych's criminal history in Manitowoc County prior to the disappearance and murder of Teresa:

November 1994: Guilty of battery, thirty days jail time, probation for one year.

---

95. State of Wisconsin versus Scott Tadych, criminal complaint, filed June 24, 2002

July 1997: Physical abuse of a child was downgraded to battery. Probation for eighteen months and sixty days jail. Charges of disorderly conduct and criminal damage to property got dismissed under the plea.

December 1997: Criminal trespass to a building, sentence involved a fine. A disorderly conduct charge was dropped under the plea.

July 2002: Disorderly conduct. Sentence withheld. Tadych got put on probation through the Department of Corrections for eighteen months. He needed to continue with counseling and take his prescribed medications, perform community service, maintain a full-time job, and pay court fines including a domestic violence surcharge. On February 15, 2004, Tadych was discharged from his probation.

Here's what Zellner has to say about Tadych and her contention that he is a suspected accomplice in the dismemberment and disposal of Teresa's remains.

"We have received several tips about Tadych being very careful not to leave anything with his DNA on it so that someone could retrieve it," Zellner told the author. "He refused to give us blood for a DNA methylation experiment. Tadych's reluctance to provide his DNA has only increased our suspicion of him. Mr. Avery's complete willingness to have further testing performed has solidified my view that he is 100 percent innocent."

But not everyone is rooting for Zellner to succeed.

There remain a number of fierce loyalists, mainly people whose family members, relatives, and dear friends either work in Wisconsin law enforcement or had a role in bringing murder charges against Avery. Along with several high-ranking members of Wisconsin's political government, people including Wisconsin Governor Scott Walker and his right-hand man, Attorney General Brad Schimel, who once played in a band with former Manitowoc County special prosecutor Ken Kratz, they have doubled down and put forth a relentless quest to make sure Avery stays a condemned and convicted murderer, just as they have done with Brendan Dassey, who most people are sure is innocent.

"I couldn't care less about the opinions of those who think I am trying to free a murderer," Zellner told the author. "All of the individuals I have exonerated were believed to be guilty until they walked out of the prison gates. I have not read a single article, social media post, or book from a 'guilter' that is not riddled with factual inaccuracies, legal misperceptions, or profound ignorance.

"The Achilles heel of this group is their leader, a discredited and disgraced prosecutor whose unethical behavior has exceeded anything my legal experts have encountered in any other post-conviction case in the country."

CHAPTER TWENTY-THREE

KEN KRATZ

"That same 'ugly picture' depicted in Kratz's offensive sexual misconduct with women appears in Kratz's solicitation of Avery. Kratz acted out of his own self-interest, in an utterly unethical way, abused his professional office, and engaged in conduct prejudicial to be the administration of justice."
– Bennett L. Gershman, state of New York, County of Westchester, sworn affidavit of May 10, 2017.

In the legal profession, prosecutors generally abide by the rules of professional conduct inside the courtroom and surrounding the rights of the accused. But every so often an oily person can infiltrate the criminal justice system in a way that does great harm to America's confidence in their public officials who take an oath to uphold the Constitution and protect the civil liberties and rights of the accused.

Every once in a blue moon, someone like Ken Kratz comes around and is able to play the system to his own advantage, because he's confident nobody else will dare challenge him.

Luckily for everyone, the voting public, police officers, and criminal defense lawyers, there are checks and balances in the legal system. That's why, in all likelihood, the same man responsible for obtaining successful murder convictions against Avery and Brendan Dassey, despite presenting two completely different scenarios in their trials of how Teresa's murder happened, will likely be the eventual fall guy, the poster child for the Avery murder case's implosion, when that day comes.

For every Ken Kratz who poisons the criminal justice system and brings shame and embarrassment to other hardworking, noble and conscientious criminal prosecutors, defense lawyers, and judges, there is someone on the opposite spectrum, someone with a sterling reputation such as Bennett L. Gershman, a highly distinguished state of New York lawyer whose credentials are a thousand times stronger than those of Kratz.

New York law professor Bennett Gershman is one of the country's leading experts on the topic of prosecutorial misconduct.

Gershman worked from 1966 to 1972 as an Assistant New York County District Attorney handling homicides, rackets, appeals, and major felonies. "I presented hundreds of cases to grand juries and tried numerous felony cases to verdict."

From 1972 to 1976, Gershman was an Assistant Attorney General in the New York State Special Prosecutor's Office that was charged with investigating official and political corruption in New York City.

"I was chief of the appeals bureau and the Bronx Anti-Corruption Bureau where I investigated cases, presented cases to special grand juries, and prosecuted many public officials including judges, prosecutors, attorneys, police officers and other public officials charged with corrupt, fraudulent, and dishonest conduct."[96]

These days, Gershman serves as a tenured professor of law at the Elizabeth Haub School of Law at Pace University in New York. He has taught there since 1976. He teaches classes on criminal law, criminal procedure, constitutional law, trial practice, and professional ethics.

"During my academic career I have served as a defense attorney representing many persons charged with serious felonies including murder, rape, organized crime, and drug cases," Gershman said. "I have testified as an expert witness in judicial proceedings and before the United States Congress, the New York State Legislature, and various professional and fact-finding commissions."

Gershman also provided a legal opinion on January 6, 2017, for the nomination of Alabama Senator Jeff Sessions for Attorney General of the United States.

Gershman has written a treatise on the ethical duties of prosecutors called *Prosecutorial Misconduct*, 2nd edition published by Thomson-West, and a treatise on the criminal trial called *Criminal Trial Error and Misconduct*, that delves into errors and misconduct involving a judge, prosecutor, defense attorney, and jury, and what can be done to challenge the misconduct after the fact.

"I often lecture to judges, prosecutors, bar associations, and other professional and civic groups," Gershman said.

One lawyer who never attended one of Gershman's lectures is Ken Kratz.

"For a prosecutor, the press conference is the most powerful forum in which to communicate with the public," Gershman said. "A press conference gives the prosecutor the

---

96. May 10, 2017 affidavit of New York attorney Bennett Gershman

opportunity to express in a dramatic way the results of an investigation, the crimes being charged, and the involvement of the persons accused of committing those crimes. Because there is a risk that the press conference can prejudice the right of an accused to a fair trial, ethics rules strictly circumscribe what a prosecutor can say at a press conference."

According to Gershman, Kratz's back-to-back press conferences held on March 1 and 2, 2006 "constituted professional misconduct. Kratz, an experienced prosecutor, knew that a prosecutor is not allowed to disparage the character and reputation of the accused, disclose the existence of a confession or other physical evidence, discuss any information that is likely to be inadmissible in evidence … and express an opinion on a defendant's guilt.

"Kratz knew that his statements would make it virtually impossible for anyone watching his press conference to keep an open mind about the case and the guilt of the defendants. Kratz knew what he had accomplished."

At the first news conference event, Kratz declared that law enforcement "now has a definitive set of answers as to what happened to Teresa Halbach" and "we know exactly what to look for and where to look for it." The next day, March 2, Kratz claimed, "we have now determined what occurred sometime between 3:45 p.m. and 10 or 11 p.m. on the 31st of October."

But why would someone in Kratz's position step over the line and commit prosecutorial misconduct, as Gershman outlines? For starters, Kratz would have known he was invincible at the time. In other words, there were no higher powers and authority to call him out and hold him accountable. Therefore, there was no misconduct except in the minds of the disenfranchised.

"More than any other government official, a prosecutor is viewed by the public with esteem and trust," Gershman said. "The public looks to the prosecutor as the official most responsible for vindicating the rule of law and punishing wrongdoers. Given Kratz's prestige and prominence as the special prosecutor by the governor to lead the investigation, Kratz's assertions that law enforcement had 'solved' the case would almost certainly be greeted by the public with both relief that the perpetrators had been apprehended and an outcry to punish them."

During the March 2 press conference, Kratz suggested Avery shackled, raped, tortured, and butchered Teresa to death. "Kratz knew at the time of his March 2 press conference that every statement he made accusing Avery of the horrific acts against Teresa Halbach ... was based exclusively on the uncorroborated confession of 16-year-old Brendan Dassey, which has recently been found by a federal court to have been coerced by police," Gershman said.

"Kratz knew that Dassey was of borderline intelligence, attended special education classes, and was known as a mild-mannered, introverted young man who was never before in trouble with the law ... Dassey's confession presented a narrative that was totally different than the version Kratz used in filing the original murder charges against Avery, and Dassey's confession was legally inadmissible against Avery for constitutional and statutory reasons. In short, Kratz had no evidence and therefore no legal basis to support the new charges of sexual assault and torture against Avery contained in the amended complaint and announced at the press conference."

Deep down, Kratz also knew something the general public did not know. And it was something he very much did not want people and the gullible lapdog members of the Wisconsin press to report.

Here's what it was:

"Kratz knew that a four-month police investigation that had conducted at least eight separate searches of Avery's trailer, garage, and every part of the property had yielded no forensic or physical evidence to corroborate Dassey's confession," Gershman said. "A prosecutor engages in professional misconduct when he makes unwarranted claims and brings unwarranted criminal charges.

Gershman determined that Ken Kratz's pretrial press conferences crossed the lines of decency and violated Avery's right to a fair and impair jury trial in America's judicial system.

"Moreover, in bringing charges that are not legally and factually sustainable, Kratz engaged in professional misconduct for another reason. Prosecutors are commanded 'not to prosecute a charge that the prosecutor knows is not supported by probable cause.' Kratz knew that he lacked sufficient evidence to charge Avery with the acts described in Dassey's confession. Dassey's confession, as Kratz surely knew, was inadmissible against Avery under the Sixth Amendment to the U.S. Constitution. Dassey's confession was also inadmissible against Avery because it violated a fundamental rule of evidence barring use of statements that are hearsay."

But what was Kratz's motivation in holding a press conference making inflammatory assertions against Avery knowing what he was saying was not true?

"He lacked probable cause, indeed, any factual basis whatsoever, to file his amended complaint charging Avery with the additional crimes of sexual assault and torture and then publicly announced those new charges to the world. In my opinion, Kratz brought these new charges against Avery in bad faith. He knew that he would not be able to present these facts against Avery to a jury, as demonstrated by his decision to drop the sexual assault and kidnapping charges on February 2, 2007. He disclosed these facts publicly knowing that they would be heard by prospective jurors and used to prejudice Avery ... By charging without a proper factual basis, and then representing in official court documents and in his public statements that those charges were validly brought, Kratz engaged in fraudulent, dishonest, deceitful, and misleading conduct."

In fact, Kratz's behavior in the case was so far over the top that he "thereby violated the 'attorney's oath' by advancing facts prejudicial to the reputation of a party without any legitimate reason by law or justice to do so," Gershman's affidavit notes.

"It is one thing for a codefendant like Dassey to make allegations that implicate himself and others. It is a far different thing for a prosecutor not only to repeat those statements publicly but also to endorse them as the truth, particularly when there is no factual basis to confirm their validity. All of Kratz's references to Avery's alleged heinous acts were gratuitous, without any legitimate basis in fact or law, without any legitimate law enforcement reason, and destroyed Avery's character, his ability to receive a fair trial, and his Constitutional right to the presumption of innocence. Collectively, Kratz's statements were offensive to the fair and proper administration of justice and the integrity of our system of justice and demonstrated Kratz's unfitness as a prosecutor."

Kratz's egregious behavior ensured Avery's life was ruined and he became a pariah in his community, just as Kratz successfully portrayed Avery during his term representing the voters of Calumet County, who kept electing and re-electing Kratz, time and time again as their arbiter of justice.

"Although the prosecutor is allowed to prosecute with earnestness and vigor and 'may strike hard blows' he is not at liberty to strike foul ones," Gershman said. "Constitutional and ethical rules impose a special obligation on prosecutors to serve and vindicate the truth and administer justice. Thus, a prosecutor violates due process and his ethical duty to serve the truth when he presents inconsistent and irreconcilable theories at two different trials against two different defendants. Such conduct is inherently unfair, disserves the truth, and renders any resulting conviction unreliable."

Many people familiar with the plight of Avery and his nephew are totally oblivious to the fact that after Kratz obtained a murder conviction against Avery, Kratz went on to convict Brendan Dassey based on a totally different set of allegations and theories as far as Teresa's murder was concerned. Something crazy and ridiculous like this only happens in Manitowoc County, Wisconsin.

According to Gershman, here were some of the many examples showing how Kratz strayed outside the boundaries of professionalism and credulity:

From Avery's trial: "All of the evidence points to one person. That's the one person being responsible. I'm going to argue at the conclusion of this case who that one person is. I bet you can guess who I'm going to suggest was responsible."

From Dassey's trial: "Kratz claimed that Brendan Dassey killed Teresa Halbach, or at least participated in her killing with Avery. Kratz claimed that she was killed by Avery stabbing her in the stomach, Dassey slitting her throat, Avery manually strangling her and then incidentally adding a gunshot. He argued she was killed in Avery's trailer, not his garage."

But at Avery's trial: "He argued no blood was found in the trailer. But since Teresa wasn't killed in the trailer, there shouldn't be. She was not killed in the trailer. Where was Teresa killed? This is an easy answer or at least it is an answer that is directed by all the physical evidence in this case. She was killed in Steven Avery's garage."

At Avery's trial, Kratz alerted the jury "we will actually be arguing to you that Mr. Avery handled, handled that weapon in his hands when Ms. Halbach was killed. Teresa's death was caused by two gunshot wounds to the head. Teresa's future aspirations were snuffed out by one act and by one act from one person."

But nobody in Wisconsin's judicial system, notably the Manitowoc County presiding judge Jerome Fox for Dassey's trial, called out Kratz's antics as being inappropriate. Kratz's ability to offer completely different theories against codefendants for the same murder drew a free pass from the judge.

"Kratz's inconsistent contentions at the Avery and Dassey trials violate due process as well as a prosecutor's duty to promote the truth and serve justice," Gershman said. "A prosecutor may not advance at separate trials theories of guilt which cannot be reconciled factually. Kratz could not in good faith argue at Avery's trial that Avery was the only killer and then argue at Dassey's trial that Avery along with Dassey killed Teresa Halbach. Kratz could not in good faith argue at Avery's trial that Halbach's death was caused by gunshot wounds and then argue at Dassey's trial that her death was caused by stab wounds to her stomach and throat and manual strangulation as well as gunshots.

"Kratz could not in good faith argue in Avery's trial that Halbach was killed in the garage and then argue in Dassey's trial that she was killed in Avery's trailer. Kratz's theories … negate one another. His claims are inconsistent and irreconcilable. Such flip-flopping conduct by a prosecutor is inherently unfair, legally and ethically, and undermines the very concept of justice and the duty of a prosecutor to serve truth. A prosecutor cannot engage in such gamesmanship, such conduct destroys confidence in the integrity of the system of justice and the constitutional and ethical precept that the prosecutor's goal is to serve justice rather than winning convictions."

But since Kratz was not a man of ethics or integrity, he also had no shame in writing a book intended to sabotage Avery's long-term prospects of ever getting justice and a new trial.

Part of the information that Kratz contained in his 2017 book, *The Case Against Steven Avery and What Making a Murderer Gets Wrong*, came from information that Avery's trial judge, Patrick Willis, had sealed and therefore was not part of the court record at the time of Avery's trial.

"Kratz's book and media appearances describe in vivid detail how he claims Avery sexually assaulted his ex-wife, his former girlfriend, his niece, and his babysitter, his horrific torture of a cat, and a variety of other violent criminal acts," Gershman said. "Indeed, these allegations parallel the inflammatory allegations Kratz made against Avery in his sealed motion to Judge Willis.

"To be sure, the First Amendment protects Kratz's freedom to publish and talk about his book. But as an attorney, and former lead prosecutor in the Avery and Dassey cases, Kratz's free speech rights are constrained by ethical rules … although Judge Willis unsealed the motion after Avery was convicted, the publishing of this information was unnecessary and would certainly be prejudicial to future jurors if Avery was successful in seeking a new trial. Kratz's book is an inaccurate and inflammatory attack on the popular Netflix series, *Making a Murderer*."

From Gershman's perspective, "there appears to be no legitimate reason for Kratz to disseminate this inflammatory information.

"Although the Avery and Dassey cases have attracted widespread interest, and were the subject of a ten-part Netflix series *Making a Murderer*, Kratz was in a unique position that was different from all other journalists and commentators. Kratz was the lead prosecutor against Avery and Dassey. Kratz was privy to considerable confidential information that had not been officially revealed. Ethical standards specifically address the question of the extent to which a former prosecutor is allowed to reveal secret information obtained in confidence while investigating and prosecuting a criminal matter."

But even more appalling behavior by Kratz began in 2013, after he had already been forced to resign from office in shame and disgrace. By that point, he had retreated to far northwestern Wisconsin where he was struggling to make it in private practice as a criminal defense attorney, in Superior, Wisconsin.

Kratz's correspondence to Avery included outlandish requests pressuring Avery to add him to his prisoner list of visitors.

Kratz further badgers Avery in his correspondence of September 6, 2015: "Since I'm the person who probably knows more about your case than anyone else, I hoped that you would choose me to tell your story to. Unfortunately, you only want to continue your nonsense about being set up. That's too bad because you had one opportunity to finally tell all the details, but now that will never happen."[97]

Gershman maintains that in all of his years of practicing law and studying the ethics and misconduct of prosecutors, he has never once witnessed someone like Kratz.

"Kratz's conduct in approaching the man he vilified, brought unsubstantiated charges against, convicted of murder, and sent to prison for life without parole, in order to

---

97. Kratz's letters to Avery are mentioned in Bennett Gershman's May 10, 2017 affidavit

'tell his story' is unlike any conduct of any ex-prosecutor I have ever encountered," Gershman said.

"Kratz's conduct is offensive to the proper administration of justice. His intimidation and manipulation for his own selfish motive of the person he prosecuted impairs the dignity of the legal profession and the ethical responsibility of lawyers to abstain from overreaching, harassing, and manipulative conduct."

In Gershman's purview, Kratz's ploy to convince Avery into believing that Kratz would be inclined to write an honest book from Avery's perspective is another falsehood that erodes at the credibility of the judicial system.

"Kratz's solicitation of Avery is akin to a personal injury lawyer's solicitation of cases from recent accident victims. Dubbed 'ambulance chasing,' such conduct has seriously impaired the reputation of the Bar. Kratz's conduct in my opinion is even more nefarious. Kratz had a personal involvement with Avery, and sought to manipulate that connection under the guise of appearing to act on Avery's behalf to help him tell his 'honest' story so that the public would 'understand both sides.' But of course, Kratz's appeal for Avery's cooperation ostensibly for disinterested motives was a sham. Kratz wanted to write a book and get the person he prosecuted to help him. His solicitation was disingenuous and prejudicial to the administration of justice."

But, here's why things get even more interesting.

"There is an uncanny parallel between Kratz's solicitation of Avery as a private lawyer and Kratz's solicitation of vulnerable women when he was a prosecutor. In 2010, Kratz was investigated by the Wisconsin Division of Criminal Investigation for sending inappropriate text and email messages to women, including victims in active domestic abuse cases Kratz was then prosecuting. There were at least ten women who complained about Kratz's improper sexual overtures to them. The state investigation led the Wisconsin District Attorneys Association to call for Kratz's resignation, for Governor James Doyle to initiate removal proceedings against Kratz, and after Kratz involuntarily resigned, for the Office of Lawyer Regulation in 2011 to bring a disciplinary complaint against Kratz alleging several counts of professional misconduct."

Afterward, Gershman notes, Kratz was suspended from practicing law in Wisconsin for four months.

In one case where Kratz was prosecuting a parental rights termination case, Kratz became lustful toward the woman involved in the case, telling her "I won't cum in your mouth" and later informing her that he was leaving on a wild trip to Las Vegas where he could have "big-boobed women serve me drinks."

"Kratz commented in court to a social worker that the court reporter had 'big, beautiful breasts" and another time he contacted a young woman almost thirty years younger than he was, inquiring if "she was the kind of girl that likes secret contact with an older elected DA … the riskier the better."

"You may be the tall, young hot nymph, but I am the prize!" Kratz had texted her.

Indeed, Kratz, the three-time divorced Wisconsin lawyer, was in a league of his own. Time after time, women found him repulsive and did not want anything to do with him.

"Kratz tried to defend his appalling behavior towards the women by raising 'incredible' 'inconsistent' 'hyper-technical,' and 'puzzling' arguments," Gershman said. "His claim that he wanted to amicably resolve the disciplinary proceedings, according to the Wisconsin Supreme Court, 'borders on the intellectually insulting.' Kratz's insistence that his conduct resulted from addiction to drugs does not change the 'ugly picture by the record.'"

But, there was also something at play. There was a pattern developing.

"Interestingly, quite similar allegations in the disciplinary proceedings against Kratz are present in Kratz's solicitation of Avery. Thus, in the disciplinary proceeding Kratz was found to have acted with a 'selfish motive,' manipulated a 'vulnerable woman,' engaged in 'exploitative behavior,' engaged in 'harassing behavior,' showed a 'crass placement of his personal interests above those of his client,' and 'crossed the line separating the unprofessional conduct from the acutely offensive and harassing,'" Gershman pointed out.

However, there is no indication Kratz was pursuing Avery for sexual reasons, like the women who were domestic violence victims he tried to seduce.

"But as a matter of professional ethics, Kratz's conduct towards Avery was as intimidating, self-interested, and manipulative as it was to the women Kratz abused. Avery was in a hopeless position and an easy target for Kratz's solicitations. Kratz knew the prison authorities had objected to Avery speaking to Kratz and that Kratz's overtures might hurt Avery. Particularly disingenuous was Kratz's ploy to suggest falsely that Kratz was simply a disinterested person trying to assist Avery to tell his story - his 'honest' story - to the world, but knowing full well that he wanted Avery's story only if Avery told his story in a way that served Kratz's selfish interests in writing a book and promoting himself. Kratz exploited his former status as Avery's prosecutor 'who knows more about your case than anyone.' Kratz disparaged Avery's 'continued nonsense about being set up.' He intimidated Avery as he did with the women he abused, trying to convince Avery to talk to him by the veiled threat that it was 'too bad' that Avery refused to talk to him 'because you had one opportunity to finally tell all the details, but now that will never happen.'"

Gershman's curriculum vitae notes he has authored four books. He has also written about two dozen law review articles including writings on "Litigating Brady v. Maryland," "Reflections on Brady v. Maryland," "Prosecutorial Ethics and Victim Rights," "Witness Coaching By Prosecutors," and "The Prosecutor's Duty to Truth."

As for Kenneth R. Kratz, the Wisconsin Bar Association online directory indicates he graduated from Marquette University's Law School in 1985 and was admitted to practice law in Wisconsin on May 20, 1985. But as of November 2018, the Wisconsin Bar Association listed Kratz's law license as being suspended for three different reasons: dues, CLE: continuing legal education and for OLR Certification; the Office of Lawyer Regulation was an agency within the Wisconsin Supreme Court.

The website domain on file with the Wisconsin Bar Association for the Kratz Law Firm was also for sale.

CHAPTER TWENTY-FOUR

CREEPY KRATZ

"Dear Governor Jim Doyle, I just want to make you aware of some inappropriate questions that Ken Kratz had asked my seventeen-year-old daughter when we had an appointment with him in July 2010 ... My daughter had a relationship with (name blacked out) who we found out is a registered sex offender."
– September 21, 2010

The jury that convicted Avery of murder in 2007 was led to believe the Manitowoc County defendant was a sexual deviant monster. In reality, special prosecutor Ken Kratz, the man who convicted Avery was the real sexual monster in the courtroom, based on a 143-page investigative file compiled in 2010 by the Wisconsin Department of Justice DCI.

For background, Kratz became licensed to practice law in Wisconsin in 1985. He worked as an assistant district attorney in La Crosse before being appointed as the Calumet County District Attorney in 1992. He would remain in that position until his forced resignation under personally humiliating circumstances in October 2010.

When Kratz was in his fifties, he appeared to be sexually aroused by teenagers, the DCI reports show.

"On our meeting with Ken, he had asked my daughter … the following questions, keep in mind these are not word for word;

Who would usually take off your clothes before sex, referring to my daughter?

Do you know what ejaculate means?
Would he usually ejaculate in you or out?
About how long did the sex last?

"Then he proceeded to ask about other sex acts, oral sex and then he asked her those questions, mouth to penis, mouth to vagina, etc.

"At the time these questions were going on, I did not feel these were appropriate as she is a victim of a sex offender, and I thought it was the D.A.'s job to make this as painless as possible for the victim. My client advocate ... was in the room also and we discussed this after we left. She felt the same way I did about his questioning. This was before the preliminary hearing, and we don't even know if this will go to trial. Some of those questions I would have a hard time believing a defense attorney would even ask a victim."[98]

The parent informed the Wisconsin governor that she now has a good idea why Kratz asked her seventeen-year-old daughter such lurid questions.

"I felt he violated and further victimized my daughter by getting some sick enjoyment out of the answers she gave to his questions. I also felt he was no better than the guy he is trying to put behind bars as a repeat sex offender. I would hope you would remove him from office so that he will not be able to abuse his powers and further victimize anyone else. As my daughter is under the age of eighteen, I would appreciate it if you would not use my name in any press reports so as to protect her privacy."

***

Ken Kratz's recurring and alarming conduct predated Avery's arrest for Teresa's murder back in 2005, though

---

98. All accounts cited in this chapter are from the DCI report concerning complaints made against Calumet County District Attorney Ken Kratz

Kratz's misbehavior intensified after the Avery case because he wanted to portray himself as if a famous sex symbol.

If Kratz had worked as the local high school janitor or garbage truck driver, it's probably less likely that his constant creepy behavior would have been tolerated, but in a small Wisconsin town like Chilton, Kratz was somebody. As a result, this gave him a great cover to engage in behavior that was unethical and a blemish on the district attorney's office.

One woman, interviewed by the Wisconsin Department of Justice in 2010, told special agents how she "first met Kratz five years ago when she got in trouble for shoplifting. Kratz was the DA on her case and he charged it out. (She) said Kratz never did anything inappropriate to her at that time."

Then in 2009, Kratz called the woman on her cell phone.

The woman told investigators "she has no idea how Kratz had her phone number. Kratz told (her) that he and his wife were getting a divorce and he wanted to talk to her about things."

After that call, Kratz visited the vulnerable woman at her apartment.

"He told her that he knew everything about her, and if she did not listen to him, he could 'get her jammed up.' Kratz talked about how he was into bondage. He said he ties women up, they listen to him, and he is in control. She said he instructed her to give him a blow job and she did."

The woman was afraid. But she went ahead and performed the sex act upon the District Attorney of Calumet County.

"He had said that he knew everything about her and (she) did not know what that meant ... Kratz had such seniority over her and it was said she had not done anything in Calumet County other than the shoplifting five years prior. (She) did not know what Kratz meant. She did not want to take the chance."

The woman later told the Wisconsin DOJ that "the blow job happened on her couch and she was bent over Kratz. She said Kratz held her hands behind her back … (she) stated that Kratz was very strong."

The woman told the special agents "while Kratz was still at her apartment, she went to the bathroom and puked. After Kratz left, she puked her brains out and stayed in bed for about a week. (She) stated that she had been raped when she was 16 and said this feels a lot like it."

On the day of the sexual tryst, Kratz showed up wearing one of his finest gray suits. When he got to the woman's apartment, he also told her to close the blinds.

"Kratz talked about being submissive and being dominant. He said that the man was dominant and would tell the woman what to do and he asked if she would be willing to be submissive to him. (She) told Kratz she did not think she would be good at being submissive because she talks a lot. Kratz continued to tell (her) what he did with women and how he takes control. He said the women have to listen to him or he hits them. Kratz spoke about a room he has where he ties women up. Kratz called the room something specific but (she) did not recall what he called it."

Prior to driving over to receive the oral pleasure, "Kratz told her I know everything about you. I can make trouble for you … she stated that she was very ashamed of what she did. He's a pig. What he did was wrong.'"

Although the State's investigative files indicated Kratz forced the woman to perform a sex act upon him, the state of Wisconsin had no interest in making Kratz into a criminal. He was not about to be branded as a sexual criminal or a rapist.

"Kratz gave her an order to give him a blow job," the reports state. "She said he told her to ask his permission to give him a blow job, and she did. Kratz then put his hands behind (her) head … She had to unzip Kratz's pants. She said he gave her instructions and told her what to do the whole time … She said she had never known what the term 'crack whore' meant until then, but that is what she felt like."

On that occasion, Kratz also indulged himself in a plethora of alcoholic beverages, pounding down beer after beer before driving himself home.

"While Kratz was at her apartment (she) continued to get him more beers and he had four or five of them. (She) did not drink with Kratz … during the sex act, Kratz called her a bitch. He said 'that's how you do it, bitch.' She said he had all the power and all the control … After the sex act, Kratz stayed at the apartment and drank three more beers. He asked how (she) felt about being submissive and she said she could not do it. Kratz also talked about his wife and how she did not want to be with him anymore."

The woman told state investigators how "he had grabbed her boobs and pulled her hair. (She) said Kratz touched her breasts under her clothing and she was a fool to have let him in."

There was also something else the woman recalled. It involved money.

"When Kratz left her apartment that night, he left $75 on the kitchen counter. (She) did not see the money until after Kratz left. (She) believed the money was given to her for what she did. When (she) was not answering Kratz's phone calls, he asked if she wanted to give the money back to him. … Kratz became angry about the money, stating that it was a lot of money and wanting it back."

In the end, the woman donated the $75 to a local church.

In the following days, Kratz became a stalker.

"Kratz called her forty to fifty times after this incident, but she would not take his calls. She said he came to her apartment a couple of times, but she pretended she was not home."

***

Around the Appleton and Fox Valley area, Kratz regularly preyed upon a number of women, including women more than half his age.

One was Renee Braun, who spoke with the DCI in 2010. The two met through the website Craigslist, but she was reluctant to pursue his advances.

"Kratz questioned why she did not like older men, and he told Braun he had money. Braun told (DCI agents) that Kratz was her father's age and that was kind of creepy to Braun. Braun further stated that Kratz never told Braun he was married."

Braun reckoned they exchanged about ten text messages starting in 2009.

At the time, she was twenty-seven. In some of his texts, Kratz wrote, "I will treat you nice, you can be with an older man, we can be good friends, he texted 'Do you know who I am? I am Kenneth Kratz, the guy who prosecuted Steven Avery.' Braun says she was not impressed and determined that Kratz was weird.

"Braun stopped the contacts with Kratz before they ever met because Braun realized he was too old for her."

Another young woman also contacted the DCI in regards to Kratz.

Maria Ruskiewicz was from Marinette, Wisconsin, and a third-year law student at Oklahoma City University School of Law. Her first bad experience with Kratz happened in 2008, the year after the Avery trial. She was attempting to get a pardon for a previous drug conviction. Kratz and the judge provided her with letters in support of her pardon.

"DA Kratz wrote Ruskiewicz back, telling her that she should make an appointment with his office to meet with him. Ruskiewicz stated that the letters from DA Kratz were very professional."

Not realizing she was being manipulated, she eventually came to Chilton to meet Kratz in person.

"She recalled that he was not wearing a suit but was wearing a black shirt with a deck of cards on it and they talked about playing poker. DA Kratz and Ruskiewicz then talked about what advice he had to give her. As expected, Kratz steered the conversation toward his favorite topic.

"DA Kratz started asking her questions related to sex, posing different scenarios and asking what she thought of them. For example, he asked her what she thought about a boss and a secretary having sex or a babysitter and child having sex. He also asked what she thought about people of different ages having sex. Ruskiewicz stated that she thought DA Kratz's questions were weird, but she thought he was just trying to see if she was tough enough to be a prosecutor."

Being naïve, she accepted one of Kratz's professional business cards. It contained Kratz's secret cell phone number. She made the mistake of sending him a text, thanking him for making the time to meet with her.

She had inadvertently opened the door into her life for Kratz.

"Ruskiewicz stated that DA Kratz started texting her back about a week later. It was in one of these texts that he asked how she would please him between the sheets."

The young woman got her uncle involved and later wrote a letter informing Kratz he needed to keep their communications on a professional level. Kratz laid low for about three months, and then like a nasty prickly yard weed, he re-emerged.

"He sent her a text stating that now they had to meet in person. Ruskiewicz stated that this text was out of the blue … She compared the situation to a domestic abuser who has been threatening to beat their victim but then suddenly shows up at the victim's door. Ruskiewicz and DA Kratz never did meet again in person."

State investigators asked the Marinette woman whether "there was any type of coercion from Kratz that she should have sex with him in exchange for his support of her pardon. Ruskiewicz stated that DA Kratz never said anything like that but she felt it was implied because of the timing of his texts to her ... She said she thinks he is a dirt bag, and she believes there are plenty more victims out there."

The DOJ documents showed that: "Attorney Kratz has rationalized his poor behavior by confessing to various addictions: to Ambien, to Vicodin, to Xanax, and to sex, though he fails to point to either medical records or expert medical testimony that would explain the exact nature and severity of his conditions or how they may have affected his ability to conform his behavior to ethical rules. But regardless of how we view Attorney Kratz's behavior, as an involuntary byproduct of addiction, or as a willful blindness to professional standards, the ugly picture painted by the record remains the same. The recommended four-month suspension is deserved."

***

Ken Kratz might still be holding down office in Calumet County to this day if not for the bravery of Kaukauna resident Stephanie Van Groll, who had just turned twenty-five around the time she visited the Kaukauna Police Department to file a report, back on October 22, 2009.

"I met with Mr. Ken Kratz the District Attorney who is handling my ex's case," her police statement reads.

"I went to his office ... to decide what was going to be done with Shannon my ex after I left there. He sent me a text saying that it was nice talking to me and that I have such potential. I said thank you and thought that would be it ... since that text I've received at least 20 plus messages. I talked to one of my friends and they told me to do something about it so here I am. I'm afraid that if I don't do what he wants me to do, he will throw out my whole case and who knows what else."

The following are excerpts from some of Kratz's text messages to the young domestic violence victim whose ex-boyfriend had his criminal case pending in Kratz's office.

"I wish you weren't one of this office's clients. You'd be a cool person to know!"

"I hope you feel better soon. Do you need me to bring you some chicken soup?"

"No text yet today? I'm feeling ignored. Are you even up yet?"

"How about a margarita? That has some fruit juice in it!"

"Seriously I hope you feel better soon. Please keep in touch. It's maybe not the wisest thing I can do, but you are awfully sweet. Just don't tell anyone, ok?"

"Are you the kind of girl that likes secret contact with an older married elected DA ... the riskier the better? Or do you want to stop right know (sic) before any issues?"

"I need direction from you. Yes you are a risk taker and can keep your mouth shut and you think this is fun ... or you think a man twice your age is creepy so stop."

"Either way I think you are very nice. I am very smart, but know this is ALL up to you and really does depend how close to the edge you live!"

"Still wondering if I am worth it? Can I help you answer any questions?"

"Why would such a successful, respected attorney be acting like he's in 7th grade? Are you worried about me?"

"Are you serious? OK? That's it? Are you in a board meeting? You are beautiful and would make a great young partner someday. But I won't beg!"

"I'm serious. I'm the atty. I have the $350,000 house. I have the 6-figure career. You may be the tall, young, hot nymph, but I am the prize! Start convincing."

"Finally an opinion. I would not expect you to be the other woman. I would want you to be so hot and treat me so well that you'd be THE woman! R U that good?"

"You forgot to write me for the last time saying you could never give me enough attention to steal me away, and you are so modest that you wouldn't know how to!"

"And that you may look good at first glance, but women that are blonde, 6ft tall, legs and great bodies don't like to be shown off or to please their men!"

Two days earlier, VanGroll met with Kratz at his office to be interviewed about the ongoing prosecution of her ex-boyfriend for trying to choke her to death.

"VanGroll indicated that during the interview she confided in Kratz about the relationship she had with her boyfriend and the abuse her boyfriend bestowed upon her. VanGroll indicated that at the end of the interview, on October 20, she thought it was funny that Kratz asked her if she would mind if he dropped the charge from a felony to a misdemeanor. VanGroll then stated that she told Kratz that strangling someone was a felony in the state of Wisconsin."

About ten minutes later, came the first of a barrage of text messages thumbed out by Kratz. "The text messages continued over a period of the next two days. VanGroll indicated she felt vulnerable because she had just told Kratz the relationship that VanGroll was in, and she felt Kratz was taking advantage of that situation."

By October 30, 2009, the Wisconsin Department of Justice got involved in the case. The DCI's Peter Thelen reached out to an agent he knew had a close long-time professional relationship with Kratz.

It was Tom Fassbender.

"Peter Thelen had contact with Special Agent Thomas J. Fassbender who confirmed (redacted phone number listed in official police report) was a cellular telephone number used by Calumet County District Attorney Kenneth Kratz. Fassbender had prior contacts with Kratz at said number when making telephone contact with Kratz in an official capacity."

Now that the Wisconsin DOJ was involved, however, the criminal case that had been turned over to them was destined to disappear.

Three days after the conversation with Fassbender, the special agent in charge at the Appleton office got a call from Kratz, who is listed on the investigate reports as being "a person of interest."

"Peter Thelen received a telephone call from Calumet County District Attorney Kenneth Kratz regarding this case," reports from November 2, 2009, show. "He inquired as to whether there was still a criminal investigation going on regarding this and SAIC Thelen responded no, that the case was done as far as Special Agent in Charge Thelen was concerned."

Kratz wanted reassurance the case was closed, which is what he got.

"Mr. Kratz then offered to apologize to Stephanie if Special Agent in Charge Thelen were able to mediate this. Thelen told Kratz that he would pass this information along."

Then Kratz made a second request.

"Mr. Kratz mentioned that he would like to keep this out of the media, if possible. Thelen advised Mr. Kratz that the complaint originated from another agency and DCI was obligated to investigate, at which time Mr. Kratz said that he understood."

Two months later, Kratz was up to his old dirty tricks again.

***

Dawn M. King of Green Bay, forty-six, met Kratz through the Match.com dating site in January 2010. It was Kratz who pursued her, rather than the other way around.

"King stated that she had reservations about DA Kratz from the beginning of his contacts with her, starting with the name he used on his Match.com profile, which was 'Exboytoy1.' King stated that she did not know who DA Kratz was when he first started contacting her. She knew he was an attorney because that fact was written in his Match.com profile."

On January 23, 2000, she agreed to meet Kratz for dinner at the Black and Tan Grille in De Pere, which is a nice suburban community along the Fox River next to Green Bay. The Black and Tan was also an upscale restaurant.

"King said that DA Kratz talked about himself during their dinner. He talked about going to Las Vegas, poker, his wife, and his divorce. He also talked about cases he was working on."

During the dinner, a detective called Kratz and Kratz had no qualms about discussing the criminal case in front of her, even though she told him she understood if he needed to step away to take the call and talk in private.

"But he continued to talk in front of her. King gathered from the conversation that she heard that the detectives were searching some place at the time. DA Kratz and the detective were talking about looking for evidence and searching a car and the trunk of a car. The detective wanted to bring the person in for questioning, but DA Kratz told the detective to wait until they found more physical evidence ... After the dinner date, she searched the Internet for information and learned that there was a missing woman from Chilton. During dinner, DA Kratz told King that the detectives were at the boyfriend's house searching. DA Kratz made some reference to her about going to the crime scene with him and made a comment about her wearing heels. King said she did not want to be 'traipsing through a crime scene.'"

It turned out that the case involved a murder. A boyfriend was accused of killing his girlfriend and the crime scene apparently crossed county lines.

"King stated that DA Kratz drank a lot the night of their date. She said they had first met in the downstairs bar and had one drink there, and then they shared a bottle of wine with dinner. King stopped drinking after dinner, but DA Kratz continued to drink several more drinks in the bar after dinner while (we) listened to a live band there. King stated that DA Kratz was not worried about drinking and driving, and she felt he thought he was above the law. DA Kratz told King that he would not have a problem if he was stopped while driving home because he had friends."

The next day, the text messages started.

"They found a body," Kratz texted her.

"King said she thought it was weird and absolutely wrong that DA Kratz was telling her this information about his professional work. She said she was surprised and shocked that he would divulge such information being in the position that he was."

If that wasn't weird enough, Kratz informed her about the upcoming autopsy for the victim and invited her to accompany him to the morgue.

"He invited King to go along with him as long as she would wear heels and act as his girlfriend. King stated that she thought this was wrong on so many levels."

But the texts did not stop.

"Bored in court," Kratz kept messaging her.

In her letter she wrote to Governor James Doyle, King added, "If I didn't answer his texts immediately, he would become insecure and question why I hadn't responded and would attack me or my character. He would remind me of who he was, how he had prosecuted the biggest case around here and what a prize he was. After a few days of contact, I finally told him not to contact me anymore. He complied."

Other women who were victims of Kratz were downright terrified he might come back and harm them if their names were publicized by the Wisconsin DOJ. They agreed to be interviewed by police investigators only on the condition their identities remained a secret in any official criminal investigation files.

One such woman was victimized by Kratz in 1999, evidence that Kratz's creepy and dangerous behavior was going on long before he got involved in prosecuting Avery.

One woman was involved in a domestic dispute with her husband in 1999. The Confidential Informant suffered a black eye and a bump on her head from her abusive husband. Kratz was the prosecuting attorney on her husband's case.

"The (Confidential Informant) indicated that shortly after the meetings with Kratz, Kratz would email the CI with comments such as 'a girl like you wouldn't be attracted to a guy like me, bald and overweight.'"

The emails turned into phone calls initiated by Kratz.

"The CI indicated on one occasion Kratz came over to the CI's house, with the CI's approval, and that the CI and Kratz sat on the couch. The CI indicated that Kratz put his hand under the CI's skirt and he caressed the CI ... The CI also indicated that Kratz had not removed any of his clothing ... while the CI and Kratz were seated on the couch, Kratz's girlfriend or fiancée called and the CI learned that it was the girlfriend's or fiancée's birthday. The CI believes that Kratz forgot ... Once Kratz got off the phone with the girlfriend or fiancée, Kratz called a florist to have flowers sent to his girlfriend or fiancée ... the CI indicated that upon Kratz leaving the CI's residence, Kratz got stuck in the snow in the CI's driveway and had to be pulled out by a neighbor."

The woman also gained insight into Kratz's dark mind.

"Very early in the conversations or emails with Kratz, Kratz made it very clear that he liked women to be submissive ... Kratz would call the CI at work and the CI was not allowed to say anything, and that was part of the game. The CI indicated women weren't allowed to say anything or make any noise ... the CI just had to listen to his sexual scenarios on the phone ... Kratz had four or five sexual scenarios and that he would request the CI choose one of the scenarios that the CI would like done to the CI ... Kratz also offered to send the CI to Chicago to learn how to be submissive."

Kratz's contacts with this woman occurred while Kratz was in the midst of a full-blown criminal prosecution of the woman's husband for domestic abuse.

"Kratz also asked ... if the CI liked to be videotaped or if they could be watched by someone else. Kratz indicated this would only be for his private viewing ... Kratz indicated Kratz had a private room at his house and that no one went into the room except Kratz ... the CI was led to believe by Kratz that Kratz had other videotapes of himself or other females being involved in sexual activity."

The woman told Wisconsin special agents that her lawyer had told her upfront that Calumet County had a reputation for usually awarding custody of minor children to the father, not the mother.

"The CI reiterated that the only reason the CI agreed to engaging in the phone conversations and emails, along with one sexual contact with Kratz, was because Kratz was prosecuting the CI's husband and the CI was led to believe that Kratz could influence the decision over the custody of the CI's children."

About five months later, the woman had moved away when she got a phone call at work.

"The CI was surprised that Kratz had tracked the CI down ... Kratz asked if the CI was married or seeing someone ... Kratz indicated that he had relatives in the area where the CI was presently living."

The two special agents from the DIA who interviewed the woman made the following observations in their summations of her interview.

"On several occasions, the CI cried and indicated that the CI had been second guessing the CI's self for a long time regarding the CI not reporting the conduct of Kratz back when it happened ... The CI indicated that the only reason the CI came forward at this time was to let Van Groll know that Van Groll wasn't alone and that Kratz had conducted this type of behavior with other females."

***

In 1998 or early 1999, Menasha resident Connie Palm ran a personal ad in *The Appleton Post-Crescent* newspaper. She was in luck, bad luck. The male suitor who responded to her singles ad happened to be Kratz. During a handful of introductory phone calls, Kratz made it a point to make sure she knew she was conversing with the District Attorney of Calumet County himself.

"Palm and Kratz met for coffee at Burger King in Kaukauna in 1998 or early 1999. After having coffee, Kratz said he would show Palm where he worked, and they left Burger King together in Kratz's car."

But first Kratz wanted to take her by his house so he could change.

"Kratz talked to her about his past marriages and the details of the demise of his second marriage. He then went into a diatribe of dirty talk, going into detail about what he wanted in a wife or girlfriend sexually and about past experiences he had with numerous women."

After visiting Kratz's house for an hour, they drove toward the government municipal building in the area of Darboy and Sherwood. "While they were parked near the municipal building, Kratz touched the back of Palm's hair. Palm said she backed away from his touch and he stopped touching her. Kratz told Palm again that he works with victims and he understands."

Eventually, Kratz drove the woman back to the Burger King so she could retrieve her car.

"Palm said that during the date, Kratz told her a couple times not to talk to Harbor House (domestic violence shelter where she went for services and support) about him and what he was telling her … when he was talking about the personal things that he prefers and about meeting women in hotels.

"Palm stated that she felt almost as if Kratz were confessing to her about what he did with other women and wanting her to 'OK' his actions. Palm said that Kratz talked about a lot of things during their date, but she only wrote in her letters the details that she could truly remember. Palm stated that during the date she was only thinking about how fast she could get home."

Kratz made the mistake of opening up too much about his deviant side.

"She said he told her he met women on the Internet, they talked about what they expected, and they agreed to meet at a hotel. Kratz told Palm he did not tell these women his real name or what he did for a living and he met them in hotels out of town.

"Kratz also told Palm that he looked at pornography and he felt that it was an addiction because he stayed up until the early morning watching it."

On September 22, 2010, Palm sent a letter to Wisconsin Governor Jim Doyle relaying some of her humiliating experiences with Kratz to the governor.

"Once we arrived at his home he offered to give me a tour and made emphasis upon showing his bedroom where he slept. I then sat down in the living room to wait for him to change clothing which he did. He sat down in the living room and began another conversation where he shared information about past marriages. I found he had been married twice then he shared intimate details about why those marriages ended … then he went into details of the second marriage and he was very explicit. He said they had done a threesome with the neighbor guy down the road and his wife felt that the neighbor had more to offer her.

"You have probably heard about my dark side," Kratz told Palm.

"He shared details about many past experiences and said that he met a lot of women on the Internet, then would meet them at hotels 'out of town,' of course, and he did not give them his real name or profession. He gave specifics about liaisons going into great detail about one woman in particular who wanted him so bad and was so turned on that she was dripping on the bed. He said this several times and would not get off that particular sentence or woman."

"Do I make you nervous?" Kratz asked Palm.

"He went on to share further details and that he does different things with the women like role playing, even using a term I had heard before but can't remember now …but he explained in great detail that it involves hurting each other physically but there is a common word agreed upon ahead of time like Rumpelstiltskin and when one partner says the word the activity is to stop."

In Palm's letter to the governor, she revealed that over the years, it became common knowledge amongst the powerful people who were movers and shakers around Calumet County that Kratz's behaviors were to be tolerated.

"As the years went on and I became employed with Harbor House Domestic Abuse programs in June 2002 and got to know other professionals, I learned of the prevalence of knowledge of Ken Kratz reputation/rumors and what I felt was a sick collective social tolerance/oblivion to look the other way of this type of behavior from a man who holds a highly regarded public office."

But there was one thing Kratz kept saying over and over during his one and only creepy date with the Menasha woman he met at Burger King.

"I am uninhibited. I am uninhibited … he went on to say that he would pay to take me to a spa and be pampered all day to get a manicure/pedicure, get my hair done and a bikini wax and he would tell the girls at the salon what he would like done to me down there …he asked me a couple of times to share my fantasies with him and I would not … I have to wonder if putting pictures of Ken in the newspapers in various poses, full body, side view of face, front view, or in other attire like jeans, pictures of him over the years with dates or years attached that he served as DA and assistant DA and aged or changed in appearance might trigger the memory of other women throughout the state of Wisconsin and nearby states … I have to think there are many women out there affected by him."

By November 2010, the Wisconsin Department of Justice had seized Kratz's office computer. For the line reading criminal offense, the report indicated "Misconduct in Public Office." On the line marked "suspect," the name listed was Kenneth Kratz. Ten different women were listed in the document as "complainants."

The DCI report indicated Kratz used the following screen names: Exboytoy1, AppletonAtty and Applnatty. The following search terms were sought: bondage, dominant, submissive, role playing.

"Former Calumet County DA Ken Kratz is accused of sending inappropriate text and email messages to women, including victims in active cases he was working on. Currently looking for a preview of text documents, and possibly Internet dating sites and pornography, if excessive," the report stated.

But in the end, criminal charges of misconduct in public office were never filed against Kratz by the Wisconsin DCI.

CHAPTER TWENTY-FIVE

COMPUTER DISK

One of the longstanding obligations in the American criminal justice system is the duty of criminal prosecutors to provide a complete inventory of their side's evidence to the defendant and the defendant's lawyer. And that evidence also includes reports and information that is known as exculpatory. In other words, police reports and investigative files that may shed light on other potential perpetrators who were also being investigated for the same crime.

Exculpatory information would consist of investigative details the police officers and lead investigators had in their files.

The notion of police officers and prosecutors hiding files and reports from the criminal defendant, notably a murder defendant, is frowned upon by the American justice system, and there is longstanding judicial precedence and case law that firmly establishes that such negligent and prejudicial behavior by police detectives and district attorneys cannot be tolerated in a court of law.

Oftentimes, however, information and evidence about over-the-top criminal prosecutors who run roughshod over the rights of the accused never sees the light of day. After all, the prosecution is the one-and-only side in complete control of the evidence. Unless the defense gets lucky, or has a mole on the prosecution team feeding them information, outright proof of prosecutors destroying files or hiding evidence that could change the outcome of a criminal defendant's case don't regularly arise in America's judiciary.

In the spring of 2018, Avery's dogged post-conviction lawyer Kathleen Zellner made a discovery that rocked her world. It was a bombshell piece of evidence that she realized Avery's original criminal trial lawyers, Buting and Strang, did not know about. It was evidence that should have been tendered to them back in 2006 long before their client stood trial for Teresa's murder.

It was a crucial item of evidence that special prosecutor Ken Kratz and his loyal lead investigator, Tom Fassbender, did not want Avery's side to gain access to.

***

On April 21, 2006, Fassbender and Mark Wiegert seized the personal computer and a dozen computer disks from Barbara Janda's home. They wrote their reports in such a way to make it appear as if the computer belonged to Brendan Dassey and that their evidence gathering focused on the sixteen-year-old boy. Nothing could be further from the truth, though.

The next day, the computer was delivered to Grand Chute Police Detective Mike Velie by Fassbender. Velie was considered the region's law enforcement expert on computer forensics in criminal investigations. By May 11, 2006, Velie returned the evidence back to Fassbender, who then decided to sit on the information, that way the defense lawyers didn't have it in a timely fashion.

Seven months later, some of the information that was extracted from the Dassey computer was shared with Strang and Buting. The most noteworthy details and evidence from the computer investigation, interestingly, was never to be shared with Avery's trial lawyers.

"On December 14, 2006, 218 days after the completion of the Velie Final Investigative Report, trial defense counsel was first provided with the Fassbender report to Prosecutor Kratz."[99]

"The Kratz letter does not refer to any enclosed CD titled 'Dassey's Computer, Final Report Investigative Copy.'"

The report furnished to Avery's lawyers was misleading in so many ways, Zellner contends.

"The Fassbender report refers to the examination of Brendan Dassey's computer. There is absolutely no proof that the computer belonged to Brendan Dassey and there is proof that it was primarily used by his brother Bobby. The Fassbender report minimizes the number of violent pornographic images, the severity of the violent pornographic images and incriminating word searches that demonstrate an obsession with inflicting pain on young females, dead female bodies and mutilating female bodies. The Fassbender report also ignores the timeline of the images being viewed which excludes other family members and incriminates Bobby."

Instead, the report was designed to ensure Strang and Buting had no clue, no idea, that Bobby was a sexually disturbed deviant, which would have raised strong suspicions that he, not Avery, was involved in Teresa's murder, according to Zellner.

After all, it's an undisputed fact, some of Teresa's charred bones were found inside Bobby Dassey's burn barrels.

"The Fassbender report refers to a few messages of Brendan's about whether he thought Mr. Avery was guilty of the Halbach murder, while ignoring Bobby's prolific, graphic, and sexually aggressive messages to underage girls. The Fassbender report conspicuously omits the date of May 10, 2006, which is when Detective Velie completed the Velie Final Investigate Report and downloaded it onto a CD."

Keep in mind the prosecution side, Fassbender and Kratz, had the Bobby Dassey computer files in May 2006. The two

---

99. Motion to Supplement Previously Filed Motion for Post-Conviction Relief, July 6, 2018

men sat on the evidence in June, July, August, September, October, and November. All of those months passed and nothing was shared with the trial lawyers representing Avery. Then in December, Kratz wrote up his letter and turned over some information to Buting and Strang, but it was not everything, and it left out the most revelatory information.

"On December 15, 2006, Prosecutor Kratz sent Attorney Strang an itemized inventory of our Steven Avery file. In the inventory, Prosecutor Kratz references: '7 DVDs: Contents of Brendan Dassey's Computer.'" Again, this statement is completely misleading to the defense because 7 DVDs were disclosed that could not be opened without the EnCase program, but the CD, which required no specialized software, was not disclosed," Zellner uncovered in 2018.

Back on December 19, 2006, Strang enlisted his paralegal to send the seven DVDs to his partner on the case, Buting. "But no CD is referenced in her letter because trial defense counsel had not been provided with this CD. Because Special Agent Fassbender kept the CD in his possession, trial defense counsel only received the seven DVDs," Zellner said.

Meanwhile, the clock was ticking toward the looming murder trial, the trial Kratz liked to call the biggest murder trial in the history of Wisconsin.

"There was not time for trial defense counsel to retain a forensic computer expert and perform the forensic analysis of the seven DVDs which took Detective Velie 16 days, by the January 10, 2007, due date for trial defense counsel to file their *State v. Denny* motion. Additionally, because they were not provided a CD with the Velie Final Investigative Report, which contained his criteria, word searches, registry, recovered pornography, Internet history, windows registry, and all MSN messages, they could not effectively use this information to impeach Bobby or establish a motive to murder Ms. Halbach, pursuant to Denny."

Then on the eve of Avery's trial, Strang got a document from Kratz called "Stipulation Project."

Kratz mentioned in his January 25, 2007, correspondence there was a computer analysis of Steve, Teresa, and Brendan's computer hard drives and Detective Velie "found nothing of evidentiary value. We may wish to introduce the fact that they looked. This stip(ulation) eliminates Officer Veile (sic) as a witness."

Five days later, Manitowoc County Judge Patrick Willis rejected the effort of Strang and Buting to utilize *State v. Denny* to present an alternative suspect as part of their case to show Avery was innocent.

"On January 30, 2007, Judge Willis denied trial defense counsel's Denny motion because there was no proof of motive for the murder provided by trial defense counsel," Zellner said.

Another week later, jury selection got underway.

Then, a decade later, "On July 15, 2017, a new Brady witness, Kevin Rahmlow, in two affidavits, came forward and described how he had remembered seeing Ms. Halbach's RAV4 on November 3-4, 2005, by the old dam on State Highway 147 and reporting this to Sgt. Andy Colborn. The RAV4 was located within half a mile of Scott Tadych's former and current residences."

Then, on July 31, 2017, Zellner retained forensic computer expert Gary Hunt to analyze the seven DVDs taken from Bobby Dassey's hard drive. "Mr. Hunt examined the seven DVDs and discovered an abundance of violent pornography and created a timeline that linked a majority of the searches for violent pornography to Bobby."

On November 13, 2017, Zellner met with Buting and Strang to get their reaction.

"Attorney Buting states that neither the CD nor the Velie Final Investigative Report were ever disclosed to trial defense counsel. Attorney Buting points out that the CD was never logged into evidence but instead Special Agent

Fassbender kept the CD in his possession. This explains why trial defense counsel never saw the CD when they reviewed all of the evidence in the case at the Calumet County Sheriff's Department."

Over the course of several months, Zellner reached out to one of the former special prosecutors who assisted Kratz in Avery's prosecution, Assistant Wisconsin Attorney General Tom Fallon. She inquired about the missing CD starting on November 14, 2017, then on December 4, 2017, and finally again on March 20, 2018.

Finally, there was a breakthrough. It came on April 17, 2018.

"Attorney Fallon finally produced the CD, which contained 2,449 pages," Zellner said. "On May 25, 2018, current post-conviction counsel filed a motion to supplement the record on appeal with the CD produced by Attorney Fallon."[100]

In turn, Gary Hunt, Zellner's computer expert, determined that Bobby Dassey's computer was manipulated by someone out to destroy and conceal data on that computer. But why would someone do that?

"Mr. Hunt, after his examination of the 7 DVDs and the CD, made the following conclusions ... Mr. Hunt detected eight periods in 2005 which are relevant to the murder of Teresa Halbach, when computer records are missing and presumably deleted from the Dassey computer: August 23-26, August 28 - September 11, September 14-15, September 24 - October 22, October 23-24, October 26 - November 2, November 4-13, and November 15 - December 3."

And here's what he extracted from Teresa's last day alive.

---

100. Zellner's Motion to Supplement Previously Filed Motion for Post-Conviction Relief, July 6, 2018

"On October 31, 2005, the Dassey computer was used to access the Internet at 6:05 a.m., 6:28 a.m., 6:31 a.m., 7 a.m., 9:33 a.m., 10:09 a.m., 1:08 p.m., and 1:51 p.m."

As for the CD that was previously withheld from Strang and Buting prior to Avery's trial, it did not require any specialized software, according to Hunt.

The CD turned out 2,632 Internet keyword searches for the following terms: body: 2,083; journal: 106; gun: 75; RAV: 74, MySpace: 61; fire: 51; gas: 50; stab: 32; cement: 23; bullet: 10; DNA: 3; bondage: 3; throat: 2; tires: 2, blood: 1.

"The CD contained 14,099 images recovered from the computer. The CD also contained 1,625 photos categorized as recovered pornography, which means that these images had been deleted and then recovered. A search of the MSN messages reveals communications between Bobby and various individuals who identified themselves as teenage girls in the age range of 14-15. Bobby identified himself as being a 19 year old. The messages have explicit sexual content."

Obviously, Avery's murder trial may have turned out drastically different had Kratz and Fassbender turned over to the defense all of the contents related to Bobby Dassey's computer.

"Bobby's trial testimony about being asleep from 6:30 a.m. to 2 p.m. would have been impeached by the contents of the seven DVDs and one CD, which would have shown that he was awake and on the computer eight times in that time frame," Zellner said in July 2018.

"The vast quantities of child pornography and the violent images of young females being tortured, sexually assaulted and mutilated on the Dassey computer at times when only Bobby was home, in addition to his MSN sexually-explicit conversations with 14 and 15 year olds, as well as the word searches after the murder that indicate an interest in skeletons, dismemberment, knives through skin, fire, handcuffs, guns, bullets and blood, could have been utilized by trial defense counsel to impeach Bobby's credibility with the jury by illustration of his knowledge and preoccupation with unique details of the crime."

The CD in question also "contains conversations between Bobby and 14 and 15 year old girls ... Bobby asks that the girls flash him using a webcam."

But during Avery's trial, Kratz lauded Bobby Dassey. He made sure Bobby was considered a brave, impartial witness the jury could trust and believe, just like Kratz.

"Again, a witness without any bias," Kratz told the jury during closing arguments. "It is an individual that deserves to be given a lot of credit. Because sometime between 2:30 and 2:45 he sees Teresa Halbach. He sees her taking photographs. He sees her finishing the photo shoot. And he sees her walking up towards Uncle Steve's trailer."

Buting and Strang both strongly assert that having access to the hidden CD that was kept from them by Kratz would have altered their defense strategy.

"I accepted without challenge Ken Kratz's assertion in a January 25, 2007, email to me that Velie's analysis of 'Steve, Teresa's, and Brendan's' computers yielded 'nothing much of evidentiary value. With the belated production of the Velie forensic analysis to Mr. Avery's current lawyers in April 2018, it now appears to me from materials that Ms. Zellner and co-counsel have filed that the Velie forensic analysis in fact did include much of evidentiary value, in direct contradiction to Mr. Kratz's claim.

"Given what I know now about the existence and content of the Velie forensic analysis, this looks to me like deceit. It looks like deceit about who used this computer; it looks like deceit about the evidentiary value of the information extracted from the computer. At a minimum, it looks like material information bearing on innocence that the State knowingly possessed, had exclusively in its possession, and withheld from the defense."[101]

What else did Strang point out in his summer 2018 affidavit?

"We would have used the information in the Velie forensic analysis to support our motion by strengthening our showing that Bobby Dassey was an alternate suspect. At a minimum, the information would have gone to Bobby Dassey's availability and opportunity to commit violent crimes against and kill Teresa Halbach on October 31, 2005; to his sexual motive or other deviant motive to do so ... and to the credibility of his alibi. We also would have sought to introduce evidence of incriminating Internet searches that likely were made by Bobby Dassey, and would have confronted him on cross-examination with those searches and other information contained in the Velie forensic analysis."

It's highly probable that if Kratz and Fassbender didn't selectively choose to keep the computer analysis CD from Buting and Strang, the trial would have had a different outcome. If Bobby Dassey's trial testimony was shown to be a complete farce, it is very likely the jury wouldn't have returned a guilty verdict for Avery.

"Information demonstrating a probability that Bobby Dassey used that computer to gain access to the Internet on October 31, 2005, during times that he claimed to be asleep and while Brendan Dassey was known to be at school that day, also would have been used in cross-examination of Bobby Dassey at trial, had we known that information in the Detective Velie and Gary Hunt forensic analyses. I note that, in the end, the jury asked during deliberations for Bobby Dassey's testimony."

101. Affidavit of Wisconsin criminal defense lawyer Dean Strang, June 4, 2018

In retrospect, one has to wonder whether Kratz and Fassbender intentionally withheld the CD from Avery's trial lawyers because they suspected Bobby was the killer and realized the case had already reached the point of no return. "Current post-conviction counsel's expert Mr. Hunt's forensic examination of the seven DVDs revealed 128 violent images of young females being tortured, sexually assaulted and mutilated," Zellner said. "There were dozens of images depicting young females in pain because of having objects and fists forced into their vaginas. The images also depicted dismembered, decapitated, and drowned bodies of young females. Many of the female images, both alive and deceased, bear an uncanny resemblance to Ms. Halbach.

"Two pictures were found in the unallocated space, the first showing Ms. Halbach and Mr. Avery, the second showing only Ms. Halbach. The pictures were in an unallocated space because someone had deleted them. There is no way to know when these images were acquired or deleted. Therefore, prior counsel was deprived of a complete compilation of all the violent images, word searches, timelines, messages, and recovered images that had been deleted during the Halbach murder investigation. The State's forensic examiner was also suppressed. All of this material could have been used to establish Bobby as a third-party Denny suspect."

But, couldn't the prosecution come back and say, hey, wait a minute, there were four boys living under the Dassey roof. Isn't it possible any one of them was the deviant pervert constantly viewing this dirty disgusting smut that was messing with their mind?

When Zellner's expert utilized his 2017 computer forensic tracking software on the computer, Hunt uncovered a total of 667 Internet searches for sexual images "on weekdays when Bobby was the only member of his family at home during the week from 6:30 a.m. to 3:45 p.m. All other Dassey family members who lived at the residence … were either at work or school during those hours."

Prior to Teresa's disappearance, Barb and her husband Tom Janda had split up and he was no longer staying on Avery Road. "According to Barb, Tom Janda moved out before October 15, 2005, and never looked at pornography on the Dassey computer. Bobby was the only person at the Dassey residence from 6 a.m. to 3:45 p.m. on the weekdays. During the week, Blaine and Brendan were in school until 3:45 p.m. Bryan lived with his girlfriend and worked during the day. Barb also worked a day shift, and Tom Janda no longer lived at the residence."[(102)]

Zellner also enlisted the expertise of retired FBI behavioral analyst, Gregg McCrary, to weigh in on the matter.

McCrary "opines that these Dassey computer searches demonstrate the obsessively compulsive nature of Bobby Dassey's Internet searches and the fascination with sexual acts that involve the infliction of pain, torture, and humiliation on females and an equally disturbing fascination with viewing dead female bodies.

"Barb hired someone to reformat the Dassey computer prior to law enforcement seizing it. The reformatting resulted in a number of images being removed during the critical period before and after the murder."

But, since Kratz was liable to say and spout out anything, couldn't the special prosecutor now pontificate this was all Steven Avery's doing? Perhaps Avery was sneaking into his sister's trailer during the daytime when she wasn't around to fill his mind with dirty and wicked fantasies that would drive him over the edge and make him murder Teresa?

"The State attempted to convince the jury that Mr. Avery's motive in setting up the appointment with Ms. Halbach on October 31, 2005, was to lure her to his property to sexually assault her," Zellner said. "During the searches of the Avery

102. Motion to Compel Production of Recent Examination of the Dassey Computer, July 3, 2018

property, the State focused on trying to gather pornography from Mr. Avery's residence. However, a forensic analysis performed by the State's examiner of Mr. Avery's computer in 2006 revealed no searches of sexual images, much less violent images and dead bodies. Mr. Avery never accessed the Dassey computer. He did not have the password for the computer, nor did he possess a key to the Dassey residence which was locked when no one was home. Mr. Avery only entered the residence with permission or a Dassey family member.'"

Furthermore, Avery would be eliminated as being the deviant culprit on all but fifteen of the 128 computer searches just by the fact that he was thrown in jail on November 9, 2005. "Brendan would be eliminated from all but 26 of the 128 searches at issue by having been arrested on March 1, 2006."

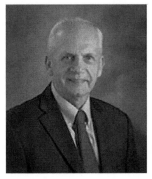

Former FBI stalwart Gregg McCrary maintains that a competent group of police investigators would have considered Bobby Dassey a prime suspect in the death of Teresa Halbach.

CHAPTER TWENTY-SIX

FANTASY LIFE

Ann Wolbert Burgess, Ph. D, has co-authored twenty-four books, thirty book chapters and more than 160 peer-reviewed articles. She teamed up with internationally noted FBI profilers John Douglas and Robert Ressler to co-author the book, *Sexual Homicide: Patterns and Motives*. It was her research on that book in particular that gave her a window into the mind of a murderer, a murderer whose mind is fried by constant visual images of violent X-rated pornography.

"We interviewed 36 sexual murderers and we concluded that, as a group, they had several traits in common: One, they had a longstanding preoccupation and preference for a very active fantasy life. Two, they were preoccupied with violent, sexualized thoughts and fantasies. In my opinion, in reviewing Mr. Hunt's affidavits, the obvious preoccupation with violent pornography, which includes torturing young females and dismembering and or mutilating female bodies, over time would result in a justification for killing.

"My opinion is based, in part, upon a review of sexual images contained in the Dassey CD and seven DVDs, Mr. Gregg McCrary's second supplemental affidavit, and Mr. Hunt's analysis of the Internet searches, including the timing and frequency of the searches as well as description of the violent pornographic images."[103]

Dr. Burgess believes that McCrary's analysis of Teresa's death being a sexually motivated crime was right on the money.

---

103. Affidavit of Dr. Ann Burgess, July 5, 2018

"The Dassey computer examination by Mr. Hunt also revealed that Bobby Dassey was untruthful when he testified that he had been asleep on October 31, 2005, until 2:30 p.m. I also agree with Mr. McCrary that Bobby should have been considered a prime suspect because of his untruthful statements during the investigation, combined with the nature of his Internet searches."

Burgess pointed out that twenty-two search terms described forcing objects into female vaginas; thirty-seven search terms described violent accidents and violent car crashes with images of dead bodies; thirteen searches for drowned, dead, or diseased female bodies; sixty-five searches for describing the infliction of violence on females including fisting and images of females experiencing pain.

Dr. Ann Burgess contends that Bobby Dassey was engaged in a dangerous and obsessive web of violent pornography and death. She said this is all too common in cases of violent sex crimes against young women including many that end in murder.

"Further, Mr. Hunt determined that 562 of the searches were performed on 10 weekdays. Mr. Hunt described folders created on the Dassey computer entitled, 'Teresa Halbach,' 'Steven Avery,' and 'DNA.'"

"The searches speak to the compulsive nature of the offender, specifically the sadism, as the fantasy life translates into the compulsion to act out the sadistic fantasy, example, a sexual homicide," Dr. Burgess said.

"A person obsessed with violence is more likely to commit a murder than someone not so obsessed."

Here's what Dr. Burgess informed the court regarding the computer disk that Kratz chose to hide from Strang and Buting back in 2006.

"The images on the CD also contain blindfolded and bound girls, dismembered bodies, and bestiality. All of these images display a fascination with dominance, control, and mutilation, which is characteristic of many sexual homicides. The mutilation of Ms. Halbach's body is consistent with a fascination with the morbid images found on the Dassey computer of dead and dismembered human bodies."

Dr. Burgess has been recognized by courts as an expert witness on child pornography, crime classification, offender typology, rape victims, rape trauma, and serial offenders.

"All of the opinions offered within this affidavit are based upon a reasonable degree of scientific certainty in the field of psychiatric nursing," she said. Dr. Burgess has been a professor of psychiatric nursing at Boston University since 2001.

"I have also reviewed Steven Avery's second supplemental affidavit in which he describes Bobby commenting on Teresa Halbach after each appointment that she had at the Avery Salvage Yard. Specifically, Mr. Avery says that Bobby would say, 'I see that your girlfriend was here again.' Since Bobby was never present when Ms. Halbach was on the property, Mr. Avery concluded that he must have been watching her from a window. Clearly, Bobby had developed an unhealthy obsession with Ms. Halbach. It is also significant that Bobby has always maintained that he did not know that Ms. Halbach was coming to the property, but there is a conflicting report from the Wisconsin Public

Defender Office dated November 23, 2005, in which Bobby admitted that he knew Ms. Halbach was coming to the property that day."

From her perspective, what was not recovered from Bobby Dassey's home computer during the police investigation into Teresa's murder case is just as important, if not more striking, than what authorities and computer forensic experts did actually find.

"The Dassey computer examination by Mr. Hunt revealed eight significant periods of deletions related to the times that Ms. Halbach visited the Avery property," Burgess said. "It is not unusual ... an organized offender would try to cover up his fantasies by deleting files from a computer. Furthermore, I agree with Mr. McCrary that it is highly significant in any investigation if there is an attempt to delete or destroy records. Clearly, the person deleting or destroying records, has to be considered as a suspect in any homicide investigation."

During the closing arguments in front of the jurors from Manitowoc County, Kratz told them, "We could start with the moment of the visual or with the image of that man, Steven Avery, standing outside of a big bonfire, with flames over the roof, or at least over the garage roof, and the silhouette of Steven Avery, with the bonfire in the background and the observations made by some witnesses. Can you all picture that? Can you picture that as a moment, as a moment in time? And that moment, by the way, although dramatic and although important, should tell the whole story," Kratz told jurors at the end of the five-week-long trial.

"That moment of Steven Avery, after the murder was committed, of Steven Avery tending the fire, of Steven Avery disposing or and mutilating the body of 25-year-old Teresa Halbach. That would be a good place to start. But I'm not going to start there. I'm going to start somewhere else. I'm going to start with the Toyota RAV4. The Toyota RAV4, which was owned by Teresa Halbach, which was discovered on the fifth of November at the Avery Salvage property ... Because the discovery of that RAV4, the discovery of Teresa Halbach's vehicle, changed the course of not only this case, but the clues and the secrets found in that vehicle changed the lives of everybody in this room. Look around, everybody. The clues found in that vehicle, on the fifth of November, changed everybody's lives. Yours included. Your lives will never be the same, ours won't. Families won't. That moment is particularly important. And that is where we're going to begin."

That was vintage Kratz.

As far as her academic background, Burgess obtained her bachelor's degree from Boston University, her master of science from the University of Maryland, and her doctorate of nursing science from Boston University. She also has an honorary degree from the University of San Diego. Here's what Dr. Burgess had to say, given her dedication and expertise in getting to know the psyche of the criminal mind, the deviant sexual offender who gravitates into the abyss.

"The offender in the Halbach murder would be classified as an organized offender who plans, thinks things through, and tries to cover his tracks by deleting incriminating files, interjecting himself into the investigation as a primary witness for the State, misleading the investigators about the timeline and events surrounding the murder, and would be very likely to attempt to plant evidence and frame another for the murder," Dr. Burgess concludes.

"The offender would keep secret his commission of the sadistic murder of Ms. Halbach. The police should have considered Bobby a prime suspect in the murder of Ms. Halbach and should not have eliminated him as quickly as they did."

While finishing this book, the author reached out to Zellner, the country's leading wrongful conviction lawyer, to gain her insight into the killing and dismemberment of the young *Auto Trader* photographer who never made it home to her family's farm on Halloween 2005.

"Bobby has been described by family members as being a very quiet, socially awkward teenager who never dated," Zellner said. "He spent a great deal of time on the computer, which was in his bedroom. Our experts have developed a profile of the individual doing the computer searches for violence pornography. The individual was obsessed with inflicting sexual violence on young females and displayed a strong interest in viewing deceased, mutilated female bodies. My experts believe the individual is very disturbed and seems to hate women."

Zellner said she has visited with Avery, one on one, about Bobby, since this was his nephew, and he saw him often, from September 2003 until his arrest in November 2005.

"According to Mr. Avery, Bobby became increasingly obsessed with Ms. Halbach in the few months before her death," Zellner said. "Mr. Tadych (Bobby's stepfather) has a history of domestic violence. Bobby and Mr. Tadych have told multiple lies about the events of October 31, 2005. The police reports demonstrate that Bobby and Mr. Tadych went out of his way to try to get the police to charge Steven. As early as November 5, 2005, Bobby tried to implicate Steven in the murder. Mr. Tadych talked obsessively about the case at work during the investigation. Both Bobby and Mr. Tadych changed their stories to fit the State's narrative. I believe Bobby in particular completely duped the cops, planted the bones and blood to frame Mr. Avery and willingly and enthusiastically became the State's star witness."

And the State's star witness was also aided by the dubious testimony from his future stepfather, Scott Tadych, who furnished him with an alibi, actually, an alibi for both men, around the exact time of Teresa's disappearance and killing.

That day, Tadych failed to show up for his work shift. He claimed he made two separate visits to a local hospital to visit his mother who was apparently undergoing back surgery in Green Bay. Keep in mind this was the same woman Tadych tried to beat up and had called several despicable vulgar names during an explosive outburst that led to his arrest by police just a few years earlier.

"That afternoon, or that morning, I was up by my mother," Tadych testified under oath during questioning by Kratz at the murder trial.[104]

"Then I left her and I went to the woods hunting. I went to my trailer and then I went to the woods hunting. Archery hunting, bow hunting, archery."

Next, Kratz asked, "About what time was it that you got out into the woods or that you got to your deer hunting stand?"

"About 3 p.m."

"On your way to deer hunting, that would be just before 3 p.m., did you observe anybody on the roadway?"

"Yes I did. I saw Bobby Dassey on Highway 147. I was going west and he was going east."

"Where is it, Mr. Tadych, that you hunt, or at least that day, where was it that you were going hunting?"

"In Kewaunee."

In the minds of the jurors, Tadych's testimony iced any suspicion toward Bobby as being the more likely killer. At the same time, Tadych helped bury Avery, a man he hated because he resented the fact that Avery was in line to collect a multi-million dollar settlement for the 1985 wrongful conviction case. And because he knew the cops investigating Teresa's death were not street smart individuals, Tadych realized he could essentially say whatever he wanted, and no one would question his statements or question his motives.

"Tadych went on to indicate that Steven has a large amount of control over Brendan as well as the rest of the

---

104. Day 12 jury trial of Avery, Scott Tadych testimony February 27, 2007

Dassey and Avery families. He states he believes this due to the large amount of dollars that Steven was possibly going to be coming into … He stated he has known Steven approximately two years. Tadych went on to indicate Brendan spends most of his time with Steven and that Steven had taken Brendan up north a lot. Scott went on to indicate his gut feeling is that Steven had some sort of sexual relationship with Brendan but he has nothing to back this feeling up."[105]

During Avery's trial, Tadych made sure that he helped the prosecution nail Avery.

"I saw a big fire," he testified. "It was a big fire. It was bigger than normal … They were almost as tall as the garage. Eight feet, ten feet. I don't know, ten feet maybe. Ten feet tall the flames were."

"It was a big fire?" Kratz asked his friendly witness.

"It was a big fire," Tadych repeated for the jury.

"Where did you go then, Mr. Tadych?"

"I went back to where I was living at the time, the trailer house on 147. About two miles away."

When Bobby Dassey was initially interviewed by the police, Bobby told them how he and Tadych had crossed paths while driving past one another, around the same time as Teresa's murder, going the opposite directions on Highway 147. Suspiciously, when Bobby was pressed to remember where the two saw one other on the road, just a matter of days earlier, he couldn't offer a definitive answer.

"Bobby indicated that as he was traveling on State Highway 147 towards the property he hunts deer on, he did observe an individual known to him as Scott Tadych. Bobby indicted that Scott would be able to verify precisely what time he had seen Bobby," Dedering's report five days after Teresa disappeared showed.

---

105. Interview of Scott Tadych, Investigator John Dedering, March 30, 2006

Dedering's report, though, was hollow. There was a lack of follow-up questioning. The most obvious question was not asked of Bobby, that is, how would Bobby know that Scott Tadych would be able to know the exact time that the two men passed one another?

When Avery stood trial, Dean Strang questioned Tadych about his whereabouts around the time of Teresa's murder as well as the story about Tadych and Bobby seeing one another on the highway.

"It's a 15-minute drive or something like that to your hunting spot?"

"Approximately, yeah."

"And this is when, on your way to hunting, is when you see Bobby Dassey?"

"Correct."

"He's going east in the other direction on Highway 147?"

"Correct."

"Speed limit on 147?"

"Fifty-five."

"And the two of you, obviously, are going in opposite directions?"

"Yes."

"And so you pass each other and you are later able to tell the police that Bobby was going deer hunting?"

"Yes."

"How do you know that?"

"How do I know that is because Bobby Dassey was going to the trailer where I live to hunt behind it."

"Let me understand. He's going to hunt deer right behind your trailer?"

"Yes."

"But you don't hunt deer right behind your trailer?"

"Occasionally, yes."

"And when did he tell you about this hunting trip that he planned right behind your trailer?"

"I don't recall him telling me. He had permission from the landlord to hunt there."

"So you figured since you saw him driving east on Highway 147 he must be going hunting?"

"Yes."

"Anybody else see you going west on 147 to go hunting, so far as you know?"

"Bobby Dassey."

"And had you told him that you were going hunting?"

"No."

"How would he have known that you were going hunting?"

"Because I was in my camouflage clothes."

"You were in your camouflage coat?"

"Yes."

"In your green Ford Ranger?"

"Yup."

"Passing one another at 55 miles an hour?"

"Nope. Where I passed Bobby I probably was only doing maybe 25 miles an hour tops. He was slowing down to turn in my driveway and I was driving up 147."

"I see. And so you surmise that he would have known you were going deer hunting because he would have seen you in your camouflage clothing?"

"Yes."

"Did you go hunting with anybody that day?"

"No."

As it turned out, Tadych, who has a reputation of being a compulsive liar, wound up giving numerous inconsistent statements to the police and in court in regard to Teresa's murder. The size of the fire he saw in Avery's backyard changed dramatically from his initial interviews with police to the point of him serving as a main witness for Kratz. He also told police he went and visited his mother at the Green Bay hospital two separate times on the day of the murder and nobody in the police investigation made any attempt to verify either visit. In addition to the dubious story about seeing Bobby on the highway, Tadych insisted Barb Janda left his place that night after watching Prison Break. Later on, he changed that story and claimed she spent the night with him. The later story gave him a rock solid alibi to refute any allegations he might have been involved in burning and dismembering Teresa's body, along with Bobby Dassey, after the skies grew dark after slaying, perhaps at the Manitowoc County gravel pit where the pelvic bones were later found.

During a tape-recorded interview with Dedering and DCI agent Kevin Heimerl, Bobby admitted that he did not leave to go into work at the Fisher Hamilton Manufacturing plant in Manitowoc until almost two hours later than normal.

"Dassey indicated he stayed home until 11:30 p.m. on October 31, 2005, and then left for work at Hamilton Manufacturing," their reports state. There appeared to be no follow-up questions as to why Dassey didn't go into work as scheduled.

On February 27, 2006, when Bobby underwent a follow-up interview, Dedering asked him again about his activities on the day of the homicide. This time, Bobby told the police "he got up at approximately 9 p.m., got ready for work… Bobby indicated that when he was leaving for work at approximately 9:30 p.m., he noticed that Steven was having a bonfire. He estimated that the flames were five to six feet in height. He stated that it was a good-sized fire and that Steven has had fires there in the past … He stated he worked from 10 p.m. until 6 a.m. the following day and when he arrived home, he noticed nothing unusual and that the fire was out."[106]

In late 2017, Gregg McCrary filed a second affidavit with Wisconsin's criminal justice system, in reference to Bobby Dassey.

106.   Interview of Bobby Dassey. Investigator John Dedering, Feb. 27, 2006

"The fact that Bobby Dassey became the key witness for the prosecution and that his testimony placed Teresa Halbach on the property 'walking over to Steven's trailer' after she completed her assignment, interjected him into the prosecution in a way that should have raised the suspicions of reasonably trained detectives if that testimony is untrue. Based upon the affidavit of Bryan Dassey, it appears that Bobby Dassey's testimony was untrue. In my opinion, a prudent investigator would have considered Bobby Dassey a suspect and would have investigated him as such. There is no evidence that authorities ever investigated, much less eliminated, him as a suspect or investigated the discrepancies in his trial testimony."[107]

McCrary also offered the same sentiments regarding Tadych, who had a lengthy history of abusing women and he was at the center of the controversial letter that arrived at the Green Bay post office, the infamous SIKIKEY letter.

The letter made reference to a body being burned up at 3 a.m. at an aluminum smelter, which is where Tadych has worked.

"Mr. Tadych worked the third shift at the Wisconsin Aluminum Foundry. The note, which was never thoroughly investigated by law enforcement, is potentially of great evidentiary value because the note was sent on November 9, 2005, and it was not disclosed to the public until November 11, 2005, that Ms. Halbach had allegedly been burned on the Avery burn pit," Zellner said.

But that's not all.

"Mr. Tadych's nickname at work was 'Skinny' and, according to a current employee, many of the shift workers are not totally literate. It is a reasonable inference that a semi-literate employee might have misspelled the word 'Skinny' in the note."

---

107. Supplemental Affidavit of Gregg McCrary, October 20, 2017

At no point during Teresa's murder probe, did anybody in Wisconsin law enforcement attempt to get the fingerprints or DNA samples from Tadych to compare with the evidence in the case, including the eight fingerprints that were recovered from the RAV4 that did not belong to Avery, Brendan Dassey, or Bobby Dassey, among others in the family.

"At a minimum, Mr. Tadych should have been asked to provide his DNA and fingerprints so that they could be compared to crime scene evidence," Zellner said. "Mr. Tadych's failure to respond to Kevin Rahmlow's text about seeing the RAV4 at the turnaround by the old dam on November 3 and 4, 2005, before the discovery of the Halbach vehicle on the Avery property, is also suspicious."

Rahmlow, of course, is the man who came forward in 2017, providing a sworn affidavit about his first-hand experience of seeing the RAV4 abandoned after Teresa's disappearance, but not on the Avery property, as Kratz represented.

"I went to the old dam with Mr. Rahmlow and my investigator," Zellner said. "He is absolutely telling the truth about seeing the Halbach vehicle. He is also telling the truth about the Cenex station missing poster in the window regarding Ms. Halbach and her vehicle. Some people think he is mistaken about speaking to Colborn being it was Colborn's day off and he would not have been in uniform. I find that point to be unpersuasive because Colborn was involved in the biggest investigation of his life. I do not believe that he would take a day off in the middle of the investigation. He wanted to run for sheriff. I believe he would have worn his uniform on his day off because it would have given him a little bit of authority.

"No cop or witness has come forward giving Colborn an alibi for Mr. Rahmlow's claim, nor does anyone say they saw him in plain clothes on November 4, 2005. This is a cop who absolutely does not write up reports, if at all, until years later.

"Mr. Rahmlow's timeline of seeing Ms. Halbach's vehicle on the early afternoon of November 4, 2005, and Mr. Siebert's timeline of seeing her vehicle drive onto Mr. Avery's property shortly thereafter, match. Mr. Rahmlow has no motive to lie and had moved from Wisconsin to Michigan years before."

Rahmlow was hardly the only person who remembered seeing the RAV4 concealed off State Highway 147 in the days prior to its startling appearance on the back end of Avery's property.

CHAPTER TWENTY-SEVEN

DAMAGED

When former Mishicot resident Kevin Rahmlow came forward in 2017, he made it abundantly clear that he saw Teresa's RAV4 being concealed at the Highway 147 turnabout near the old dam toward Mishicot. It turns out Rahmlow was hardly the only person in Manitowoc County who remembered seeing Teresa's vehicle being concealed off the road near the Old Dam.

"I lived in Mishicot in 2005. On October 31, 2005, I was driving east on Highway 147 toward Mishicot when I saw a vehicle by the old dam on the north side of the road. It was around dusk, but there was enough light for me to make out its shape and color," said Paul Burdick, a long-time resident of Mishicot.

"It was a small SUV, greenish in color. It was facing northwest and parked facing a tree."[108]

However, when Burdick drove past the old dam another time, in the coming days, he made another observation.

"Several days later, the vehicle was gone," he said. "I did not report what I saw to the police. The talk around town was that some people in the community called in the vehicle to the police."

However, at the Manitowoc County Sheriff's Office, there are no written documents indicating anybody responded to a call of an abandoned vehicle, Teresa's RAV4, being dumped near the old dam.

---

108. June 28, 2018 sworn affidavit of Paul Burdick

Interestingly, Zellner also discovered Manitowoc County's radio transmissions concerning calls and efforts to find Teresa or her RAV4 on Friday, November 4, 2005, no longer exist.

"Ms. Halbach's vehicle was observed parked by a tree at the old dam by witness Paul Burdick on October 31, 2005," Zellner said. Then, over the next few days, Zellner noted, "Ms. Halbach's vehicle was observed parked in the same location at the old dam by witness Kevin Rahmlow.[109]

The sightings of Teresa's RAV4, dumped behind the tall trees and wild brush along the state highway, also point to the suspected involvement of Tadych in the murder, according to Zellner. The distance between where Tadych lived in November 2005 and the location of the abandoned vehicle, was roughly a half mile.

Provided this was the murder victim's vehicle, then how did it get to Avery's property and why did it sustain front-end damage? There is no denying the fact that Teresa's RAV4 was damaged after she visited Avery Salvage. But nobody in Wisconsin law enforcement made much of an effort to find out why her vehicle was damaged.

What caused the driver's side blinker light to get knocked out? Where did this occur? Why did the culprit make it a point to stop what he was doing, get out of the vehicle and pick up the broken vehicle debris, and place it into the cargo area?

Photos of the vehicle also make it clear the front bumper was torn as well.

A few logical scenarios remain. The killer may have struck an object driving the victim's vehicle after dark, panicked, and retrieved the blinker light. The other scenario is that the police, and perhaps one of the searchers such as

---

109. Defendant's Reply to the State's Response to Defense's Motion to Supplement Previously Filed Post-Conviction Motion for Relief, August 3, 2018

Ryan Hillegas, the ex-boyfriend of Teresa, were involved in the car mess up.

Zellner suspects that the RAV4 may have been moved from the Old Dam Turnabout to the Radandt Sand & Gravel pit that Friday afternoon of November 4, and then after dark, it got towed onto the Avery property where it was spotted the next morning.

Steven Avery has told his lawyer he believes the RAV4 had to be towed onto the perimeter of the Salvage Yard property at some point in time because the vehicle was facing west, meaning it may have been unhitched at that point because the tow driver could not turn it around.

"Also the RAV, according to Steven, is parked too close to the vehicle next to it so that there is not room to exit the driver's door of the RAV for a man to exit," Zellner said. "Steven believes the parking light damage was the result of towing."

Zellner has been attempting to gain access to the broken blinker light in order to have to it tested for trace evidence and DNA, but the state of Wisconsin has put up a vigorous fight to thwart her attempts to have the blinker light tested. It is also fighting her efforts to have the pelvic bones undergo testing to confirm whether these charred bones positively belong to Teresa.

"The parking light on Teresa Halbach's car was damaged after she left the Avery property on Halloween 2005. We know the car was not damaged before Halloween," Zellner said.

"The specific damage was located in the area of the driver's side parking light and is consistent with the vehicle being driven through the Radandt Gravel Pit and colliding with one of the metal property stakes on Radandt's property or the red Pinto blocking access to the Avery property.

Over the past couple years Zellner's investigators have tried repeatedly to interview Halbach's ex-boyfriend, Ryan Hillegas, the young man who organized the search party efforts to find Teresa. Hillegas was the individual who met up with Pamela Sturm on the Saturday morning of November 5, 2005. That was the day that Sturm and her daughter showed up late and told Hillegas they wanted to go and search the Avery Salvage yard themselves. In turn, Hillegas and Teresa's roommate, Scott Bloedorn, supplied Sturm with a camera and they also furnished her with the phone number to reach Calumet County Sheriff Jerry Pagel.

However, Zellner's repeated attempts to interview Hillegas about any facets of Teresa's disappearance and the front-end damage to Teresa's RAV4 have been unsuccessful. Hillegas has refused to be interviewed by Zellner's investigators, Kirby & Associates, she said.

"Mr. Hillegas injected himself into the police investigation by taking an active role in the volunteer search," noted police procedural expert witness Gregg McCrary.

"He gave a female volunteer a camera and a direct phone number to the sheriff. It appears that he directed her to the area where the victim's vehicle was located. He also appears to have misled police when he told them that Ms. Halbach had damaged the front driver's side of her vehicle months before her disappearance, had filed an insurance claim for that damage and had taken the cash payout without repairing her vehicle. However, it appears that particular damage was done more contemporaneously with the crime and a check with Ms. Halbach's insurance company revealed that she never filed an insurance claim for the front end damage."[110]

On May 26, 2017, the insurance company for Teresa Halbach responded to the subpoena sent to them by Kathleen T. Zellner & Associates. "Pursuant to your subpoena, ERIE has made a diligent and exhaustive search of its records and finds no such claims to have been presented … between the years 2003 and 2006 pertaining to Teresa M. Halbach. As

---

110. Affidavit of Gregg McCrary, May 8, 2017

such, The ERIE has no records to provide," advised Kevin F. Nelson of the litigation/claims examination department.[111]

***

When Zellner filed her original post-conviction relief on June 7, 2017, the 221-page document outlined a number of explosive Brady violations she said were committed by Kratz. In many cases, the existence of even one Brady violation warrants a conviction reversal and sends the case back for a new trial.

"In *Brady v. Maryland*, the Court held that the State violates an accused's constitutional right to due process of law by failing to disclose evidence. A Brady claim requires a showing that the undisclosed evidence is favorable to the accused because it is either exculpatory or impeaching; the evidence was suppressed by the State either willfully or inadvertently and the accused was prejudiced because the evidence is material to guilt or punishment," Zellner's motion argues.

Zellner's team uncovered a number of key pieces of evidence that were never furnished to Avery's original trial lawyers, Buting and Strang.

One was the voicemail CD taken from George and Jolene Zipperer's home.

"When Ms. Halbach first arrived in the vicinity of the Zipperers' residence, she made a phone call which was answered by the Zipperers' answering machine. Allegedly, Ms. Halbach left a voicemail that she could not locate the Zipperer residence. On November 3, when the Zipperers were interviewed at 9:30 p.m., they told the investigators that Ms. Halbach had left a voice message on their answering machine. The voicemail was listened to by Detective

---

111. Exhibit 59, Response to Subpoena to Erie Insurance, May 26, 2017

Remiker of the Manitowoc County Sheriff's Office and it was copied by Manitowoc County Sheriff's Office Detective Dennis Jacobs onto a CD. The CD of Ms. Halbach's voicemail recording on the Zipperer answering machine was never turned over to trial defense counsel and has allegedly disappeared.

"Mr. Fallon confirmed in a letter to current post-conviction counsel on April 20, 2017, that neither Calumet nor the Manitowoc Sheriff's Offices have been able to locate the CD of Ms. Halbach's voicemail left on the Zipperer answering machine."[112]

The disappearance of the voicemail, however, may have something to do with Kratz's professional misconduct, Zellner contends.

"Suspiciously, Mr. Kratz never played the recording of the 2:12 p.m. voicemail for the jury. It is reasonable to conclude that Mr. Kratz concealed the 2:12 p.m. voicemail because it confirmed that the Zipperers' residence was Ms. Halbach's last stop … Clearly, the destruction and or concealment of Ms. Halbach's voicemail to the Zipperers leads to the reasonable conclusion that her voicemail refuted Mr. Kratz's timeline and so it was concealed from trial defense counsel. Investigators concealed the voicemail left by Ms. Halbach on the Zipperers' answering machine because it refuted their theory that Ms. Halbach's final appointment was Mr. Avery."

The second Brady violation allegation pertains to Teresa's fuel tank.

"Although the odometer reading from Ms. Halbach's vehicle was noted at the Wisconsin State Crime Lab, no reference was made by law enforcement or the Wisconsin State Crime Lab to the amount of gas remaining in the RAV4's fuel tank, which would have provided vital

---

112. Motion for Post-Conviction Relief, June 7, 2017

information about how far the car had traveled since its tank was filled to capacity on October 29, 2005," Zellner said.

Police obtained Teresa's credit card statements which show that two days before her death, Teresa spent $37.94 to purchase a full tank of gas at the Exxon station in De Pere, a suburb adjacent to Green Bay. Zellner determined her 1999 Toyota RAV4 had a fuel capacity of 15.3 gallons.

"Mr. Fallon has confirmed on April 20, 2017, that the State failed to determine and document the gas level remaining in Ms. Halbach's vehicle when it was discovered on the Avery's property. Clearly, the State did not want the mileage revealed because it would have completely refuted its theory that Ms. Halbach and her car were driven many more miles after she left the Avery property," Zellner said.

A third Brady violation allegation concerns the highly questionable flyover conducted by Calumet Sheriff Jerry Pagel and his investigator, Wendy Baldwin. Their reports showed they were up in the sky for several hours flying over the terrain and specifically over the Avery property under the guise of searching for Teresa's vehicle. But they may have had ulterior motives. Their flyover may have been a shifty way for them to survey the Avery property to find the perfect spot to put Teresa's RAV4. A video of their flyover was provided to Strang and Buting but the video they got was only a few minutes long.

"Wendy Baldwin and Sheriff Pagel were in the air for around four hours yet the State produced only three minutes of footage," Zellner informed Judge Angela Sutkiewicz during the summer of 2017. "Mr. Kratz saw the unedited flyover video and knew that the RAV4 was not there at that time, but knew that the State's case might fail if the RAV4 was not present before 6 p.m. on November 4.

"The video was intentionally edited to conceal the fact that the RAV4 was not present at the time of the flyover on November 4."

Back in 2006, Strang and Buting notified Kratz about the questionable flyover videotape. "We currently have a spliced copy on a DVD which is obviously from several different dates, times, or aircrafts with no separation or designation as to their date and time. Thus I assume there must be a master copy of the complete videos," Buting wrote to Kratz back on July 24, 2006.

The lawyers for Avery asked Kratz to provide a complete copy in 2006, but that never happened.

A fourth Brady violation outlined by Zellner concerned the Wisconsin police investigators maintaining an oath of silence about their knowledge that Teresa's vehicle was driven through the Radandt quarry properties. Zellner has an affidavit from the quarry owner who swears under oath that the criminal investigators from the Wisconsin Department of Justice told him such.

"DOJ investigators never authored a report documenting their conversation with Mr. Radandt about the RAV4 being driven from his property and planted on Mr. Avery's property," Zellner said. "Mr. Kratz did not call Mr. Radandt as a witness at Mr. Avery's trial. The failure to produce this evidence to trial defense counsel was a clear Brady violation because this information could not only have been used to impeach the State's witnesses it also would have provided exculpatory evidence for Mr. Avery that the RAV4 was planted on his property."

One of the biggest pieces of overlooked evidence in Avery's 2007 trial concerned the front-end damage to Halbach's vehicle.

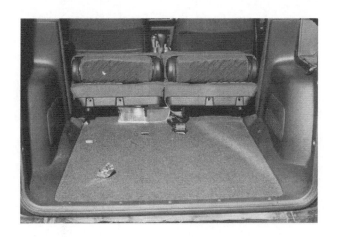

Attorney Kathleen Zellner has offered her theory explaining the date and circumstances for when the murder victim's blinker light got damaged.

CHAPTER TWENTY-EIGHT

AVERY'S BRAIN

Across the Missouri River from Omaha, Nebraska, sits the gateway into Iowa, the city of Council Bluffs. On July 22, 1977, a retired police captain was cruelly murdered by someone brandishing a shotgun. The murder victim was working overnight security at a car dealership. Four months later, two black teenagers, Terry Harrington and Curtis McGhee from Omaha, were rounded up and presented as the ruthless murderers. In August 1978, an all-white jury from Pottawattamie County rejected Terry Harrington's claims of innocence. Harrington insisted he was at a music concert and was later visiting one of his former high school football coaches. The prosecution found a crime lab analyst who testified at Harrington's jury trial that gunshot residue was recovered from a jacket seized from Harrington's home.

The prosecution's case came together after a young man named Kevin Hughes was arrested for involvement in a stolen car ring. After promises of leniency from the police and a $5,000 reward, Hughes agreed to testify that he, Harrington and McGhee tried to steal a car at the lot in Council Bluffs and that Harrington fatally shot the 56-year-old John Schweer, at the dealership.[113]

Harrington served out of his life prison sentence at the Iowa Department of Corrections. The 1980s rolled by, so did the 1990s. Then, in 1999, he had his first encounter with Lawrence Farwell, PhD.

---

113. The National Registry for Exonerations, Curtis McGhee

"I am a Harvard-educated forensic neuroscientist and founder of brain fingerprinting. I have testified in court as an expert witness on brain fingerprinting. I have conducted research on brain fingerprinting at the FBI, the CIA, and the U.S. Navy. TIME magazine named me one of the TIME 100: The Next Wave, the top innovators of this century who may be 'the Picassos of Einsteins of the 21st Century," Farwell said.[114]

In 1991, Farwell published literature on brain fingerprinting and was awarded a patent in 1994 and 1995.

Brain fingerprinting expert Dr. Lawrence Farwell has been honored by TIME magazine as one of the magazine's future Einsteins of the 21st century.

One of Dr. Farwell's brain fingerprinting clients, Terry Harrington of Omaha was in an Iowa prison for decades for the murder of a retired Iowa police officer that Harrington did not commit.

---

114. Affidavit of Lawrence Farwell, PhD. April 26, 2017

"The technique has a known and very low error rate. The science underlying brain fingerprinting is well accepted in the scientific community."

"For national security reasons, I was not allowed to publish the details of the research conducted by myself and my colleagues at the FBI, the CIA, and the U.S. Navy until 2012," Farwell said. "Abstracts and brief reports that were published prior to that time did not disclose the specific methods that produced the highly accurate and reliable results reported in these studies."

On March 5, 2001, Farwell presented his brain fingerprinting analysis in the Iowa District Court for Pottawattamie County, in the murder case involving condemned Iowa prisoner Terry Harrington.

So how does this revolutionary testing procedure work?

"Brain fingerprinting detects information stored in the brain. It does not detect how that information got there. Information that the suspect knows from reading a newspaper, from interrogations, or from hearing testimony at a trial is not applicable in a brain fingerprinting test," Farwell said, because, "A finding that an individual knew such information would prove nothing about his participation in the crime. Knowledge of such information could be explained by his having read the newspaper, participated in the trial, etc."

To do the test, Dr. Farwell uses EEG, electro-encephalography, to measure an electrical event starting three hundred milliseconds after the exposure to the stimulus.

"If the person is a witness to or perpetrator of the crime, his response to stimuli that embody accurate details of the crime will evoke a P300 response," Farwell said.

Farwell has used the test on people and their purported alibi statements, but he admits there are some drawbacks in that area.

"However, in the case of an alibi, all that can usually be determined is whether the alibi story has validity as the subject's remembered experience. It is not usually possible to determine whether the exact timing of the alibi experience places the subject away from the crime scene at the time of the crime," he said.

And that's helped Dr. Farwell perfect his patented brain fingerprinting test.

"Brain fingerprinting provides definitive, reliable, valid scientific evidence regarding whether specific information is stored in a particular brain or not. Brain fingerprinting, like other forensic sciences, does not make a scientific determination of guilty or not guilty. That is a legal decision to be made by the judge and or jury," Farwell said.

In 2000, Terry Harrington attempted to overturn his 1978 Council Bluffs, Iowa, murder conviction for killing the retired police captain by arguing the Farwell brain fingerprinting test amounted to newly discovered evidence. "In the Harrington case, I developed a series of probes for the crime scene and a separate series of probes for the petitioner's alibi, from previously undisclosed police files, interviews with witnesses, examination of the location where the crime took place, and other evidence," Farwell said.

"I administered the test of Harrington in May 2000, and in October 2000 I rendered a report to the Iowa District Court analyzing the P300-MERMER responses. I supplemented the report with a separate analysis based solely on P300 brainwave responses on November 10, 2000. Both analyses produced a result of 'information absent' regarding the crime scene probes and 'information present' regarding the alibi probes, with a high degree of statistical confidence, over ninety-nine percent.

"This indicates that the record stored in Harrington's brain does not match the crime scene and does match his alibi," Farwell said.

Judge Timothy O'Grady of the Iowa District Court held a one-day hearing on the brain fingerprinting evidence presented by Dr. Farwell, on November 14, 2000.

"At the November 14 session, I testified and was cross-examined on the basis of my test reports. After the briefs were submitted and other unrelated grounds for post-conviction relief were tried, District Judge Timothy O'Grady issued his ruling on March 5, 2001, the court determined that brain fingerprinting was new evidence not available at the original trial and that it was sufficiently reliable to merit admission of the evidence. However, the court did not regard its weight as sufficiently compelling, in light of the record as a whole, as meeting its exacting standard, and thus it denied a new trial on this and the other grounds asserted by Harrington."

On the other spectrum, Dr. Farwell was involved in a 1999 brain fingerprinting experiment on James Grinder in Missouri.

"A Brain Fingerprinting test I conducted in 1999 showed that Grinder had the record of the 1984 murder of Julie Helton stored in his brain. Grinder and other alleged witnesses and suspects had previously given several contradictory accounts, some involving his participation and some not. The Brain Fingerprinting test showed that the account that matched the record in his brain was the one in which Grinder perpetrated the crime," Farwell said. "One week later, faced with a certain conviction and almost certain death sentence, Grinder pled guilty in exchange for a sentence of life without parole."

On May 2, 2016, Dr. Farwell performed his patented court-approved brain fingerprinting test on the man condemned to life imprisonment for Teresa's brutal killing in Manitowoc County, Wisconsin.

"The data analysis program that I applied … in the Avery case was more sophisticated than the previously available analysis methods," Dr. Farwell said. "As in every crime, the brain of the perpetrator was central to the phenomenon revealed by the newly discovered blood-spatter evidence in the Avery case. The perpetrator's feet stood behind the car. The perpetrator's hands wielded the object and struck Teresa. The perpetrator's feet and hands, however, cannot operate independently. The perpetrator's brain controlled the actions of his hands and feet.

"The perpetrator's brain is different from the brain of an innocent person. The perpetrator's brain processed the information that, one, Teresa was behind the car and, two, the cargo door was open when the perpetrator attacked and struck Teresa."

Farwell noted his brain fingerprinting test would detect the difference between the brain of the perpetrator and an innocent person.

Obviously, Avery already knew lots of information about Teresa's murder case, based on his interactions with her on the day of her disappearance, from his interviews and interrogations with police, and from sitting through a five-week jury trial in 2007.

"Mr. Avery acknowledges knowing all of this. He claims that he knows information about surrounding events only through innocent participation in these events and not through participation in the murder itself," Farwell said.

"Prior to the Brain Fingerprinting test, Mr. Avery explicitly stated that he did not commit the attack on Teresa, nor did he witness the crime. He explicitly stated that no one had told him the specific details of the perpetrator's initial attack on the victim."

Here are some of the key questions that arose during Dr. Farwell's interview.

"Do you know where the victim was in relation to her vehicle when the perpetrator attacked and wounded her?

"Do you know if she was behind the car, in the driver's seat, or on the passenger side?"

"Such questions obtained a denial from Mr. Avery that he knew the relevant information, without revealing the correct information about the crime. If Mr. Avery did not commit the crime, he would have no way of knowing that the perpetrator attacked when, one, she was behind the car and two, the cargo door was open. He explicitly denied knowing these details about the crime on the basis of his contention that he did not commit or otherwise participate in the crime," Dr. Farwell said.

"This test was structured to determine definitively and scientifically whether or not two specific salient features of the murder of Teresa Halbach were stored in Mr. Avery's brain: A) where the victim was in relation to her vehicle when the perpetrator attacked and wounded her: **behind car.** B) The configuration of the victim's vehicle when the perpetrator attacked the victim: **cargo door open."**

According to Dr. Farwell, the probe stimuli for brain fingerprinting test he conducted on Avery were "behind car" and "cargo door open."

"I told Mr. Avery that he would see a phrase correctly specifying where the victim was in relation to her vehicle when the perpetrator attacked and wounded her but did not inform Mr. Avery that the correct information probe stimulus was 'behind car.' I told Mr. Avery that he would see a phrase correctly specifying the 'configuration of the victim's vehicle when the perpetrator attacked the victim' but I did not inform Mr. Avery that the correct information probe stimulus was 'cargo door open,'" Dr. Farwell said.

Also, a number of irrelevant stimuli were developed for the test such as the victim having had a Saab 9 5 and Volvo S40. The irrelevant stimuli regarding Teresa's death were a deep stream and a golf club.

"For Mr. Avery or anyone else with a basic knowledge of the crime, clearly the target stimuli were correct, crime-relevant information and the corresponding irrelevant stimuli were irrelevant and had nothing to do with the crime."

Here's what Dr. Farwell told Avery prior to giving the test.

"The perpetrator attacked the victim, wounded her, and ultimately killed her. At trial, one specific attack with one specific weapon was extensively discussed, so everyone knows about that attack, including you. Just because you know about it, does not mean you did it, only that you heard about it at the trial.

"There was another attack with another method that was not mentioned at the trial. The perpetrator knows about that other attack, where it took place, and what happened, but an innocent suspect does not know these things.

"If you are innocent, you do not know anything about the other attack that took place because you were not there. If you are guilty, you know details about the other attack because you did it. This Brain Fingerprinting test will determine whether or not you know specific details about this other attack that was never mentioned at the trial; that no one ever told you about."

Farwell's experiments don't make determinations based on a visual inspection of the brainwave data, he emphasized. Instead, he uses mathematics to compute whether the "information present" or "information absent" is stored in the person's brain.

So what did he find for Avery?

"These results mean that scientific testing has determined with a 99.9 percent statistical confidence that Mr. Avery does not know certain specific details about the attack on Teresa Halbach," Farwell concluded. "This salient, crime-relevant information, which was experienced by the perpetrator when he committed the crime, is not stored in Mr. Avery's brain. Specifically, this information comprises the details that were revealed by the newly discovered blood-spatter evidence and embodied in the probe stimuli.

"This provides scientific evidence that Mr. Avery does not know specific critical, salient crime-relevant information regarding what actually took place at the time that the perpetrator attacked Teresa Halbach."

In the case of the condemned Omaha man, Terry Harrington, an Iowa judge allowed the experiments performed by Dr. Farwell that revealed his client was not involved in the murder of the retired Council Bluffs, Iowa police captain, but in the end, District Judge O'Grady rejected Harrington's post-conviction appeal and chose to keep Harrington incarcerated for the late 1970s murder that Harrington did not commit.

In 2003, Harrington's long fight to bring his injustice to an end came to a successful resolution when his case went before the Iowa Supreme Court. In April 2003, the Iowa Supreme Court ordered Harrington get a new trial. That October, Harrington was finally freed and prosecutors announced they would not retry the murder case against Harrington, who lost about twenty-five years of his life to a shotgun murder committed by somebody else.

Harrington and his codefendant, McGhee, were both exonerated and their case is now featured on the National Registry of Exonerations. Harrington and McGhee later obtained settlements from the cops in Iowa who were responsible for pinning the retired cop's murder on them, allowing the real killer, believed to be a white person, to walk free.

In 2013, the Omaha newspaper reported "Council Bluffs To Pay $6.2 Million To Settle Lawsuit with Wrongfully Convicted Omaha Men."

The article indicated Harrington and McGhee would be paid $2.3 million immediately and the rest would come in six annual payments of more than $528,500. A final payment of $728,500 would come in July 2020.

"The two were freed in 2003 when the Iowa Supreme Court determined that prosecutors committed misconduct by concealing reports about another man seen near the crime scene with a shotgun. The pair sued Pottawattamie County, eventually settling for $12 million," the article noted.

While housed in the Iowa Department of Corrections with his life wasting away, Harrington begged for the chance to take the brain fingerprinting test, insisting it would prove his innocence to the district court judge.

It eventually did.

As for Avery, his lawyer tells this author: "He was adamant about taking Dr. Farwell's brain fingerprinting test. Mr. Avery believed that the test was one hundred percent accurate in detecting if he was lying. Guilty people absolutely do not request new forensic testing or submit themselves to a test that could reveal their deceptions."

Zellner said there have been countless times during her representation of Steven Avery where he has made it clear to her that he is completely willing to undergo any kinds of testing and questioning if it helps prove his innocence.

"One of the biggest breakthrough moments was when Mr. Avery was so adamant about wanting all of the additional forensic testing done on the RAV4 and any other items we wanted to test," Zellner told the author.

For her, the recent scientific testing upon the bullet that was likely planted on the floor in Avery's garage in March 2006, was a huge deal for her side, and will be crucial as Avery's appeal moves forward. That item of trial evidence became known as Item FL.

"The second breakthrough moment was the discovery of the wood and paint on the bullet, but no bone," Zellner said. "I knew the State's entire theory about FL was false. The third breakthrough moment was the cumulative effect of not being able to replicate any of the State's forensic evidence.

"All of it was flawed."

But like she has had to do in many of her most high-profile wrongful convictions, Zellner will have to win Avery's innocence at the appellate level. Since she became involved in the case in 2016, following Judge Willis' retirement at the Manitowoc County Courthouse, the case got passed off to a judge from neighboring Sheboygan County, Angela Sutkiewicz.

She has a reputation for being a terrible judge and unfair judge. She was the subject of an unflattering investigative article produced by the USA TODAY NETWORK Wisconsin's investigative reporter Eric Litke, who is the state's leading reporter when it comes to analyzing Wisconsin's judicial system.

One of Litke's pieces revealed Sutkiewicz had an astonishing record that no judge should be proud of.

She was the fourth most substituted judge in the entire state of Wisconsin, an amazing feat because she isn't even in one of the state's most populated counties. Being the subject of repetitive substitution requests illustrates that the judge is not considered fair and not considered a knowledgeable person when it comes to interpreting the law. In other words, she's basically known as a hack judge, lazy and uninformed, not an exemplary member of Wisconsin's judiciary.

When it came to Avery's case, Sutkiewicz made it clear in her rulings that this was not a case to which she wanted to devote considerable time and attention. When she issued her first ruling on October 3, 2017, rejecting Avery's post-conviction appeal, her entire review of Zellner's motions and exhibits was less than six pages long.

"The reports submitted by the defendant are equivocal in their conclusions and do not establish an alternate interpretation of the evidence," Judge Sutkiewicz's ruling states. "Given the totality of the evidence submitted at trial and the ambiguous conclusions as stated in the experts' reports, it cannot be said that a reasonable probability exists that a different result would be reached at a new trial based on these reports. Finally, in light of the discussion of the evidence above and the conclusion with relation to the ability to appeal and venue for an appeal, the defendant has failed to establish any grounds that would trigger the right to a new trial in the interests of justice. As such, no further consideration will be given to this issue."

Wisconsin's Court of Appeals later kicked the case back to Judge Sutkiewicz after determining the lower court judge still needed to address an item Zellner had raised in her post-conviction motion regarding the computer disk Kratz had withheld from Buting and Strang regarding the violent pornography on Bobby Dassey's computer.

Realizing she got stuck with a stinker of an elected judge, Zellner filed a motion on June 14, 2018, asking Judge Sutkiewicz to step aside from the case.

"Moreover, for the convenience of the judiciary, the parties, and witnesses, Mr. Avery respectfully requests that his case be reassigned to a judge in Manitowoc County," Zellner said. "The record, evidence, and many of the witnesses in this matter are located in Manitowoc. All pleadings are filed with the clerk of the circuit court of Manitowoc. In short, at this juncture holding further proceedings in Manitowoc before a Manitowoc judge would be the most efficient use of judicial resources. At this juncture in Mr. Avery's case, all of the prior reasons for holding the legal proceedings outside of Manitowoc no longer exist ... Mr. Avery respectfully requests a substitution of judge in accordance with Wisconsin Statute 801.58."[115]

Judge Sutkiewicz ruled the motion before her was "premature."

She explained the Court of Appeals had kicked the case back to her to make a decision in regard to the new evidence, namely the CD. However, it was clear that under no circumstances did Judge Sutkiewicz want to allow Zellner's side to present evidence and call witnesses in her courtroom.

---

115. Defendant's Motion for Substitution of Judge, filed June 14, 2018

Instead, the Sheboygan judge had two objectives: one, being to prolong Avery's case on her court docket as long as practical and, secondly, to ensure that the state of Wisconsin, namely the Office of Attorney General Brad Schimel, did not, under any circumstances, lose the case.

Finally, on September 6, 2018, Judge Sutkiewicz issued an eleven-page ruling, again rejecting Zellner's bid for a new trial related to the Brady violation allegation surrounding the violent pornography computer disk Fassbender and Kratz chose to withhold from Buting and Strang as they prepared for trial, and were trying to build a strong case for a third-party alternative suspect defense.

"This matter is back before this court for a limited review pursuant to an order from the Court of Appeals," the judge wrote. "The defendant alleges that the prosecution withheld a CD created from a seized computer drive and that the failure to turn over this item of discovery directly impacted the defense in both the trial and appellate courts."

In her final analysis, Judge Sutkiewicz concluded, "In order for the defendant to establish that there was a Brady violation in a criminal prosecution, the defendant must prove that evidence was suppressed by the State. In this case, the defendant fails on this first burden."

In embarrassing fashion, the judge's written ruling showed her true colors and how little she even knew about Teresa's murder case. In her September 8, 2018 ruling, Judge Angie Sutkiewicz referred to the seized computer in question as being the computer of "**Brandon**" Dassey. As everyone familiar with the case knows, the 16-year-old nephew's name is Brendon Dassey, not **Brandon Dassey**.

"I believe we have an excellent chance of getting Mr. Avery's case reversed on appeal," Zellner assured this author. "It is much easier to get a case reversed for a hearing than to get a reversal of an adverse ruling after an evidentiary hearing."

In Avery's case, Judge Sutkiewicz staunchly refused to grant Zellner a chance to present evidence to show why the defendant should be granted a second trial.

For that reason, Zellner is upbeat and positive.

On September 8, 2018, Zellner proclaimed on her Twitter account: "So far only 1 Judge has ruled on Avery. At least 10 more will review before a final decision is made – on this evidence. If he is not freed we will file again. Never going to end until he is free."

At one point in time, before Zellner's involvement on Avery's case, Judge Sutkiewicz was simultaneously handling Mr. Avery's post-conviction motion in 2013 and the Halbach family's wrongful death lawsuit against Mr. Avery.

"Judge Willis immediately recused himself from the wrongful death lawsuit when he was given these dual assignments. Judge Sutkiewicz kept both cases and then delayed the voluntary dismissal on the wrongful death case of the Halbach's until Mr. Avery finally filed a motion complaining about her failure to dismiss, despite the Halbach's request to do so. She quickly granted the voluntary dismissal after Mr. Avery's motion to the appellate court was filed," Zellner said.

But it's also Judge Sutkiewicz's ties to Kratz that has Zellner concerned about justice and fairness for her client. Even though Kratz became an outcast in Wisconsin's legal community, there are still a number of lawyers and judges who worked with him over the years who don't want to rock the boat or say anything disparaging about Kratz.

"We are aware that Judge Sutkiewicz sat on the Wisconsin Crime Victim's Rights Board, as a private citizen, with former prosecutor Ken Kratz," Zellner said. "We attempted to have another judge substituted for her but she denied our motion as being 'premature.'

"We will re-file that motion if the appellate court reverses her dismissal of the Avery post-conviction motion. Her dismissal orders fail to address the vast majority of issues we raised."

In preparation for this book's publication, Zellner told this true-crime author "it is impossible to predict how long it will take to get the conviction reversed. The case was dead in the water for eleven years when I came on board. I think it is remarkable all of the evidence we have uncovered despite this significant lapse of time."

Overall, Zellner is very proud of what her team has accomplished in less than three full years on Avery's case, starting on it from scratch.

Sooner or later, other courts, other more sophisticated judges, other more experienced judges, will take notice.

"We have demonstrated that all of the State's forensic evidence used to convict Mr. Avery is flawed because none of this evidence can be replicated," she said. "By that I mean the blood was selectively dripped in the RAV4. Neither the quantity or location of the blood came from an actively bleeding finger."

The bullet used to persuade jurors of Avery's guilt is another major component of Zellner's quest to prove her client got convicted on manufactured evidence.

"The bullet with Teresa's DNA on it did not go through her head or any other part of her body," Zellner says convincingly.

"The quantity of DNA on the key and hood latch shows it was planted. No human body was ever burned in Mr. Avery's burn pit. The license plates and electronic devices were easy to plant. If the results of a scientific study cannot be duplicated, the results are considered invalid. The same principle applies here to the State's forensic evidence. It cannot be replicated."

CHAPTER TWENTY-NINE

BOBBY'S GARAGE

When Strang and Buting were preparing for trial, they had retained the services of Pete Baetz, the retired Illinois police detective whose claim to fame was that he was involved in the congressional investigation of James Earl Ray surrounding the 1968 assassination of Martin Luther King Jr. After retiring from law enforcement, Baetz moved back to his native Manitowoc County. However, the defense was handicapped at trial because Kratz had failed to turn over the computer disk with the violent pornography on Bobby Dassey's computer. As a result, Strang and Buting were unable to aggressively present a convincing case pointing the finger at Bobby Dassey as the more likely killer of Teresa Halbach.

Baetz has remained unwavering in his belief that the most likely people involved in Teresa's murder and dismemberment were Bobby Dassey and Scott Tadych. In 2016, he reached out and spoke with Kathleen T. Zellner about his suspicions and never heard back from the firm. Then, in 2018, he got a call out of the blue. It was Zellner.

Baetz told the author that Tadych had apparently become paranoid since Zellner has aggressively put him and Bobby under the microscope. Baetz said he learned from Zellner that Tadych is making sure he picks up all of his cigarette butts for fear that somebody would retrieve them since he could leave his DNA on them.

"The background we had done on him is that we had an individual who had no respect for women and he was aggressive with them," Baetz said. "He is what we cops would call an asshole."

Baetz said the story presented at trial suggesting that Teresa's body was burned in Avery's outdoor burn pile pit was preposterous. Baetz said the burn pit was almost on top of the garage and if the flames got as high as Tadych testified at trial, the entire garage would have gone up in flames and the propane gas tank that was also nearby likely would have caught fire and caused a great explosion.

Baetz said that any old-school detective, someone familiar with flames and burning trash, would have realized Teresa's body was incinerated inside of a fifty-gallon steel drum. Nobody in their right mind would have taken the chance of simply tossing the body outside because the weather elements are too unpredictable.

The use of a burn barrel would allow the killer to conceal the crime because nobody would see there was a body inside unless they physically walked to the barrel and peered inside.

And, the fact remains, several of Teresa's bones were recovered from the bottom of Bobby's burn barrel and nobody else's, Baetz said.

Although Baetz suspects the police from Manitowoc County were involved in rampant evidence planting and manufacturing during the case against Avery, he always doubted the notion that the scattered bones found at Avery's burn pile pit were put there by the cops. For starters, two of the biggest bones that were found turned up on the edge, not within the burn pit itself. Another reason why Baetz didn't think the police put the bones there was because of Bear, Avery's mean and vicious junkyard dog. Baetz said he had a chance to encounter Bear during his time working as the criminal investigator for Strang and Buting.

Bear was the type of dog that would attack and constantly bark if a stranger or prowler ever set foot on Avery's trailer property. The dog was on a metal chain and kept outside. The fact that the dog never went berserk leads Baetz to believe that Teresa's bones were transported under the cloak of darkness from Bobby's yard to the burn pile pit, where the barrel was spilled, but unknown to Bobby at the time, he failed to remove all of the bones, and that's why some of the bones remained at the bottom of his barrel when it was confiscated by the Manitowoc County Sheriff's Office on Sunday, November 6.

Baetz said there were two dubious actions taken by Tadych and Bobby around the time of the crime that also factored into his suspicions that both men had something to do with the killing.

The first was Bobby's first statement to the police, on November 6. That was when Bobby told Dedering he and Tadych both passed each other traveling on State Highway 147 but that the investigator should interview Tadych because Tadych would remember the area where they passed each other going in opposite directions on the two-lane state highway.

"It was very valuable for them to have a mutual alibi," Baetz said. "Again, that was so self-serving."

Whoever killed Teresa also dismembered her body, removing her arms, her legs, her torso, Baetz said. Most people don't realize that dismembering a body is an extremely messy and nasty job, Baetz said. Unlike most of his family, Steven Avery was not an avid hunter, Baetz added, but on the other hand, Bobby and Tadych were both avid hunters and both men had substantial experience at dismembering the carcass of a dead deer.

Both men claimed they were out deer hunting at separate locations around the time of Teresa's murder. However, in the aftermath of Teresa's disappearance, after the Manitowoc County Sheriff's Office was becoming a regular presence on Avery Road investigating Teresa's disappearance, it seems Bobby took the initiative to scour the country roads and find a dead deer carcass, throw it into the back of his truck, and bring it home.

In addition, he also made it a point to visit one of the local convenience stores to make them aware of the deer carcass he retrieved. He obtained a deer tag, which also generated a paper trail, which was handy to have when the police arrived and sought to question him about the blood spatter in his garage.

In the days after the Manitowoc County police began poking around Avery Road following Teresa's disappearance, Bobby Dassey scoured the countryside to retrieve a dead deer. He then kept the butchered deer carcass and hung it inside his garage for many days while the homicide investigation was still ongoing.

At 7:33 p.m. on Friday, November 4, authorities were notified that a deer was struck by a car just east of Larabee.

The following morning, the RAV 4 was identified on the Avery property. A massive police presence took over Avery Road for the next eight consecutive days and when the police opened Bobby's garage to look around, a dead deer carcass was strung up in the air.

The deer, Baetz said, was another perfect diversion to fool the police.

When the police arrived, it appeared as if Bobby was skinning a deer. "It was BS," Baetz said. "And if they dismembered the victim there, the police never did any forensic examination of that spot itself."

Baetz suspects Bobby either saw the deer or heard it on the police scanner and ran out to get it as soon as he could. "It would have been great for covering up the blood," Baetz said.

During the murder investigation, the Dasseys made the police aware they had lawfully taken the deer off the road, furnishing a tag they got at the local store to allow them to keep it.

"I think the deer being hit was a propitious incident. The deer gets hit and they take advantage of a situation that would help. They're always thinking of how can we cover up? There's a backup plan, and that's why they got it certified with a tag through the Department of Natural Resources," Baetz said. "Everything is covered."

Baetz said that dismembering the body inside the garage would be the perfect place to do the dastardly act. The garage would be closed, and it offered the comfort of privacy, unlike taking apart the body out in the woods, for example.

"You do it in your garage. You will be able to control it. That's when it was done and it was done in those burn barrels," he said.

Josh Radandt's affidavit indicates he saw a fire reminiscent of a burning barrel, in the area of where Bobby Dassey lived. "The electronic components of Ms. Halbach were burned in the Dassey burn barrel behind the residence at approximately 4:30 to 5 p.m. That fire was observed in the Dassey burn barrel by Josh Radandt," Zellner's filing states.

Baetz said he's also pretty sure what was used to take apart Teresa's body.

"I think they used a meat saw," he said. "Actually, dismembering a human body is not an easy task. It's extremely difficult. And if you get to take off the limbs, it's a nasty job. But if you've done this to deer before, you're comfortable."

Here are some of the key events of October 31, 2005, concerning Bobby Dassey's behavior, as outlined by Zellner, on August 9, 2018.

"Bobby had developed an obsession with Ms. Halbach and on a number of occasions watched her from his residence and commented on her visits the next day."

"Mr. Avery did not leave the Dassey phone number with *Auto Trader* because he was waiting for a return call on his cell phone or landline to confirm the appointment. Because Bobby was awake, he would have heard the voice mail message left by Ms. Halbach on the Dassey answering machine at 11:43 a.m. … Bobby was the only person who could have listened to Ms. Halbach's voice message to the Dassey residence at 11:43 a.m. and known that Ms. Halbach did not have an address for the appointment."

"Bobby lied to the police when he denied knowing that on October 31, 2005, Ms. Halbach was coming to the property."

"Bobby told police that he saw Ms. Halbach by her vehicle for approximately 10 seconds. However, Bobby was able to describe Ms. Halbach's clothing, physique and hair style, indicating that he had more direct contact with Ms. Halbach than simply seeing her out of his window for 10 seconds."

"The Dassey computer Internet browsing data indicates that 22 pornographic searches were made on October 31, 2005. Bobby's computer was in use on October 31, 2005, which impeaches his trial testimony that he was asleep from 6:30 a.m. to 2 p.m. The computer was used to access the Internet on October 31, 2005, at 6:05 a.m., 6:28 a.m., 6:31 a.m., 7:00 a.m., 9:33 a.m., 10:09 a.m., 1:08 p.m., and 1:51 p.m."

"As Ms. Halbach left the property, Bobby followed her in his Blazer."

"Ms. Halbach's cell phone records indicate that she had left the Avery property by 2:41 p.m. and headed west on

State Highway 147 and south on County Highway Q. It was established at trial that Ms. Halbach frequently did hustle shots. Because Bobby lied about following Ms. Halbach from the Avery property, he most likely is the person who waved her down for a hustle shot. Ms. Halbach was in the area of Kuss Road, so it is a reasonable inference that she stopped her vehicle for the hustle shot at the Kuss Road cul-de-sac."

"The blood spatter on the inside of the RAV4 cargo door demonstrates that a struggle ensued between Ms. Halbach and her attacker."

"The dog alerts indicate that Ms. Halbach was in the area of the suspected burial site for a period of time where she may have been assaulted."

The scientific testing by Zellner's crew of world-renowned experts validates her position that the killer put Teresa's unconscious body into the back of Teresa's vehicle and drove the sports utility vehicle back to Avery Road near 4 p.m.

"The hair bloodstain patterns ... were created by Ms. Halbach being placed in the rear cargo area of the RAV4 and her injured head bouncing on the inside panel as the RAV4 was moving. It is a reasonable inference that Ms. Halbach and her vehicle were brought back to the Avery Salvage Yard after she left the property the first time."

There are two supporting eyewitnesses who back up her theory. One individual is John Leurquin, who was a propane truck driver for Valders Co-Op who spent time on Avery's property on Halloween.

He was called as a defense team witness by Strang and Buting. He testified matter-of-factly that "a vehicle similar to Ms. Halbach's drove past him at 3:45 to 3:50 p.m. Mr. Leurquin was uncertain whether the driver was male or female or which direction the vehicle turned as it exited the Avery property."

During the trial, Leurquin testified he loaded his propane truck for commercial and residential customer deliveries "on the southeast corner of Avery Road and 147."[116]

His work schedule was 7:30 a.m. to 4 p.m.

Buting: "Now on October 31, 2005, do you recall seeing any particular vehicle that later it became of interest to you?"

"Uh, yes. I recall seeing a green SUV. Uh, midsize SUV. Not the large size. It was smaller."

"OK. So tell us what you saw?"

"I seen a vehicle pass by the front of my truck, and I just glanced up, and it was a green SUV and that's all."

"Well, which direction was it going?"

"Back towards Avery Road. So that would be to the north. I mean, towards 147. It was leaving."

When asked on the witness stand if he was "a friend of the Avery's" the witness testified, "No."

"Did you happen to see which direction that green SUV went when it got to the intersection of Highway 147?"

"No, I didn't pay attention."

That same afternoon sixteen-year-old Brendan Dassey and older brother Blaine arrived home on their yellow school bus.

"I do not have any personal knowledge of who made the appointment with Auto Trader to have my mother's van photographed but I did help clean the van so that it could be sold," Blaine Dassey said.

"On October 31, 2005, when the school bus driver brought Brendan and me home as we traveled west on State Highway 147, I saw Bobby on State Highway 147 in a bluish or greenish vehicle heading towards Mishicot. Bobby was not driving his black Blazer. Bobby was not home the rest of the evening while I was home."[117]

---

116. John Leurquin, direct testimony March 8, 2007, Avery trial

117. Affidavit of Blaine Dassey, June 25, 2018

Blaine's affidavit also addressed the dark Internet searches made from the Dassey personal computer, the one that his mother hired someone to reformat as the murder case was widening in early 2006.

"There was only one computer at the residence and it was always in Bobby's room sitting near a desk. The computer had a password. The computer had an AOL dial-up Internet connection. Bobby was the primary user of the computer.

"At no time did I ever do searches for pornographic images or words related to pornography, words related to violence, words related to death, words related to mutilations, words related to torture, words related to guns or knives, words related to Teresa Halbach, words related to Steven Avery, words related to DNA, or words related to dead, mutilated, or dismembered female bodies."

Blaine Dassey's sworn statement indicates the only time he used the computer was for homework and occasionally to send instant messages to people.

"At no time did I ever create a folder for Teresa Halbach, my Uncle Steven, DNA, or news stories on the murder."

***

On August 9, 2018, in her thirty-second month representing Avery, Zellner unveiled to Wisconsin's criminal justice system how she suspects the murder was orchestrated and why the property next to Avery was the real site of suspicion.

"It is a reasonable inference that Ms. Halbach was shot by Bobby's .22 LR because Scott Tadych attempted to sell Bobby's .22 LR the next week to a fellow employee at the Wisconsin Aluminum Foundry. The Dassey garage was never luminoled or checked for forensic evidence of any type; however, blood, which was never tested, was found between the Dassey garage and residence."

As far as the victim's vehicle, Zellner argues it was backed into Bobby's garage and then it was dumped by a tree near the Mishicot dam. On Halloween, before sunset, eyewitness Paul Burdick remembers he saw the vehicle. Witness Kevin Rahmlow saw the RAV4 in the same spot over the next few days, including November 2 and 3.

The distance to the old dam is 1.7 miles, a twenty to thirty minute walk, according to Zellner.

Zellner has submitted to the court the police statement of Bobby's mother, who was questioned about the deer carcass back on November 6, 2005, which was two days after the deer was killed. However, her statement gave the police the impression the deer was hit on November 3, when that was clearly not the case.

"Barbara Janda told the agents that her son, Bobby, had gotten a deer and that a deer carcass was hanging in Janda's garage. Barbara stated that the deer was gutted out and skinned. Barbara told agents that the deer hanging in her garage had been road kill, which Bobby had received Thursday evening, November 3, 2005."

The statement goes on to explain that mother and son gutted the deer at the site where it was killed. "After Bobby gutted the deer, Barbara and Bobby went to 310 Mobil located between Mishicot and Manitowoc on Highway 310 in order to register the deer … After they hung the deer up, Barbara and Bobby skinned the deer the same night … Barbara told the agents that the deer has not moved from where they had hung it since that time. Barbara told the agents that they only took the inner tenderloins out while the deer was hanging in Barbara's garage."

"It is a reasonable inference that Ms. Halbach was dismembered in the Dassey garage because of Bobby's attempt to conceal evidence by hanging a deer in the Dassey garage and lying about the time frame of when that happened."

On Halloween, the victim's body was put into one of the Dassey family burn barrels and taken over to the Manitowoc County Gravel Pit after dark, Zellner believes. The gravel pit is massive and it's bordered by other gravel pits.

Zellner said that her client asserts that Bobby was the only one in the family who regularly hunted inside the county-owned gravel pit, that Bobby knew the terrain and topography and that he often burned his deer carcass inside a burn barrel.

"Ms. Halbach's body was burned in the Dassey burn barrel and the odor was detected by Travis Groelle as he was working on County Highway Q after sunset. On October 31, Bobby was two hours late leaving for work from the Avery property. He did not leave for work until 11:30 p.m.

"Once the burning of the body finished at the gravel pit, somewhere in the neighborhood of 60 percent of the bones and most of the teeth got taken elsewhere for burning," Zellner maintains. "Some of her bones were inadvertently dropped on the ground in three locations in the Manitowoc gravel pit."

From her review of the Calumet County evidence tag numbers, Zellner realized there were actually three separate locations in the county gravel pit where piles of human bones were recovered by the police. Pile 1 was where the charred pelvic bones were found. However, there was a great distance within the quarry from Pile 1 to Piles 2 and 3. Pile 1 was 474 yards away from Pile 2. The distance from Pile 1 to Pile 3 was 518 yards. On the other hand, the human bones found in Piles 2 and 3 were much closer to each other, a distance of only 48 yards apart.

Zellner said she discovered the existence of the two other human bone piles, in addition to the one with the pelvic bones, after analyzing the evidence tags. The tags contained identifiers for where the bones were found as part of the DCI's investigative police report that was reviewed by Dr. Leslie Eisenberg, the state's forensic anthropologist, who testified for the prosecution at Avery's trial.

The realization that there were multiple sites within the quarry with charred human bones has Zellner convinced that someone was attempting to scatter the bones there by dumping them out of a burn barrel under the cover of darkness.

However, the barrel was put back on Bobby's property still containing a number of charred human bones of Teresa.

On November 3, news broke about Teresa's disappearance and Avery told Bobby and others about Sgt. Colborn's visit to Avery Road to question Avery. At that time, Avery's middle finger injury from two weeks earlier had busted open.

"When Mr. Avery left the property to go to Menard's, Bobby entered Mr. Avery's trailer and wiped up blood from Mr. Avery's sink. He transported the blood to the RAV4 and selectively dripped the blood into Ms. Halbach's vehicle in order to frame Mr. Avery for the murder. Bobby was the only one who could have planted Mr. Avery's blood in the sink during the crucial time period before the blood complexly coagulated."[118]

It's an undeniable fact that Avery saw tail lights by his trailer shortly after he and his brother Chuck headed over to Menard's. "It could only have been the taillights from Bobby's vehicle that Mr. Avery saw by his trailer because no one else could have driven to Mr. Avery's trailer in that time frame. Bobby is the only family member on the Avery property who was present and had access to the blood dripped in Mr. Avery's sink on November 3, 2005."

There were also the physical injuries to Bobby's body.

---

118. Defendant's Reply to State's Response to Motion to Compel Production Of Recent Re-Examination of the Dassey Computer, August 9, 2018

"Bobby had scratches on his upper back in close proximity to the time of the murder, that were consistent with human fingernails," Zellner argues.

She provided the police photographs that were taken the medical examination room of Bobby's back the week after Teresa disappeared.

In November 2017, Dedering was brought out of retirement and made a special investigator on the case to help the state of Wisconsin which remains in a win-at-all-cost mode in regard to keeping their convictions of Avery and Brendan intact.

When Dedering questioned Bobby during an interview about the computer and the violent pornography, Bobby claimed it wasn't him. He also told Dedering the personal computer was not even kept inside his bedroom.

"In Bobby's 2017 re-interview by the police, he denied that the computer was in his bedroom even though the crime scene video shows the computer in his bedroom," Zellner found.

Zellner said the computer forensic evidence shows in convincing fashion that Bobby gave false testimony during the trial claiming he was still sound asleep until 2 p.m. and woke up shortly after Teresa rolled up to photograph his mom's van.

She said her investigator Steve Kirby interviewed Bobby in 2017 and confronted him about all of the violent pornography on the computer.

She also said he remained steadfast to his story that he was watching from the distance, inside his kitchen window, as Teresa walked over to Steven Avery's red trailer and that he never saw her again.

"He stuck with his story. He was given a chance to admit he was pressured by the cops and he would not," Zellner said. "That's because the lie is his. It isn't a cop lie. It's his lie. He made it up on November 5 (2005) and he's stuck with it ever since."

When asked about the hard-core violent pornography, "my investigator confronted him and he looked ill. He looked like he wanted to throw up," Zellner said. "It's the only thing they talked to him about that elicited some display of emotion."

Zellner said she has been recognized by other lawyers, including prosecutors, for her credibility and willingness to work hand in hand with the other side.

She said she has had a long-standing policy and made it clear to the prosecution side that they can interview her client in the post-conviction process, with the only stipulation being that she can be present during the line of questioning.

She said that many prosecutors have taken her up on her offer because she realized they were interested in fairness and justice, however, in Avery's case, she has always gotten the cold shoulder treatment from the police involved in the Avery case. She said nobody from the state of Wisconsin team of the Attorney General has reached out to her in hopes of re-interviewing Avery about the case or the other people she has identified as the more likely culprits, Bobby Dassey and Scott Tadych.

"We have recently Luminoled the Dassey garage and collected buccal swabs for DNA testing because the police failed to do this," Zellner told the author on October 4, 2018. "There was a blood drop collected between the Dassey garage and house which was never tested. The most damning evidence linking Bobby Dassey to the crime, in addition to the multiple lies he has told, is the presence of Halbach's bones in the Dassey burn barrel which Bobby used frequently to burn deer remains.

"Ms. Halbach was dismembered and burned in a burn barrel according to Dr. John DeHaan and Dr. Steven Symes. The timing of the crime makes the Dassey garage a place of interest that has to be considered as the site of the murder and mutilation of Ms. Halbach."

***

In 2017, authorities in Wisconsin started to become jittery about the prospect of having their murder conviction against Avery fall apart. In other states, such as Nebraska, it's quite common for the Attorney General to call upon an outside police agency to conduct an independent and impartial re-investigation of the entire case, starting from scratch. That's how the Beatrice 6 case came to fruition. The Nebraska Attorney General, a Republican conservative, called for a task force to examine the case. The end result was that six people convicted of the 1985 rape and murder of Helen Wilson, a small-town widow, were ultimately freed and pardoned by the governor of Nebraska. The attorney general, despite backlash from the local sheriff's office, announced in 2008 that the wrong people had been put in prison and that a different person, through DNA, was the real killer.

But with Zellner making the waves rise in Wisconsin, the State's response was to bring John Dedering of the Calumet County Sheriff's Office out of retirement and appoint him to be a special investigator. It seems clear that his role on the case was to maintain the status quo, to make sure Avery and his nephew remain vilified, and that suspicions swirling toward Bobby Dassey and Scott Tadych are minimized or downplayed. In other words, Dedering's task wasn't to reexamine the case with a critical eye, to investigate allegations of evidence planting against some of his long-time work colleagues, such as Mark Wiegert.

Dedering knew what he needed to do. Report back to Wiegert and the Wisconsin Attorney General Brad Schimel with words and written reports of reassurance.

But reading between the lines, Dedering's sixty-two-page report makes it obvious which items he and the others who are interested in the preservation of their cases against Avery and Brendan Dassey are deeply concerned about regarding Zellner's probe into the crucial pieces of overlooked evidence from their investigation in 2005.

"Radandt was asked about the lights that he mentioned in the Manitowoc County pit. Radandt stated they were large search lights. Radandt was asked about the pelvic bones. Radandt stated that attorney Kathleen Zellner's team or the media mentioned the pelvic bones. Radandt stated he was never made aware of any pelvic bones by law enforcement."[119]

Dedering also interviewed Ryan Hillegas, the ex-boyfriend of Teresa, who has also been mentioned at times as a possible suspect in her death.

"I asked Ryan about the damage to the left front directional assembly of Teresa's RAV4. Ryan indicated he could not recall who he had spoken with or where he had gotten the information he relayed to Special Agent Tom Fassbender in 2005 regarding the damage and the insurance claim. Ryan stated it was unknown to him who told him about the damage or the claim. I then displayed photographs of the damaged area and the damaged directional to him, but the photographs did not jog his memory."[120]

Another interview involved Bryan Dassey, the older brother of Bobby Dassey and the other Dassey boys. He was twenty at the time of the killing. "Bryan indicated that the reason he did not spend any time around his mother Barbara Janda's residence was that he could not stand Scott Tadych and was not happy with his mother's conduct of still being married while being involved with Scott. Bryan stated he spent enough time at his mother's residence to clean up and then leave on the majority of the days. I asked Bryan if he

119. Interview of Josh Radandt, October 4, 2017, special investigator John Dedering

120. Interview of Ryan Hillegas, October 23, 2017, spec. inv. Dedering

could remember what day the deer carcass was placed in the Dassey garage and he indicated he could not remember."[121]

Finally, it was time to question Scott Tadych. Dedering teamed up with Wisconsin DCI special agent Jeff Wisch and they decided to interview Tadych in a laid back environment to make Tadych feel at ease and not under pressure. The Subway restaurant on Main Street in Mishicot was chosen as the location.

"Scott was asked if he was in any way involved in the homicide of Teresa Halbach and he indicated, 'No, not at all.' Scott was specifically asked if he killed anyone, including Teresa Halbach, and his answer was 'No.'"

At the time of the killing, Tadych lived at a mobile home on State Highway 147, the property was about five hundred yards from where Teresa's SUV was believed to have been put for several days after her disappearance.

Here's what Tadych told the two investigators he was doing on Teresa's last day of life:

"Scott stated his mother had back surgery at Aurora Bay Care in Green Bay on that date. Scott was unsure if the surgery was in the late or early morning. Scott stated that after visiting his mother, he came back to his residence … in Mishicot between 2:30 and 3:30 p.m. but thought closer to 3:30 p.m. Scott then changed into his hunting clothes and went hunting … Scott stated after hunting he changed out of his hunting clothes and went to pick up his girlfriend at the time, who is now his wife, Barbara. Scott stated he and Barbara then went back to the hospital in Green Bay to visit his mother some more …"

As the interview dragged on, another question came up regarding Teresa.

"Scott was asked if he knew or ever met Teresa Halbach and he denied knowing or having ever met her."

---

121. Interview of Bryan Dassey, November 3, 2017, spec, inv. Dedering

It became apparent Dedering's interview had less to do with questioning Tadych about whether he helped conceal Teresa's bones or conspired with Bobby Dassey. The only question concerned their relationship. "Scott stated he gets along OK with Bobby Dassey."

Dedering mostly wanted to talk about Avery, to help reinforce his side's justification for keeping Avery locked away from the outside world.

"Scott went on to indicate that Steven controlled and ruined the Avery family life in the two years that Steven was out of prison."

"Scott was asked if he had done anything that would minimize Steven's involvement such as 'fudging' statements and he indicated he had not."

Curiously, Dedering and his tag along did not ask Tadych the very same question about Bobby Dassey.[122]

The interview took a weird twist when Tadych, at the request of the two police, summoned his wife to the Subway to speak with them as well.

Their questions to her concerned the desktop computer inside her home.

"Barbara was asked about files on the computer titled, 'Teresa Halbach' and 'DNA.' Barbara stated she knew nothing about the files. Barbara stated she had never seen them and had no idea who would have created the files. Barbara denied seeing the page that showed Steven and Teresa together."

Dedering sought to pepper her with a barrage of questions about Zellner.

"Barbara was asked how many times attorney Zellner has been out to the Avery property. Barbara stated she was unsure of how many times attorney Zellner had been at the

---

122. Contact with Scott Tadych and Barbara Tadych, November 10, 2017, spec. inv. Dedering

property, and, at this point, Scott indicated this is pretty 'hush hush.'"

Minutes later, with her husband sitting with her at the Subway, she was asked why the country's foremost leading expert in exposing wrongful convictions, would be focusing so much attention on people close to her.

"Barbara was asked why she thinks Attorney Zellner is pointing the finger at Bobby and Scott and she indicated she did not know why. Barbara indicated that she never actually provided any evidence to Attorney Zellner concerning this matter."

Back in 2005, Dedering didn't bother to take steps to corroborate Tadych's alibi claiming he had spent much of the day at the hospital in Green Bay. Now, with Zellner lighting fire on the case, twelve years later, Dedering realized he needed to follow up on some of his shortcomings. On November 14, 2017, he contacted Aurora Bay Care Security in Green Bay. "I asked the representative whether there would be any existing video of the parking area or any other video from 2005. The representative indicated no videos exist from 2005 as their hard drive records override existing video every couple of months."

Zellner spent nearly three entire years dissecting the murder investigation before introducing evidence showing why she believes Bobby Dassey and Scott Tadych were involved in the murder and or dismemberment of the body.

Twelve years after conducting his first interview of Bobby Dassey, Dedering went back to question Bobby, now thirty-one. But this was hardly an interrogation. The interview took place on Bobby's terms, in a friendly setting, at his house on Horse Road in Mishicot. In fact, Dedering finished in only fifty minutes.

Zellner's filings to the Wisconsin's courts have made repeated assertions that Bobby has lied repeatedly to the police and during his trial testimony. When Dedering re-interviewed him with Jeff Wisch of the DCI on November

17, 2017, "we asked Bobby if he would be honest and truthful with us."[123]

In 2005, just five days after Teresa vanished, Bobby claimed remembering passing Tadych on the highway, which would have been around the time of Teresa's violent attack, but he urged them to interview Tadych because he would be able to remember exactly where the two passed each other and waved.

Now, with Zellner hot on his tail, the same question came up again, a dozen years later. Bobby, who was foggy before, now had a clear response.

"Bobby stated he saw Scott Tadych on State Highway 147 in the area of Jambo Creek Road. Bobby stated there is a large gravel pit in that area. Bobby stated he met Scott at approximately 3 p.m."

Questions turned to the sequence of events involving Teresa's visit to Avery Road, the last place she was seen alive.

"Bobby stated after he had awoken to go deer hunting, he looked out the front window of his mother's ... residence and saw Teresa's vehicle parked opposite to a van that his mother was going to sell ... Bobby stated the lady got out, started taking pictures and at this point, he got ready to take a shower before hunting. Bobby stated the lady was alone. Bobby stated he spent a couple of minutes in the shower and then got dressed and looked out of his window, again, and saw the lady walking toward Steven's trailer.

"Bobby stated he did not see Steven during this encounter. Bobby stated he spent maybe a couple of seconds looking out the window and during this time she was halfway to Steven's trailer ... Bobby stated he then went out to his vehicle and he did not see her when he got into his vehicle.

123. Interview of Bobby Dassey, Nov. 17, 2017 spec. inv. Dedering

Bobby stated he had no idea who she was so he really did not pay a lot of attention."

He was also questioned about his prior contacts and observations of Teresa, after all, she was a regular at Avery Salvage, having been there about a half dozen times during the previous year or so to photograph various vehicles the family wanted to sell through Auto Trader.

The question was posed if he had ever met or knew Teresa?

"Never."

Another question was asked if he knew Teresa was arriving on October 31?

"Nope."

Bobby didn't have a compelling answer when reminded that Bryan Dassey, his older brother, had given a statement to police back in November 2005, suggesting Bobby saw Teresa leave on Avery Road.

"Bobby was asked why Bryan would say something like this and Bobby responded, 'Your guess is as good as mine.'"

At this point, Dedering was obviously aware that Zellner was poking holes in the State's case concerning the dark secrets hidden on the Dassey computer, the one that was the subject of morbid, sadistic violent pornography searches only at times of the day when Bobby was home alone.

Had Bobby used the Internet and the computer, they asked him?

"If I did, it wasn't often," he answered.

"Bobby stated he thought the computer was on a desk in the living room at the time."

A police video captured by Dedering's colleague, Sgt. Bill Tyson, after Teresa vanished, conclusively showed the tower computer stationed at a desk in Bobby's own bedroom.

"Bobby stated he never downloaded any pornography. Bobby stated he may have watched porn at some point on it, but 'I don't know.'

"Bobby stated there were five guys with access to the computer and he doesn't know if they would have downloaded or viewed pornography ... Bobby identified his brothers, Blaine, Brendan, Bryan, himself, and Tom Janda as being the individuals with access to the computer.

"Bobby stated he did not use the computer much as he was working third shift at the time."

At that point in time, Bryan had a room in the basement, Blaine and Brendan shared a room and Bobby had his own room.[124]

Regarding the computer, the questions persisted.

"Bobby was asked if he knew who created the folder with the page depicting Steven and Teresa's photographs. Bobby indicated he knew how to create folders, but he had no idea as to who created those folders."

Questions about three specific computer folders then arose.

There was a 'Teresa' folder, a 'Halbach' folder, and a 'DNA' folder.

"Bobby was specifically asked who created 'Teresa' and 'Halbach' and 'DNA' folders that were on the computer and he stated he had no idea who did this. Bobby was asked if he did it and he indicated 'No.'"[125]

Finally, the topic of Kuss Road, which was about a half mile away from Avery Salvage, also came up during Bobby's follow-up interview in 2017.

This was the spot where, back in 2005, several cadaver and scent-tracking dogs were all led by their noses to this desolate seldom-traveled road, that was just over the other side of the Radandt gravel pits behind Avery Salvage.

---

124. Telephone contact with Barbara Tadych, Feb. 28, 2018, spec. inv. Dedering

125. Bobby Dassey interview with Dedering, November 17, 2017

"Bobby was unfamiliar with where I was talking about when I mentioned Kuss Road," Dedering's report states. "I then produced a map I had from the Josh Radandt interview and showed him where Kuss Road was located. Bobby indicated he had never hunted on the Radandt property or in the gravel pit. Bobby stated he had never hunted on the area off of Kuss Road."

At no point during the short interview that lasted less than an hour did Dedering and Wisch ask Bobby about why Teresa's bones were inside of his burn barrel, the one he used to slice up and burn his dead animal parts that were part of his hunting escapades. They also did not ask him if he had removed the missing blood taken out of his uncle's sink on the night of November 3.

"Bobby was asked why he and Scott Tadych were being singled out as suspects and he indicated, 'I don't know.'"

"Bobby was asked if he had any involvement in the death of Teresa Halbach and he indicated 'No.'"

Dedering touched on Bobby's testimony against his uncle at the trial, but it was only brief. "I asked Bobby if he had made anything up or had lied during his testimony. Bobby stated everything he said was true and he had no reason to lie during the trial."

Of course, on the other hand, if Bobby Dassey had culpability in the killing and the gross dismemberment of Teresa's body, he would have every reason under the sun to lie.

In 2005, Teresa Halbach had made at least six confirmed visits to Avery Salvage to photograph cars being sold. She was there June 20, August 22, August 29, September 19, October 10, and lastly October 31.

***

Curiously, the Subway restaurant interview of Barbara and Scott Tadych did not bring an end to Wisconsin's re-investigation of the case.

There was still something within Barb's home that Dedering, Wiegert, and others at the Wisconsin Attorney General's Office of Brad Schimel were deeply concerned about. It was a piece of evidence they had scrutinized back in 2006. Now eleven years later, they didn't know whether it might jeopardize their murder convictions.

"After the interview, I returned home to my residence ... in Mishicot. At this time, the investigators requested I turn over my computer tower, which was the same one that was in my home in 2005 and had been examined before. I agreed to turn the computer tower over to the investigators."[126]

On November 10, 2017, the state of Wisconsin law enforcement authorities seized the Hewlett Packard Pavilion computer of Barbara Tadych for the second time. The computer was first seized as evidence in 2006.

This time, something happened. Something was said that gave Barb pause.

"I distinctly remember at the time I turned over the computer tower to the investigators saying, 'I'm thinking of getting rid of this computer.' After I made the comment, Investigator John Dedering replied, 'That would be a good idea and you should not give the computer to Kathleen Zellner.'"

Actually, Zellner has undergone a remarkable transformation herself since she received a handwritten letter addressed to her, dated September 26, 2011. The letter was brief, only four lines long. It was written on a sheet of notepad.

"Ms. Zellner, I saw you on a case on TV. I need you to help me on my case, I'm innocent please let me know. Thank you! Steven Avery."

---

126. Affidavit of Barbara Tadych, August 2, 2018

Seven years later, in September 2018, Zellner was being honored by Maryville University in Missouri with the distinguished Sister Mary Byles Peace and Justice Prize. Sister Byles had served on the Maryville faculty as a professor from 1972 until 1990. The honor bestowed on Zellner was given for her achievements in fighting for civil justice on behalf of people of all walks of life.

"He had written to us and we had looked at it from just what the courts had filed and I saw there was all this forensic science against him," Zellner remarked. "His blood was in the car. His DNA was on her car key in his bedroom. Her bones were in his burn pit. The bullet in his garage had her DNA on it. It's like "Whoa, we were like 'No way. We don't want to take this case.' Then I watched the documentary and I thought, 'Oh, wait a minute. This forensic stuff is bogus. I can tell by watching it how unbelievably superficial it is. No photographs are even taken when they find the bones. They keep the county pathologist from coming on the property."

And that's essentially how Zellner became involved in Avery's crusade to overturn his murder conviction.

"So I thought, I'm going to take and I'm going to hire world renowned experts. I'm going to do ballistics, blood, and if I dump a ton of money in it, I'm going to do it. Because I think this guy is innocent. I'm even going to do brain fingerprinting, that the CIA does, on him."

One of the biggest revelations, according to Zellner, concerns Dr. John DeHaan's analysis of the bones found in Avery's backyard burn pit.

"So I hired John DeHaan, probably the leading fire forensic expert in the world, and he said, 'There wasn't a body burned in that burn pit. He said there's absolutely no evidence.' And he's actually burned human bodies more than anybody in the world, which is a weird occupation. But this is the guy that knows … He said a barrel was used and forty percent of the bones were tipped into the burn pit. So someone poured bones into the burn pit. He said 'The teeth are missing.' He said, 'The teeth never melt.' And he said if you had burned at a crematorium level of heat at this burn pit, outdoors, you would have burned down the garage and blown up the propane tank. He said you could not sustain the temperature degree for the bones. He said it's totally fabricated. No body burned in there."[127]

And then there was the DNA on the hood latch. Her client's DNA was on the hood latch. "Guess what we found out, we found out that the amount of DNA on the hood latch is ninety, nine-zero, times the quantity that would have been left if a person had just opened a hood latch."

And that led to the quest to track down the elusive swab that had to be taken from Avery and substituted in as the hood latch swab.

"And we found it. They took two groin swabs from him when they had arrested him for a gun charge. So we're like what are you doin' doing groin swabs when somebody's arrested for a gun charge? They pocketed the two groin swabs, because we knew they would be epithelial DNA, and they turned those into the crime lab."

But Zellner's favorite find, she said, was dismantling the prosecution's theory that Teresa was shot in the head with a .22 caliber bullet, which was laying in Avery's garage, but they had just missed finding it the first six times they searched the garage for hard evidence.

"They couldn't find it, couldn't find it, couldn't find it, couldn't find it, then they found it. And they said. 'Whoa, it's got her DNA on it.'"

And then, with the state's permission, Zellner got to bring the bullet to the Microtrace laboratory, which solved the Unabomber case and numerous airline crashes. "It's probably the best forensic trace laboratory in the world. And they looked at it under a microscope, very advanced

127. Zellner presentation at Maryville University, September 2018

sophisticated microscope, 'Oh, that bullet, that bullet's got red paint on it and wood. So, wait a minute! Where's the bone. If you shoot a .22 through somebody's head, I don't care how many times you shoot it, the lead is so soft it's like a sponge. It's going to have bone on there. So then I flew to Arizona. I hired Luke Haag. We shot out in the desert .22s through bovine bone and every single one of them was embedded with bone. So what do we know? We know that .22 was stuck in the Avery wood in the garage and they just pried that thing out of there. Again, we found her DNA that traced back to what DNA of hers they used to put on there. Because it also had wax on it and they just happened to have her Chapstick."

Zellner's message to her legions of supporters all around the world is this: don't lose faith in her. Her quest to undo Avery's murder conviction and regain his freedom still remains in the early steps of the post-conviction appeals process.

"It's just staying on it, that's what we did. We're going to be like a wrecking crew with this evidence, and we're going to expose what they thought was a dunk-shot case."

On Nov. 6, 2018, Zellner posted the following statement to her Twitter account, which had ballooned to more than 459,700 followers: "It would be so much easier to walk away, close the door, not spend another dime, believe all the unproven allegations IF we could have just duplicated the State's forensic evidence but neither we nor anyone else can do so.

"Why? Because he is INNOCENT."

Pete Baetz maintains that Avery's vicious junkyard dog Bear would have growled and barked like crazy if a nighttime stranger tried to dump Teresa's bones out of a burn barrel into Avery's backyard. But if the person was someone familiar, Bear would not have barked.

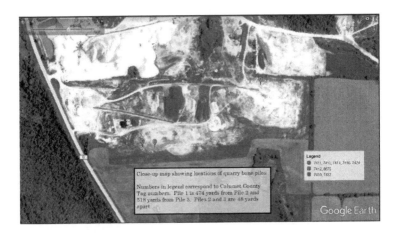

This geographic map shows the terrain for the Manitowoc County Gravel Pits where three different piles of human bones were discovered by authorities.

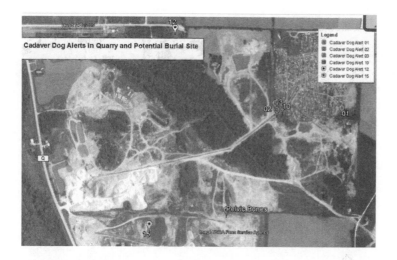

This map shows the areas where the police cadaver dogs picked up Teresa Halbach's scent; notice these are all areas far away from Steven Avery's trailer including near Kuss Road.

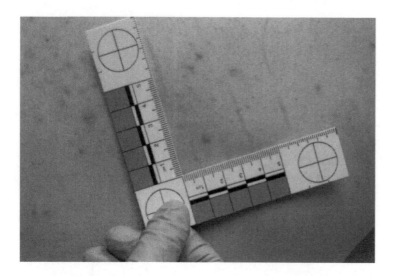

Bobby Dassey claimed these scratch marks on his back were caused by his Labrador puppy jumping on him earlier that same morning, just hours before he was interviewed by two police investigators on the afternoon of Nov. 7, 2005.

Mark Wiegert, at right, with Jerry Pagel, who was the Calumet County's Sheriff at the time of Halbach's murder. In 2018, Wiegert won a close election to become the new sheriff. Meanwhile, Attorney Kathleen Zellner has uncovered strong evidence indicating that Wiegert was perhaps intimately involved in fabricating DNA evidence later used to convict Avery.

FIVE YEARS LATER

NEW WITNESSES EMERGE

After the November 2018 publication of *Wrecking Crew*, world-famous exoneration lawyer, Kathleen Zellner, sharpened her focus suggesting Bobby Dassey, Steven Avery's dark and disturbed nephew, was Teresa Halbach's real killer. On a beautiful fall afternoon of September 29, 2023, Zellner and I met on the patio of a Starbucks coffee shop near her suburban Chicago law offices near Naperville.

During the interview, I told her, "It seems like you and your staff go above and beyond, not only to prove the innocence of your client to the court, but to show the court, show the police, show the public, and everyone else interested, who the real killer was in that particular case. That's been true in many, many of your famous cases. With *Making a Murderer* and Steven Avery, I was curious how you feel about Bobby Dassey, Steven Avery's nephew … What's led you to be convinced that Bobby Dassey, in your eyes, is the killer of Teresa Halbach?"

"We have tried to create, and the best way to create reasonable doubt in a murder case is to point the finger at someone else," Zellner explained. "And we've done that over the years very successfully. So in the Avery case, we started out looking at the police. There were people who actually thought that the police had arranged the murder. And we were able to quickly dispel all of that. We also learned that the blood vial was not the source of Steven Avery's blood. So then I knew that it had to be somebody very close to Steven and had to be somebody inside the family. So we began to really look at the individuals on the property at the time of the murder, and everything led back to Bobby Dassey.

"We uncovered that he had lied in his (trial) testimony about seeing Teresa walking towards Steven's trailer; Teresa left the property, and he knew that. We believe that he followed her. He told numerous lies, including where the computer was in the house. He told lies about seeing Scott Tadych on the road. There were a number of things that pointed back to him. Steven (Avery) has always felt that he was involved because he was very obsessed with Teresa Halbach. And so all of those things have led us to file the various motions. Now, we've got a direct connection with the crime because we've got an objective witness who's got no stake in the case who's identified Bobby with the murder victim's car. So we've got the direct connection. We think we've established motive and opportunity."

During these past five years, since *Making a Murderer* Season 2 aired, millions of people have continued a spirited debate on various social media platforms regarding the Wisconsin judicial system's staunch refusal to grant Steven Avery a new murder trial. Despite the political shift in power from Republican to Democratic control of the governor's office and Attorney General's Office, both of Wisconsin's political parties remain unsympathetic toward Avery and his condemned nephew, Brendan Dassey, the younger brother of Bobby Dassey.

While Avery and Brendan Dassey remain heroes to the wrongful conviction movement, the simple-minded uncle and mentally challenged nephew remain banished from society, locked away from the outside world at their respective Wisconsin prison facilities. On July 8, 2021, Steven Avery lost his biggest supporter, and he was not able to be at his mother's bedside when Dolores Avery died after battling dementia. She was 83. "Fate has dealt another cruel blow to Steven Avery today right before his birthday tomorrow," Zellner declared on Twitter in July 2021. "His mother Dolores Avery passed away at 6:50 a.m. He needs your support now more than ever."

Dolores Avery had stuck with her son since the beginning of his horrible nightmare way back in 1985. She never wavered in her belief of his innocence when corrupt Manitowoc Sheriff Tom Kocourek framed her son, derailing his life for 18 years, for the barbaric and brutal rape of Manitowoc businesswoman, Penny Beerntsen, along the sandy shores of Lake Michigan during the sweltering summer of 1985. Years later, Avery's mother remained in her son's corner during the Teresa Halbach murder trial, insisting to everyone willing to listen that Steven was innocent of the killing.

In May 2022, less than one year after his mother's death, Avery left the maximum-security prison in Waupun, but it wasn't to regain his freedom. The Wisconsin Department of Corrections moved Avery to the medium security prison, Fox Lake Correctional Institution. The distance from Manitowoc to Fox Lake is 94 miles.

"Steven Avery, the biggest blow to him was when his mother died," Zellner explained during our interview on September 29, 2023. "But he's got some very real friends, and he's got one friend from Australia who has been consistently bringing his father to visit him. He's in a new relationship with a female, and she's just a breath of fresh air. She's educated, very successful, very stable. I'm not going to mention her name. She has no interest in publicity. So she is just a gift, and so is the friend from Australia. I'm not going to mention their names, but he's doing quite well considering he's been wrongfully convicted twice. But he's definitely got these very loyal people who have helped him get through this."

Meanwhile, across the state border in Illinois, Zellner remained committed to uncovering the truth. One of her strongest attributes is her patience. She has an uncanny ability to remain even-keeled, to stay the course, to not get frustrated, even after a post-conviction ruling does not go her way. Because Avery's case had garnered international prominence, Zellner had encountered her share of online critics who have wanted her to fail. On the other hand, there are ordinary people out there who simply seek the truth, people who did not know Steven Avery or Kathleen Zellner at the time of *Making a Murderer*. One was a man who moved to Colorado. His name was Tom Sowinski.

At the time of the Halbach murder, in 2005, Sowinski had lived in Manitowoc County for more than 20 years. He used his trusty four-door sedan, tan and gold, to bring people their daily newspaper. Sowinski worked as a motor route carrier for Gannett Wisconsin Media, parent company of *USA Today*, and owners of 10 daily newspapers across Wisconsin at that time, including *The Herald Times Reporter* in Manitowoc. For Sowinski, most of his early morning newspaper deliveries were dull and uneventful. Every so often, Sowinski might encounter deer darting across the highway or see the flashing red and blue lights of a police car speeding to an emergency. For Sowinski, the early morning events of November 5, 2005, stayed on his mind for several years. As the years went by, he wondered to himself, did he, of all people, possess the key to unlock one of the biggest clues surrounding the Teresa Halbach murder mystery?

***

While most of Manitowoc County's citizens remained comfortably asleep in their beds, Sowinski's newspaper delivery route put him near Avery Salvage Yard for what became a scary, unforgettable encounter. Before sunrise, Sowinski steered his sedan along State Highway 147, then he turned left, bringing him down Avery Road. "Soon after I turned onto Avery Road, I witnessed an individual who I later realized was Bobby Dassey, and another unidentified older male pushing a dark blue RAV4 down Avery Road on the right side towards the junkyard," Sowinski recalled in his affidavit. "Bobby Dassey was shirtless, even though it was early November. The second man appeared to be in his fifties or early sixties, had a long gray beard, was wearing a worn, puffy jacket, had a larger frame, and was around six feet in height.

"The RAV4 did not have its lights on," Sowinski remembered. "I drove down Avery Road towards the mailboxes, left *The Herald-Times* in the mailbox and turned around. I felt very afraid as I approached the two individuals because Bobby Dassey attempted to step in front of my car, blocking my exit. I was within five feet of Bobby Dassey, and my headlights were on the entire time. The older man ducked down behind the open passenger door. I swerved to the right and drove in the shallow ditch to avoid hitting Bobby Dassey. I called out, 'Paper Boy, Gotta Go' (sic) because I was afraid for my safety."

Sowinski's encounter with Bobby Dassey took place hours before the police made the Avery Salvage Yard the focus of their murder investigation for the next several days. "Bobby Dassey looked me in the eye, and I could tell with the look in his eyes that he was not happy to see me there," Sowinski noted. "I knew that Bobby Dassey and the older individual were doing something creepy." Unbeknownst to Sowinski, Halbach's RAV4 would be discovered later that Saturday morning. Someone had even covered it with several boards, not necessarily to hide it, but to make it easy for someone to discover the car. And sure enough, when the mother-daughter volunteer search party members, Pamela Sturm and daughter Nikole, arrived mid-morning, they quickly found the RAV4 along the outer ridge of Avery Salvage Yard. "After I learned that Teresa Halbach's car was found on November 5, 2005, I contacted the Manitowoc Sheriff's Office and spoke with a female officer," Sowinski remembered. "I reported everything I have stated in this affidavit to the officer. The officer said, 'We already know who did it.' I provided my phone number, and they said they would contact me soon. I never heard back from the police."

Ten years later, in December 2015, Sowinski joined millions of people across the globe immersing themselves in the brand new 10-part true-crime Netflix documentary, *Making a Murderer*. "After watching season one of *Making a Murderer*, I contacted Avery's trial attorneys to inform them of what I saw and never heard back. Nothing has been promised or given to me in exchange for this affidavit," Sowinski declared.

In December 2022, as her seventh year of legal representation for Avery drew to a close, Zellner filed a 51-page motion for post-conviction relief with Manitowoc County. Of note, Sowinski, her new witness, now provided her with a direct connection between Bobby Dassey and Teresa Halbach's murder. Moreover, Zellner informed the Wisconsin courts that Sowinski had not contacted Avery's original criminal defense lawyers, Jerry Buting and Dean Strang, as he originally believed and stated in his affidavit. Actually, Zellner discovered he had emailed the New York-based Innocence Project in 2016 after watching *Making a Murderer* Season 1. Consequently, Sowinski's email to the Innocence Project did not get passed along to Avery's lawyers. In fact, Sowinski's first attempt at contacting Zellner happened in December 2020, a full three years after Avery already filed his second post–conviction motion.

"Further, Mr. Sowinski's memory was refreshed, with a recorded dispatch that was recently discovered, in that he made the call to the Manitowoc Sheriff's Office on November 6, 2006," Zellner's December 2022 filing declared. "The Sowinski evidence provided by Mr. Sowinski to Mr. Avery's current post-conviction counsel is newly discovered evidence, which provides the missing direct connection between Bobby and Ms. Halbach's murder, making him a Denny suspect."

Of importance, Avery did not have the Sowinski evidence until Tom Sowinski came forward to Zellner's law firm in April 2021. "Rather, the Sowinski evidence was reported to the Manitowoc Sheriff's Office by Mr. Sowinski, but the evidence was suppressed from Mr. Avery by the prosecution," Zellner reminded Wisconsin's post-conviction judge. "Neither Mr. Avery nor his counsel were on notice that Mr. Sowinski had any knowledge about Bobby's actions on November 5, 2005. The Sowinski evidence is material to several issues in Mr. Avery's case. Most importantly, it is material for establishing Mr. Avery's defense, that is, that a third party committed the crime against Ms. Halbach. It is material for establishing the direct link to Bobby as a third-party Denny suspect and to opening the door to reconsidering the 'Velie CD' as establishing a sexual motive for the murder. Additionally, the Sowinski evidence is material to the evidence in the RAV4 being planted by Bobby, including Mr. Avery's blood and DNA. The RAV4 also contained the Halbach vehicle key and Ms. Halbach's electronic devices, which were discovered in Mr. Avery's bedroom and burn barrel, respectively."

Next, Zellner's December 2022 filing detailed how the Sowinski evidence impeaches Bobby Dassey's murder trial testimony. Taking the witness stand for the prosecution, Bobby Dassey suggested Halbach never left the Avery property, that he last saw her walking toward Avery's red trailer. "Bobby's testimony was the most determinative of Mr. Avery's guilt because the State used it to establish that Ms. Halbach never left the Avery property alive," Zellner emphasized. On the witness stand, prosecutor Kratz asked Bobby Dassey, "after seeing this woman walking toward your uncle Steven's, did you ever see this woman again?" "No," Bobby told the courtroom.

To prevail on a Denny motion, defense lawyers must persuade the judge the third party had motive, opportunity, and a direct connection to the crime. "Law enforcement considered pornography as evidence of motive in Ms. Halbach's murder," Zellner pointed out in her filing. "The clear working theory of the investigators was that the murder of Ms. Halbach was motivated by sexual assault. Pursuant to that theory, the Dassey computer was seized by law enforcement on April 21, 2006."

According to Zellner, "There is sufficient evidence that it was only Bobby who had access to the Dassey computer during the day on weekdays between approximately 7 a.m. to 3:30 p.m. ... Moreover, 128 searches for the most violent porn images primarily occurred on weekdays when only Bobby was in the Dassey residence. It is undisputed that Mr. Avery never accessed the Dassey computer. He did not have the password for the Dassey computer, nor did he possess a key to the Dassey residence, which was locked when no one was home. The only time Mr. Avery ever entered the Dassey residence was when one of the Dassey family members was home ... The depicted acts in the violent pornography that Bobby was viewing are sufficiently similar to the violent murder of Ms. Halbach. The evidence of Bobby's searches for violent pornographic images is not so remote in time as to be inadmissible, but rather, so close in time to Ms. Halbach's murder that the searches are direct evidence of Bobby's motive to kill Ms. Halbach ... The Sowinski evidence greatly strengthens the opportunity argument because Bobby is in possession of Ms. Halbach's vehicle, where her murder likely occurred ... The vehicle is a key piece of evidence in the crime. The new evidence that Ms. Halbach's vehicle was returned to the Avery Salvage Yard from a different location is corroborated by the fact that a witness saw a vehicle similar to Halbach's leave the property on October 31. In Mr. Avery's trial, Mr. Leurquin, a propane driver, testified he saw a green, midsize SUV leaving the Avery Salvage Yard driving towards Highway 147 between 3:30 and 4 p.m. on October 31. He informed law enforcement about this when he was stopped at a roadblock a few days later and had heard about the news of Ms. Halbach being missing."

**

One of the most interesting developments from Zellner's investigative legwork on Avery's behalf has been her focus on some of the figures who remained in the shadows. One such person was Michael Osmunson, an avid hunter and close friend of Bobby Dassey who was a nearby resident of Mishicot. According to Zellner, Bobby Dassey was with Michael Osmunson when Halbach's vehicle was discovered at the Avery Salvage Yard party on November 5, 2005. Zellner's post-conviction filing noted that her investigator met with and interviewed Osmunson about whether he was the person with Bobby pushing the RAV4 onto the Avery Salvage Yard. According to Zellner, the interview was necessary because Osmunson fit the height, weight, and beard description provided by Mr. Sowinski of the person helping Bobby push the car.

"When Osmunson was asked if he was the person who helped Bobby push the vehicle on the Avery property, on November 5, 2005, Osmunson responded he 'could not remember' if he was that individual," Zellner's December 2022 post-conviction filing revealed.

Osmunson said something else to the Wisconsin police that drew scrutiny from Zellner as her legal team had dug into the Manitowoc County murder mystery several years later.

Back in 2005, Halbach's mother first reported her daughter as missing on November 3. "Remarkably, Osmunson stated to law enforcement that he first learned about the missing girl on Tuesday, November 1, 2005, when Halbach had not yet been reported missing," Zellner pointed out. "Further, the record reveals that Osmunson and Bobby were either suspiciously calling each other repeatedly or with each other at relevant times after Ms. Halbach's murder. Bobby's phone records reflect that on October 31, 2005, there were seven phone calls between Bobby and Osmunson occurring between the following times in the morning and evening: 6:12 a.m., 6:36 a.m., 3:56 p.m., 3:57 p.m., 4:53 p.m., 5:10 p.m., and 6:01 p.m. Bobby's phone records reveal that Bobby called Osmunson a total of 66 times from October 24, 2005, to November 9, 2005."

Avery was arrested on Nov. 9, 2005.

"If Bobby is established as a viable third-party Denny suspect, the forensic evidence in this case is completely undermined," Zellner implored the court. "The newly discovered evidence that Bobby was in possession of Ms. Halbach's vehicle means that he had opportunity and access to plant evidence in the vehicle and from the vehicle. Because Bobby has been directly linked to the murder of Ms. Halbach, there is a reasonable inference that he planted the bones in Mr. Avery's burn pit. This new evidence creates a reasonable probability that had the jury heard the new evidence, it would have had a reasonable doubt as to the defendant's guilt. Therefore, Mr. Avery should be granted a new trial."

Not only was the Sowinski evidence newly discovered, Zellner argued it signified a monumental Brady violation by the prosecution. As outlined back in Chapter 26, American prosecutors have a duty to share certain evidence with the defense, including evidence favorable to the defendant. And from Zellner's perspective, she also needed to investigate the veracity of Sowinski's information. Avery's lawyer wanted to be absolutely positive Sowinski's credibility was in check. After all, there were all sorts of scam artists trying to make a name for themselves by cashing in on the *Making a Murderer* hysteria. Zellner needed to find out whether Sowinski was nothing but a glory seeker.

She directed one of her law firm's private investigators, Steven Kirby, to conduct a thorough background probe of Sowinski. As part of his research, Kirby obtained Sowinski's date of birth, relatives, employment history, phone numbers, and email addresses. Kirby researched Sowinski for any civil and criminal court cases, plus his ownership history for homes and automobiles. Indeed, financial records obtained by Zellner's private investigator from the Wisconsin newspaper confirmed Sowinski worked as a carrier in 2005 and 2006 for *The Herald-Times Reporter*. After confirming Sowinski's work history, Kirby's background check led him to contact Avery's original criminal defense lawyers. "Mr. Avery's current post-conviction counsel contacted Mr. Avery's trial defense counsel, Mr. Buting, who confirmed that Mr. Avery's trial counsel had not received any emails from Mr. Sowinski," Zellner's post-conviction filing alerted the judge.

The world-famous wrongful conviction lawyer and her staff undertook a rigorous review of all the discovery materials, along with any prior Freedom of Information Act requests made to the Manitowoc Sheriff's Office pertaining to Avery's murder case. Once again, they came up empty. Avery's lawyers uncovered no information in regard to Sowinski and his claim of speaking with Manitowoc sheriff's officials back in 2005. As for Sowinski, he had moved to Denver, Colorado, by 2021. That spring, he received a certified letter notifying him to contact Zellner immediately. From there, Sowinski called Avery's lawyer and her private investigator arranged for a face-to-face interview, on April 10, 2021. Two days later, Zellner had the Sowinski affidavit notarized for the court.

"The affidavit described the evidence Mr. Sowinski reported to the Manitowoc Sheriff's Office about what he observed on the Avery property while delivering newspapers on November 5, 2005, as well as the actions he took afterwards. His affidavit included a map indicating where he observed the two males pushing the RAV4," Zellner's motion stated.

By August 28, 2021, Zellner had listened to all of her law enforcement audio recordings from Avery's case. She found no recording that matched the description of events provided by the former Manitowoc newspaper carrier. Not ready to give up on her quest for the elusive information, Zellner submitted three new Freedom of Information Act requests to the Manitowoc sheriff's joint dispatch center on March 15, 2022. She focused on the agency's audio recordings between 12:01 a.m. November 3, 2005, through 11:59 p.m. on November 9, 2005. By May 3, 2022, the Manitowoc sheriff's office complied with Zellner's information request.

"For the first time, the time and date of the calls were revealed on the track files," Zellner's filing declared. Contained within the numerous audio calls was one made at 10:28 p.m. on Nov. 6, 2005. That particular call captured Zellner's attention. Armed with the newly discovered evidence, private investigator Steven Kirby tracked down Sowinski's former girlfriend, Devon Novak, for an interview. On August 6, 2022, Novak identified the voice on the recorded call to the Manitowoc Sheriff's Office as being Tom Sowinski's voice. Later, Kirby met with Sowinski and played the audio recording for him. Sowinski recognized the voice as being his own. "Mr. Sowinski provided Mr. Avery's current post-conviction counsel with an affidavit regarding his voice identification," Zellner's December 2022 filing declared.

As Zellner pointed out for the judge, Avery's conviction for first-degree intentional homicide was largely based on his trial defense counsel's unsuccessful efforts to name a third-party Denny suspect that met all the Denny requirements. "The Sowinski new and material evidence was suppressed when the Manitowoc Sheriff's Office failed to disclose the November 6, 2005 10:28 p.m. audio recording pursuant to defense discovery requests," Zellner argued in her appeal.

"The disclosure of the audio recording would have led to the identification of Mr. Sowinski and the evidence he has provided which directly connects Bobby to the murder and the framing of Mr. Avery ... The Sowinski evidence also impeaches Bobby's testimony and refutes the State's theory that Ms. Halbach's RAV-4 never left the Avery property and that Mr. Avery was the last person to see Ms. Halbach alive. Further, 'materially favorable' evidence not only includes exculpatory evidence, but also evidence that is impeaching a prosecution witness."

In closing, Zellner's December 6, 2022, post-conviction relief motion asked Wisconsin Judge Angela Sutkiewicz to grant Avery an evidentiary hearing or a new trial "and all relief this court deems appropriate."

As of 2023, Sutkiewicz had served as a Sheboygan County judge since 2010. On August 22, 2023, Judge Sutkiewicz issued her 31-page ruling. To her, the newspaper delivery driver seeing Bobby Dassey and someone else pushing murder victim Halbach's RAV4 along Avery Road was not important enough to grant Avery a new trial, or even an evidentiary hearing in the judge's courtroom. The judge's ruling left Wisconsin's political establishment breathing a sigh of relief. Influential Democrats and Republicans throughout the Wisconsin government were counting on Sutkiewicz to rule against Avery. Wisconsin's politicians and its judiciary were thoroughly embarrassed by their state's portrayal during both seasons of *Making a Murderer*, in 2015 and 2018. If Judge Sutkiewicz ruled in Zellner's favor, the judge realized she would, in effect, leave the barn door wide open for *Making a Murderer* filmmakers Moira Demos and Laura Ricciardi to make yet another trip back to the Dairy State. By 2023, the last thing Wisconsin's powerful establishment wanted was for the Emmy-award winning, internationally celebrated *Making a Murderer* film producers to release a Season 3. For that reason, Wisconsin's politicians had put their faith and trust in the middle-aged

Sutkiewicz. They considered her their sacred goalkeeper. For Wisconsin's mighty political bureaucracy, the strength of Zellner's newly discovered evidence needed to be treated as irrelevant and the judge from Sheboygan was expected to treat her courtroom gavel like it was a fly swatter. Avery, the condemned prisoner from Manitowoc County, and Zellner, his celebrity status exoneration lawyer from Illinois, were considered obnoxious insects in the eyes of Wisconsin's justice system. However, for judges like Angela Sutkiewicz, it seemed as if Zellner would not make like a bee and buzz off, no matter how many times a fly swatter was waved in her direction. Finally, on August 22, 2023, with the weight of Wisconsin's justice system resting on her broad shoulders, Angela Sutkiewicz released her highly anticipated ruling on Avery's latest post-conviction motion.

The ruling consisted of 31 pages, of which, more than half rehashed the crime's background and other chronology. If you were an avid Steven Avery and Brendan Dassey supporter, the judge's ruling was like finding all four of your vehicle's tires deflated in the driveway. Perhaps most frustrating, the long-time Sheboygan judge continued to mess up important relevant facts of Halbach's murder, as the judge also inexplicably listed the wrong names of key people in her ruling.

For instance, one of the biggest question marks facing the prosecution concerned the fact that several of Halbach's charred bones were discovered inside Bobby Dassey's burn barrel. That particular barrel was kept on the Dassey family property, not part of Steven Avery's yard. Avery had his own burn barrel near his red mobile home trailer, but Halbach's bones were not found inside it. And yet Judge Sutkiewicz got this basic fact wrong in her ruling as she wrongly characterized Halbach's bones as being found inside Avery's burn barrel rather than Bobby Dassey's burn barrel in her August 22, 2023, decision when Sutkiewicz wrote, "the defense argues that Mr. Dassey's possession of the RAV4 also provided to him access to the key to the victim's car, found in the defendant's home, as well as the victim's electronics, found in the burn barrel along with the victim's remains." Then, on page 20, the Wisconsin judge incorrectly labeled the names of the Dassey brothers when she wrote, "No physical evidence directly linking Brian Dassey to the homicide was found in the house."

If you analyze the rest of the judge's ruling carefully, you will notice that Sutkiewicz treats the prosecution's evidence as iron-clad truth.

Page 12 of Sutkiewicz's ruling: "The state argues that the defendant has fallen short of establishing that Bobby Dassey was, in fact, the person who conducted the computer searches in question or that the searches conducted were probative or relevant to prove that anyone had motive to commit murder in October of 2005."

Page 13: "The state notes that there are no citations to any facts of record establishing Mr. Dassey's whereabouts at the time the searches were conducted or any evidence that conclusively establishes that no other person had access to the home or computer at the time in question."

Page 13: "The state further disputes the defendant's conclusions that law enforcement considered pornography or sexual assault as a motive for the murder in this matter."

Page 15: "Assuming, for the purposes of this motion, that those three searches were conducted by Bobby Dassey, the state argues that a mere three searches conducted prior to the murder of Ms. Halbach fail to demonstrate that Mr. Dassey was a voracious consumer of violent pornography prior to the murder, thus failing to establish that theory of motive offered by the defendant."

Page 16: "The state further states that the images and search results from the Dassey computer did not directly mirror the manner in which the victim was killed ... the state notes that evidence offered by the defendant as proof of motive cannot be proved to have been obtained by or have been in the sole possession of Bobby Dassey."

Page 18: "The defendant rests his motive argument on the premise that Bobby Dassey had an obsession with violent, sexual pornography involving young women and a fascination with gruesome homicides and deaths. However, the defendant's arguments are not supported by the evidence submitted ... The defendant could have offered a witness who saw Mr. Dassey actually conducting any of the searches in question. Even more simply, the defendant could have offered evidence that the defendant was actually home at the time of the searches rather than speculation based on typical schedules of the family to prove that Mr. Dassey conducted the searches."

Page 20: "No search results offered by the defendant directly mirror the elements of the crime in this case. There is no evidence, only generalized assumptions, that Bobby Dassey was the individual who conducted the searches on the family computer. The computer was not in the exclusive possession of Bobby Dassey prior to or after the murder. Only a very small number of searches were conducted prior to the murder of Ms. Halbach."

Despite several of Halbach's bones being inside Bobby Dassey's burn barrel and that Zellner introduced her new eyewitness, Tom Sowinski, who saw Bobby Dassey pushing the victim's vehicle several hours before it was found, Judge Sutkiewicz made this declaration in her August 2023 ruling:

Page 20: "The defendant has not met the burden under Denny to establish that Bobby Dassey had motive to commit the crime alleged and, as such, failed to meet the burden to admit the evidence offered to prove the existence of a third-party suspect for the commission of this crime."

Page 22: "The state goes on to argue that the defendant has offered no evidence to establish that Bobby had the necessary skills available to manipulate the evidence in a manner that would implicate the defendant. The state notes at the time of the murder, Bobby Dassey was an 18-year-old high school graduate with no criminal record. Mr. Dassey was employed as a third-shift worker at a furniture factory. The state posits that there is no evidence of record that establishes how an individual of Bobby's age and experience would have obtained the scientific knowledge or skill to collect, transport and plant the defendant's blood from his bathroom."

On the other hand, Judge Sutkiewicz was unimpressed with the discovery of Zellner's two new witnesses, in spite of the fact that both men independently put Halbach's RAV4 in the control of Bobby Dassey after her disappearance.

Page 25: "Finally, the defendant asserts that the Sowinski affidavit supplies a direct connection between Bobby and the murder of Ms. Halbach. The defendant asserts that because Bobby was in possession of the victim's RAV4, it proves that he had access to the key to the defendant's car and her electronics that were found in the burn pit. These items are links that are central to proving Bobby Dassey's involvement in the murder of Ms. Halbach. The defendant argues that Bobby's possession of the car provides a direct evidentiary link between Bobby and the crime committed, making him a viable third-party suspect ... Even if Bobby was found in the possession of the victim's automobile on the night of November 5, 2005, there is only speculation and no evidence to prove that Bobby was in possession of the car or that he had exclusive control over the vehicle prior to that night."

Page 26: "The defendant further asserts that Bobby's possession of the car gave him access to the victim's car keys and her personal electronics. Again, this is speculation by the defendant. Mr. Sowinski's affidavit does not mention seeing Bobby with the key to the victim's car. In fact, the affidavit establishes that Bobby was pushing the victim's car without power on the night in question, placing doubt on whether he was in possession of the victim's car key ... the victim's key and electronics could have been taken directly from the victim or taken from her car at any time prior to or after the murder by another individual long before the auto was in Bobby's possession. There is no evidence of record taken from the car that links Bobby directly to the actual homicide of Ms. Halbach."

Page 27: "While the defendant asserts that the only logical conclusion to be drawn from Bobby's possession of the vehicle that night is that Bobby is the individual who actually murdered Ms. Halbach, this assumption is flawed. There are other reasons that Bobby could have been in possession of the car that night, including that Bobby was trying to help hide evidence to protect the two individuals directly linked by forensic evidence to this murder and convicted of the crime. The defendant's conclusory assumptions drawn from the evidence offered in the affidavit do not amount to evidence directly linking Bobby to the homicide itself. As such, the defendant failed to meet the final standard of the Denny test to establish Bobby as a valid third-party suspect in this crime."

***

Say what you want about now-retired Manitowoc County Judge Patrick Willis, the judge who presided over Avery's sensational murder trial in 2007 and later declared at the sentencing that Avery was the most dangerous man who ever set foot in his courtroom. Unknown to most people, Willis actually took the initiative to properly research the evidence brought forward against Avery's mentally impaired teenage nephew, Brendan Dassey, who was tried and convicted by a jury, in a case assigned to a different Manitowoc judge, Jerome Fox. Like millions of people who watched Brendan Dassey's videotaped interrogation and purported confession during *Making a Murderer*, Judge Willis also watched the videotapes himself, back around 2007. And the Manitowoc judge had major problems with them, so much so that Judge Willis composed a written note, entered into Avery's voluminous court file, informing anyone inspecting the court file that "the physical evidence and forensic evidence introduced at Mr. Avery's trial failed to provide corroborating support for a number of the allegations attributed to Mr. Dassey." As one significant example, Avery's sentencing judge wrote, "there was no physical or scientific evidence demonstrating that Teresa Halbach was ever present in Mr. Avery's trailer."

Fast-forward 16 years to the summer of 2023. The judge from Sheboygan assigned to replace Patrick Willis for handling Avery's post-conviction appeals, Angie Sutkiewicz, struggled to come up with legitimate reasons to deny Avery an evidentiary hearing or a new trial.

Then, upon further reflection, the judge had an idea. She would cite the Brendan Dassey confession to justify her decision in the Avery case.

Page 24: "The defendant further failed to offer any facts of record to establish a consistent plan to frame the defendant, or any theory including or excluding law enforcement involvement which implicates the defendant in this crime," Sutkiewicz opined. "The defendant's theory that Bobby framed him for this murder also fails to acknowledge a significant fact in relation to this crime - to which Brendan Dassey confessed and was convicted of participating in the murder of Ms. Halbach. Brendan specifically implicated the defendant in this crime, and his conviction has been affirmed by the appellate courts and remains of record. All of the allegations implicating Bobby in the murder and the framing of the defendant are pure speculation and are not supported by any evidence submitted by the defendant. As such, the defendant failed to satisfy the tests in Edmunds, Denny and Wilson."

On May 26, 2023, Zellner submitted another affidavit for Avery's appeal from someone who previously never stepped forward. Zellner notified Wisconsin's judiciary system she just became aware of Tom Buresh on May 10, 2023. His observations concerned Halbach's RAV4 during the late-night hours of Friday, November 4, 2005, or early morning hours of Saturday, November 5, 2005. "Mr. Thomas Buresh corroborates the previously filed affidavit of Thomas Sowinski that Bobby Dassey was driving the RAV4 vehicle of Teresa Halbach on Friday night, November 4, 2005 or early Saturday morning, after her disappearance on October 31, 2005," Zellner declared.

According to the May 24, 2023, affidavit, Tom Buresh indicated that back in 2005, he worked as a self-employed repossession agent. He remembered that sometime before 2 a.m. on Saturday, November 5, 2005, Buresh was driving his tow truck to repossess a vehicle in rural Manitowoc County near the tiny town of Larrabee. He was in the area of State Highway 147 and County Road Q in Manitowoc County.

"I noticed a vehicle in the Park N Ride on Highways 147 and 43 that had just struck a deer and had a broken headlight," Buresh remarked. "I gave the driver a roll of duct tape to repair the car. After that, I was driving down Highway 147 and made a wrong turn to go south on County Road Q. After I realized my mistake, I turned around and was heading back north. As I was heading back north, I noticed a RAV4 driving south on County Road Q. The RAV4 turned left off on County Road Q after it passed me. I noticed the RAV4 because it was unusual to see any other cars out on the road at that time of night."

As for his tow truck, Buresh recalled it had bright illuminating lights. The bright lights illuminated the oncoming RAV4 and that allowed Buresh to see the people inside the vehicle as it passed him. On that particular night, Buresh recalled he had another helper with him inside his tow truck, who also saw the oncoming RAV4. The man's name was Mike, and Mike has since died. Anyway, Buresh remembered that in either 2006 or 2007, he was watching the television news coverage of Avery's murder trial and that's when he noticed Bobby Dassey in the courtroom. Buresh remembered how he had seen Bobby Dassey driving the RAV4 during the late-night hours of 2005.

In his 2023 affidavit, Buresh acknowledged he was no saint. He had his share of ups and downs in life, and in November 2006, he found himself in Green Bay at the Brown County Jail, facing a domestic violence charge. Then, in February 2007, he was back in jail, accused of bail jumping. "During the time I was incarcerated, I told a Brown County detective that I had information about the Halbach murder but was ignored and told that 'I was already in enough trouble' and 'to shut up,'" Buresh noted.

To this day, Buresh said he cannot identify the passenger seated inside the RAV4 following Halbach's disappearance. "But I am 100 percent sure it was not Steven Avery," he insisted. "In 2017 or 2018, I told my brother, Ron, about my observation of the RAV4 back in 2005. I do not know any of the Avery or Dassey family members personally, but I may have dropped towed vehicles at the Avery Salvage Yard on a few occasions. I believe I have encountered Steven Avery on one occasion at a local McDonald's but did not converse with him."

Lastly, Buresh was asked by Zellner's associates whether he knew a man named Mike Osmunson. "I do not know Mike Osmunson," Buresh declared. "Nothing has been promised or given to me in exchange for this affidavit."

In the end, Judge Sutkiewicz was not persuaded to give much weight to Buresh's affidavit, either.

Page 29: "Once again, assuming for the purposes of this motion, that the facts in the Buresh affidavit were true, the facts do not directly link Bobby Dassey with the murder of Ms. Halbach. The affidavit asserts that two people were in the car when it was seen driving down the road. While

Mr. Buresh states that he can conclusively identify Bobby Dassey in the car, he cannot identify the other individual in the car other than to eliminate the person being the defendant. Once again, the affidavit links Bobby Dassey to being in possession of the RAV4 after the homicide took place. There is nothing in the affidavit that establishes that Bobby had possession or conclusive possession of the vehicle prior to that time. The affiant states that a second individual was in the car at the time that he saw it driving down the road. The affidavit does not establish that Bobby was the individual who was in possession of the key to the car or the car itself prior to that night. The affidavit only, taken as true, establishes that Bobby was in possession of the car on November 4th or 5th."

The judge went on to add, "Nothing in the statement links Bobby to the homicide itself. One would have to leap to the conclusion that if he were in possession of the RAV4 that night, he must be the individual who committed the murder. As previously discussed, no direct evidence in this matter links Bobby directly to the murder. Furthermore, in this affidavit, a new unnamed individual could be implicated as the murderer in this case under the theory offered by the defendant. The unnamed individual had equal access to the car and the key on that night in question. That individual could have been the individual who, if the defense theory is correct, could have moved the car back and forth from the property, removed the personal electronics from the car, possessed the key, and then planted it at the defendant's home. As such, the affidavit offered also fails the test in Denny to be admissible to prove the existence of a third-party suspect for this crime."

On August 22, 2023, the last 13 words of her 31-page ruling, all typed in capital letters, felt like a bee sting for many *Making a Murderer* fans who maintained faith in America's justice system. Avery's supporters had clung to the hope that in an act of fairness, Judge Sutkiewicz would grant Zellner the chance to argue her client's case inside her Wisconsin courtroom. There, the television news cameras could chronicle the testimony and those being summoned to the witness stand.

Instead, they got stuck with this: "FOR THE REASONS SET FORTH ABOVE, THE MOTION OF THE DEFENDANT IS **DENIED**."

Not only was the word 'denied' in capital letters, the judge made sure to type it in bold.

****

At the time of my interview with Zellner on September 29, 2023, more than a month had passed since her post-conviction motion was turned down by the judge in northeastern Wisconsin. "No question in my mind, if we were in Illinois, we would have had an evidentiary hearing several years ago," Zellner remarked. "We would have had a full court analysis and witnesses of all the evidence. It would have gone much more smoothly. There's tremendous fear in Wisconsin of being exposed. I think that *Making a Murderer* had that effect, and so the name of the game with the rulings that we've gotten so far is that no one wants us back in court. I think anywhere else we would have gotten a hearing, but we will just be persistent because there is no statute of limitations on this. Steven Avery's got many, many more chances to get out."

Incidentally, two years earlier, I wrote an opinion column for Patch headlined, "Is Making a Murderer 3 Preoccupying Wisconsin's Supreme Court?"

"In 30 years of doing post-conviction work all over the United States, we have been granted evidentiary hearings in 99 percent of our cases," I quoted Zellner as telling me in September 2021. "The other 1 percent were denied and then reversed on appeal. My question is, 'Why is Wisconsin so fearful of having a public hearing about the integrity of this conviction?"

In my opinion column, I wrote that Avery's case may be all about Wisconsin's judiciary preventing a third season of *Making a Murderer* from airing on Netflix. I asked readers to step back for a moment and assess whether they thought the Wisconsin Supreme Court wanted to make the bold declaration that Steven Avery was indeed the victim of not just one, but two state of Wisconsin wrongful convictions, both involving jury trials in front of Manitowoc County citizens?

Furthermore, I asked whether the Wisconsin Supreme Court wants to fall out of favor with the rest of Wisconsin's politicians and bureaucrats by giving the producers of *Making a Murderer* enough raw footage to compile a third season, one certain to be more compelling and dramatic than the 2015 and 2018 seasons 1 and 2 combined? And then there's Wisconsin's legacy. A pronouncement of a second wrongful conviction for Avery would give Wisconsin the disgraceful distinction of being the only state in the country with such an embarrassing mark.

The real reason why Avery may not ever get a courtroom evidentiary hearing, let alone a new murder trial, is because so many of Wisconsin's politicians, both Republicans and Democrats, public officials and law enforcement officials, retired and present-day employees, have reached the conclusion that this *Making a Murderer* hysteria needs to come to an immediate crashing halt. In their minds, mighty Wisconsin cannot continue to be vilified and ostracized to the outside world by the likes of Netflix filmmakers Demos and Ricciardi ever again. A season 3 of *Making a Murderer* could certainly focus on Avery's inevitable second wrongful conviction lawsuit, one that would demand gigantic monetary compensation, like in the hundreds of millions of dollars. A multitude of Wisconsin insurance companies could be on the hook for an enormous amount of liability. Ask yourself, would these deep-pocketed insurance adjusters employed by the local and state government entities gleefully write Steven Avery a check that makes him one of Wisconsin's richest residents to redress all the wrongs caused to him by the Badger State's criminal justice system?

For Judge Sutkiewicz, along with Wisconsin's court of appeals and the state supreme court justices, the easiest way to halt any further movie production of *Making a Murderer* season 3 is to make sure Avery and Zellner lose their post-conviction appeals. It seems that in the eyes of Wisconsin's criminal justice system, there cannot and will not be a *Making a Murderer* season 3. The prospect of new MAM episodes showing Steven Avery smiling, hugging and waving to his adoring fans as he walks out of the Wisconsin Department of Corrections - for a second time in his life - would upset many people who built their careers and professional reputations around the notion that Avery was a deviant, psychopathic killing monster. They might rather scale the top of the stadium lights at Green Bay's Lambeau Field and leap to their deaths in the parking lot, then be forced to endure a third season of *Making a Murderer*.

And you don't have to be Demos and Ricciardi to imagine the movie script: a jovial Avery returns to Manitowoc and after acquiring a $100 million wrongful conviction settlement, the hero of *Making a Murderer* buys up the downtown buildings and businesses. Long-time Manitowoc restaurants and bars owned by the community's wealthy and well-to-do disappear overnight as Avery takes them over. In their place, Avery opens his own brand of steakhouses and seafood-themed supper clubs. And with tens of millions of dollars remaining in his bank account and little time to waste, the 61-year-old Avery decides to launch his own line of bourbon, brandy, and whiskey. He turns his family's 40-acre salvage yard into the Avery Road Distillery. The new tourist attraction draws people from all over the world for a chance to sip Avery's whiskey and pose for a photograph with the short, stubby, smiling man who became the face of the wrongful conviction movement, not just once, but twice.

But before Steven Avery's saga can have a happy ending distributed to the masses through the airing of *Making a Murderer* season 3, he and his lawyer must remain determined and committed to the cause of freedom. As the alternative rock band U2 sang in their 1987 *Joshua Tree* album, "I Still Haven't Found What I'm Looking For."

One person convinced that Avery will not die behind the mighty concrete fortress operated by the Wisconsin Department of Corrections is his attorney.

During the September 2023 interview, Zellner remarked, "I do think we will win the appeal because I think the judge has made a number of errors. One of the things that's just perplexing to me is her lack of grasp of the facts. She actually thinks that Teresa Halbach's bones were in Steven Avery's burn barrel, which, of course, is untrue. They were in the Dassey burn barrel. But she's made a number of legal errors on the case. She's applied the wrong standard for evaluating new evidence. She's applied the wrong evaluation for Denny. So we do think it will be overturned by the court of appeals. And we actually went back to her with this evidence because the court of appeals indicated in their opinion two years ago, that the evidence could be very significant, and we should revisit it with the lower court, so we did that, and is typical in many of these cases, the Circuit Court judges just don't have the knowledge a lot of times or experience with post-conviction work … Usually, if there's relief granted to the inmate, it's going to be from a higher court, so Steven Avery has years to go on his appeals, unlike Brendan Dassey, whose case is pretty much finished."

***

Just when it seemed Zellner and Avery's luck had run out, they caught an unexpected and pleasant surprise. Judge Sutkiewicz came up with a case load excuse as a justification for the courts to take Avery's case off her docket. The official announcement came during the work week on Friday, October 26, 2023. "BIG AVERY NEWS," Zellner shared with her 737,000 Twitter followers. "Case is going to be reassigned to a new judge in Manitowoc. NO OBJECTION."

"There's no question she was aligned with the prosecution and even in the most recent ruling in our post-conviction motion, she is regurgitating the state's briefs," Zellner told this author on Oct. 29, 2023. "It's clear she wanted out of the case. Her biggest hope was not getting a new judge who has long-standing ties to the key police and public officials associated with Avery and Dassey's murder cases from 2005-2007.

Avery's lawyer just wanted the next judge to be open-minded and willing to analyze the evidence that she continues to uncover.

"And Sutkiewicz was aligned with Ken Kratz, the two of them served on state of Wisconsin committees together. She knew the state prosecutors," Zellner explained. "So we'll have to see."

On Monday, Oct. 30, 2023, Zellner learned that Avery's case would no longer be sent to a judge from neighboring Sheboygan County, an hour away. The newest judge on the bench for Manitowoc County, Judge Anthony Lambrecht, learned that he will handle Avery's post-conviction rulings from now on. In 2023, Manitowoc County had added a fourth circuit judge for their downtown Manitowoc courthouse, and Lambrecht ran for the position unopposed in the spring. During an April 2023 interview with *The Herald Times Reporter*, Lambrecht said he began his career as a police officer and after nearly six years in law enforcement, he chose to pursue a career in law. After he became an attorney, he worked in Manitowoc at the Wisconsin State Public Defender's Office. Before he ran for Manitowoc County judge, Lambrecht served as an assistant district attorney for Manitowoc. "I think it's really all prepared me for kind of a unique insight into the role of judge," Lambrecht told Manitowoc's newspaper six months before Avery's case became his. "Of course, it's not all criminal law, but a majority of what the judges in Manitowoc County deal with involves criminal law. I think those roles have prepared me well."

Zellner's key message for her admirers and followers all over the world is to realize that she still has plenty of avenues and paths to pursue as she works to bring Avery home from prison a free and innocent man. She remains focused on determining more facts and details surrounding the mysterious death of Halbach, the 25-year-old photographer. Zellner said she is not convinced Halbach actually died on Oct. 31, 2005. "She could have been tied up and held somewhere as a hostage," Zellner suggested recently. "No one really knows when she was murdered. There's this huge window. She could have been alive even after Bobby was seen in her RAV4. There's all those abandoned houses out there. The truth was, Teresa Halbach, was into pretty dangerous boudoir photography and she had some very strange relationships. She had someone calling her all the time and the person would always hang up and the cops never figured that out. She was not afraid of Steven Avery, and she seemed to know who this (stalker) was, and she was afraid of this person. She never thought it was Steven Avery, and she would have told (co-worker) Tom Pearce, and that wasn't the case."

Avery's lawyer said she remains focused on finding out what really happened to Halbach's personal artifacts including her purse, her full set of keys, her shoes, and the money that was in her RAV4. All of the items remain missing. She also said an unknown sample of DNA was found on the license plates that were taken from Halbach's vehicle and discarded into one of the junked vehicles on the Avery property.

"Part of our case moving forward will involve more scientific testing, including the DNA on the license plates," she said.

From her perspective, one matter that involves Sowinski's middle of the night eyewitness account of observing Bobby Dassey and a second person pushing Halbach's RAV4 along Avery Road needs further clarification. Sowinski described the person helping Bobby Dassey as being an older man. However, Zellner said that Sowinski's physical description of the person matches Dassey's close friend, Michael Osmunson. "That big hulking guy fit like a T. It didn't fit the description of Steven Avery's brother, Chuck, and it definitely was not his other brother, Earl. The person fit Michael Osmunson. He was very heavy set and had a long beard. And his statement was kind of incriminating," Zellner insisted.

Zellner suspects that Bobby Dassey and Osmunson drove the RAV4 from the turnaround on Highway 147 and they decided to push it once they reached Avery Road because they knew they needed to be quiet. Otherwise they would wake up Steven Avery and his relatives. "They had to be so quiet and disconnect the headlights and push it past Chuck Avery's," Zellner said. "Steven Avery has said that if anybody came in that driveway, my mother and I would have heard that, too."

In addition to Sowinski and Buresh, Kevin Rahmlow also signed an affidavit, giving Zellner three separate independent witnesses who saw someone other than Steven Avery in control of Halbach's RAV4 after her disappearance and probable death.

"I think she was dismembered in Bobby Dassey's garage like a deer," Zellner said. "Sixty-percent of her bones were never recovered, including the spine and ribs."

Two months after *Making a Murderer* season 2, Manitowoc County Sheriff's Detective Andy Colborn was back in the national spotlight, this time by his own choosing. On December 17, 2018, Colborn filed a defamation lawsuit against Netflix, Chrome Media, Synthesis Films, Laura Ricciardi, Moira Demos, Lisa Nishimura, Adam Del Deo, and Mary Manhardt. Ricciardi, Demos, Nishimura, and Del Deo were executive producers of *Making a Murderer* and Manhardt and Demos were its editors. With an estimated 117 million subscribers world-wide, Netflix distributed the true-crime documentary and Chrome Media and Synthesis Films were the independent film companies owned by Ricciardi and Demos, according to the lawsuit.

"Despite overwhelming evidence proving Avery and Dassey's guilt and the utter absence of evidence supporting defendant's accusations of police misconduct, defendants falsely led viewers to the inescapable conclusion that plaintiff and others planted evidence to frame Avery for Halbach's murder," Colborn's defamation lawsuit declared. "Defendants omitted, distorted, and falsified material and significant facts in an effort to portray plaintiff as a corrupt police officer who planted evidence to frame an innocent man. Defendants did so with actual malice and in order to make the film more profitable and more successful in the eyes of their peers, sacrificing and defaming the plaintiff's character and reputation in the process."

According to Colborn's lawsuit, Avery's murder trial attorneys Dean Strang and Jerry Buting played the audio portions of Deputy Colborn's call to Manitowoc County police dispatch; this was intended to convince the jurors Colborn discovered Halbach's SUV at an undisclosed location on November 3, 2005, two days before it was found. "Ricciardi and Demo, in concert with other named defendants, heavily edited portions of plaintiff's testimony in order to manipulate viewers to falsely conclude that he and other officers planted Halbach's SUV at the salvage yard," Colborn's lawsuit asserted. "Defendants Ricciardi and Demos strategically spliced 'reaction' shots of the plaintiff appearing nervous and apprehensive at trial into other portions of his testimony where he did not appear nervous or apprehensive in fact. The edits were part of defendants' overall attempt to manipulate viewers to falsely conclude that plaintiff and other Manitowoc County officers planted Halbach's SUV at the salvage yard."

Colborn's defamation lawsuit against Netflix also took issue with the film's portrayal of his role of finding Halbach's spare ignition key for her RAV4 on Avery's bedroom floor. "Defendants, separately and severally, with actual malice, led viewers to the inescapable but false conclusion that plaintiff and MTSO Lt. James Lenk planted the ignition key for Halbach's SUV in Avery's bedroom. They did so by splicing trial testimony, omitting other testimony, and failing to include essential photographic evidence that would have given viewers a complete view of what occurred," Colborn's lawsuit contended.

Three days after Halbach's RAV4 was discovered on the Avery property, Colborn and Lt. Lenk searched Avery's bedroom for evidence more remotely connected to the crime, including pornographic material, the defamation lawsuit outlined. Calumet County Deputy Daniel Kucharski accompanied them, and this was not their first time searching Avery's tiny bedroom. Days prior, Colborn noted, Manitowoc County's deputies saw "handcuffs and leg irons, apparent sex toys and pornographic materials in a bookcase that were not collected at that time." Then, on November 8, 2005, as Colborn "roughly returned a large binder," he and Lenk discovered Halbach's ignition key on the carpet next to Avery's bedroom bookcase.

"At trial," Colborn's lawsuit points out, Colborn, Lenk, and Kucharski "each offered a reasonable explanation as to how the key was missed on the earlier search and miscellaneous entries. All three testified they believed the key had fallen from a crack in the particle board backing of the bookcase when plaintiff roughly returned the binder into the bookcase. They believed Avery hid the key there with plans to retrieve it later and dispose of the SUV ... defendants Ricciardi and Demos filmed the entire trial and ... chose to fabricate testimony by splicing or omitting those portions not consistent with their false and defamatory account of the facts. In truth, plaintiff and Lenk did not plant the key, and MAM's aspersions that they did are false and have caused irreparable harm to plaintiff's reputation."

Colborn's lawsuit against Netflix claimed his "reputation has been irreparably harmed. Devoted husband, parent, decorated United States Air Force veteran, and dedicated public servant, plaintiff enjoyed an impeccable professional reputation prior to December 18, 2015, when MAM first aired. During the intervening three years, plaintiff has been subject to worldwide ridicule, contempt, and disdain as a result of the baseless and false assertions in MAM that he planted evidence to frame an innocent man or strengthen the case against a guilty one."

Prior to the Netflix release of *Making a Murderer*, Colborn noted that his name appeared on Internet search engines for only two different news articles about a routine crime near Manitowoc. "The same search now yields more than 1.8 million hits, nearly all of them painting plaintiff in a negative light," his lawsuit stated. In addition, there have been 732 YouTube videos about Colborn and his "perceived nefarious role in the Avery case. National and international news and entertainment media have published hundreds of articles, television and radio segments adopting the defendants' foregone but false conclusion that plaintiff and other Manitowoc County police officers planted evidence.

Social media, including Facebook, Twitter, YouTube and Reddit is replete with threats and insults directed at plaintiff because of the baseless accusations against plaintiff forced upon viewers of MAM," the defamation lawsuit claimed.

Colborn and his Manitowoc-based lawyer, Michael Griesbach of Griesbach Law Offices, insisted that people have made countless tweets, memes, insults and threatening social media posts portraying Colborn as a corrupt police officer and a prime mover in framing Avery. The defamation lawsuit suggested Demos, Ricciardi and the rest of the co-defendants could have mitigated the harm to Colborn's reputation "by admitting their distortions and omissions of fact when the above-mentioned articles were published and in the sequel to the original series, *Making a Murderer*, part 2. Instead, with actual malice, defendants doubled down by distorting and omitting additional facts to bolster their pre-ordained conclusion that plaintiff participated in the framing of Avery."

Colborn revealed he has received serious and ongoing threats to his and his family's safety, giving him extreme anxiety on a daily basis. The recorded telephone threats fill the capacity of 28 compact discs.

"Avery sympathizers have threatened to kill plaintiff and members of his family, kidnap and sodomize him and gang rape his wife," his lawsuit maintained. "Photographs of plaintiff's children have been posted online by hateful viewers under the spell of MAM. Repeat late night telephone calls to plaintiff's residence were commonplace in the aftermath of MAM's release, with callers screaming profanities and threatening to do physical harm. Defendants' tortious conduct has changed nearly every aspect of plaintiff's life, from travel plans to whether and where he and his wife go out to eat. Constantly on alert for danger to his family's safety whenever they leave their home, plaintiff suffers from extreme exhaustion and anxiety."

Lastly, Griesbach asked that Netflix and the other defendants provide his client with a retraction and an honest clarification of the erroneous and false statements and depictions cited in Colborn's lawsuit "to clear his good name and restore peace of mind." Their lawsuit sought unspecified monetary damages for defamation, intentional infliction of emotional distress and negligence.

Originally filed at the Manitowoc County Courthouse, Colborn's lawsuit was later refiled on April 3, 2019, in Wisconsin's federal court system. The case was later assigned to U.S. District Judge Brett Ludwig. In 2020, the Senate confirmed the 51-year-old Ludwig, a federal district judge for the Eastern District of Wisconsin, based in Milwaukee. A resident of suburban Mequon, Ludwig obtained his bachelor's with high honors from the University of Wisconsin at Stevens Point in 1991 and his law degree from the University of Minnesota in 1994. After law school, he served as a clerk for the U.S. Court of Appeals' Eighth Circuit.

By 2022, the defamation case against Netflix remained unresolved, but the plaintiff's case appeared on the verge of collapse. On September 18, 2022, my online news article for Patch reported that Colborn was forced to admit that his marriage had fallen apart, and that was not the fault of Netflix or the filmmakers of *Making a Murderer*. On July 21, 2022, Colborn gave a sworn statement for his federal lawsuit that certainly was not helpful: "For purposes of this case, I have agreed not to assert that *Making a Murderer* caused my divorce. I had a romantic relationship with Jodi Maurer prior to my divorce from Ms. Colborn. *Making a Murderer* did not cause Ms. Maurer to avoid romantic involvement with me. My relationship with Ms. Maurer harmed my relationship with my ex-wife, Ms. Colborn," Andy Colborn testified.

Colborn's divorce became final in February 2022.

"My relationship with Ms. Maurer also harmed my relationship with my adult children," the now-retired sheriff's detective further testified. In addition to Colborn's testimony regarding the fall of his marriage, several other statements attributed to him were made part of his court file against Netflix. The 2022 court documents indicated Colborn had wanted to sue Avery's original criminal defense attorneys, Dean Strang and Jerry Buting. The following were some of the lawsuit stipulations entered into Colborn's court file against Netflix:

"I believe that Jerome Buting has damaged my reputation in out–of–court statements about me that were made after the release of *Making a Murderer*."

"At one point, Mr. Colborn wanted to sue Mr. Buting for defamation."

"At one point, Mr. Colborn wanted to sue Mr. Strang for defamation."

"Mr. Colborn has not watched *Making a Murderer* in its entirety."

"Upon announcing his retirement, Mr. Colborn received supportive calls from dozens of people."

"In 2016, Mr. Colborn was already preparing to retire from the Manitowoc County Sheriff's Office in no more than three years."

"Mr. Colborn voluntarily retired in 2018.

"Mr. Colborn had a retirement party."

"Since his retirement, Mr. Colborn decided to return to the workforce and was able to find new employment."

"Mr. Colborn's faith community supported him after the release of *Making a Murderer*."

"No one has confronted Mr. Colborn as a result of *Making a Murderer*."

"Mr. Colborn has not lost income due to *Making a Murderer*."

"Mr. Colborn had an affair with Jodi Maurer while married to Ms. Colborn.

"Mr. Colborn's infidelity irreparably harmed his relationship with his ex–wife, Ms. Colborn."

"Mr. Colborn's infidelity also harmed his relationship with his adult children."

"Mr. Colborn filed for divorce from his now ex-wife, Barb Colborn, in March 2021."

"Mr. Colborn's divorce from Ms. Colborn was finalized in February 2022."

***

Four years after Colborn's defamation lawsuit moved to Milwaukee's federal court, his case came to a stunning and abrupt halt. On March 10, 2023, U.S. District Court Judge Brett Ludwig issued a 31-page ruling granting Netflix's motion for summary judgment, granting Ricciardi, Demos, and Chrome Media's motion for summary judgment and denying plaintiff Colborn's motion for partial summary judgment.

Zellner was not surprised Colborn lost his lawsuit. "Defamation cases against public figures are notoriously hard to win. You have to prove actual malice," Zellner told me on September 29, 2023. "I was flabbergasted the suit was filed. It was completely ill-conceived, cost a lot of money, and it was completely without merit, and the judge dismissed it on a summary judgment, finding there was no evidence at all that the producers had distorted any of the facts of the case. And I think, really with Colborn, it backfired on him. I don't know who advised him to file it. I mean, I could take a guess. But it was one of the most frivolous lawsuits I've seen in a long time. I think they probably should have been sanctioned for filing it, and I think it was maybe a publicity stunt ... in a way it just backfired because there's a written opinion by the judge saying that there was no defamation, and there was no distortion, so it actually reflected really well on the producers of *Making a Murderer*."

For crusaders of the First Amendment, especially the news media, Judge Ludwig's ruling in Colborn V. Netflix may become one of the most significant modern-day legal rulings for defamation lawsuits brought against the press or filmmakers. The judge showed a deep understanding of *Making a Murderer* and the evidence from Avery's 2007 murder trial. As a result, Judge Ludwig crafted a masterfully written 31-page decision addressing the tenets of Colborn's defamation lawsuit. Even the opening summary of Ludwig's decision reads like something out of a John Grisham novel:

"On December 18, 2015, Netflix released the ten-part docuseries *Making a Murderer* and turned small-town sergeant Andrew Colborn into a household name. He now very much wishes it had not. His unflattering portrayal in the series transformed his '15 minutes of fame' into what felt like a far longer period of infamy, as a mob of outraged viewers flooded his voicemail and email inboxes with vile and hostile messages. Some called him a crooked cop.

Others wished him a long, unpleasant stay in fiery perdition. At least one person threatened to harm his family. Meanwhile, two thousand miles away, *Making a Murderer*'s producers were basking in accolades and consorting with major media outlets. Critics lauded their journalistic tenacity and unique ability to synthesize the legal and dramatic. Colborn received no such flattery — as the producers took the stage at the Microsoft Theatre to accept their Emmys, he was busy boarding up the front door to his own house. Outraged by what he believed to be grossly unjust, inverted life trajectories, Colborn filed this lawsuit, accusing Netflix, Inc., Chrome Media LLC, and producers Laura Ricciardi and Moira Demos of defamation.

Next came the probative question before the court, had Colborn provided sufficient evidence to make a defamation case out of his portrayal in *Making a Murderer*? "He has not," the judge in Milwaukee ruled. "The First Amendment does not guarantee a public figure like Colborn the role of protagonist in popular discourse — in fact, it protects the media's ability to cast him in a much less flattering light—so Defendants are entitled to summary judgment on all counts."

Of note, the judge revealed, Colborn only watched about one hour of the entire two seasons of *Making a Murderer*. To prove defamation under Wisconsin law, Colborn needed to prove Netflix and the filmmakers published a false, defamatory, and unprivileged statement. Furthermore, for public officials such as Colborn, the First Amendment requires "clear and convincing evidence that the defendant published the defamatory statement with actual malice, i.e., with knowledge that it was false or with reckless disregard of whether it was false or not."

The following is a condensed summary of Ludwig's findings:

Page 5: "His summary judgment motion adopts an overbroad view of defamation, identifying 52 allegedly defamatory statements. But most of his gripes read more like media criticism better suited to the op-ed section; they are not actionable statements that could even potentially be defamatory under Wisconsin law. Those few statements that might conceivably be actionable fail for other reasons. Colborn's 'defamation by fabricated quotation' claim fares no better because the record shows no instance in which Defendants did not convey the gist of a changed quotation. Colborn's final theory, a claim for 'defamation by implication,' also fails because he has not produced sufficient evidence to sustain it ... his kitchen-sink approach identifies 52 instances of alleged defamation. He cites the series' use of music and graphics, its inclusion of certain statements of and concerning other people, its incorporation of true statements or protected opinions and the alteration of reaction shots from Avery's homicide trial. None of these can support a claim for defamation."

Page 7: "Other parts of Colborn's case reflect his own dissatisfaction with what is in fact the verifiable truth.

It is well-established that 'truth is an absolute defense to a defamation claim.' Thus, in defamation lawsuits at least, verity still prevails, even if the audience lacks the temperament for it ... Altogether, Colborn complains seven times of statements that no one, not even he himself, can prove false. In these instances, it is the facts that aggrieve Colborn, and there is no legal remedy for that."

Page 9: "Colborn's complaint includes a 'defamation by fabricated quotation' theory. The idea here is that, in the course of condensing the trial footage, Defendants deliberately altered Colborn's words to make him appear more contemptible. Of course, some alteration is necessary. No documentary is 'true' in the strictest sense of the word; they all abbreviate, edit and emphasize. But there are degrees of falsity, and, for defamation purposes, the question is where to draw the line."

Page 17: "Colborn also challenges the producers' decision to show him agreeing that he could understand how someone might think he was looking at Halbach's Toyota based only on the audio of his dispatch call. In fact, Colborn never answered that question because his attorney objected and the judge sustained the objection. But, though not depicted in *Making a Murderer*, Colborn later affirmed on the witness stand that the call sounded like hundreds of other license plate or registration checks he had done before. In essence, he testified that the audio closely resembled a mine-run dispatch call. Thus, Colborn implicitly admitted that, based only on the audio of his dispatch call, it sounded like he had Halbach's license plate in his field of vision."

Page 20: "Moreover, by excluding certain portions of his deposition testimony, *Making a Murderer* may have actually enhanced Colborn's credibility. At his deposition, Colborn unequivocally denied ever broaching the 1994 or 1995 phone call with District Attorney Rohrer. Rohrer's testimony called that into question. Were *Making a Murderer* the calibrated hit piece Colborn claims, its producers surely would have leapt at the chance to catch the object of their disdain in an outright lie."

Page 22: "Colborn argues that *Making a Murderer* falsely implies that he committed criminal acts (planting evidence) and is thus defamatory per se. Defendants assert that Colborn's case falls short for at least three reasons: 1) the implication that Colborn planted evidence is not reasonably conveyed and attributable to Defendants; 2) Colborn cannot prove that he did not plant evidence; and 3) Colborn cannot satisfy defamation by implication's heightened actual malice standard. The first two arguments fail; a reasonable jury might find that 'Making a Murderer' falsely implied that Colborn planted evidence. But because the Defendants are correct that Colborn cannot show actual malice, this theory also fails. A faithful recreation of the entire trial, framing defense and all, would also have defeated any claim for defamation. Yet *Making a Murderer* is not always so evenhanded in its presentation. To the extent it qualifies as journalism, it often hews closer to gonzo than objective, and its visual language could be read to suggest something perhaps more nefarious than the totality of the evidence warrants. Thus, a fair-minded jury could conclude that *Making a Murderer* not so subtly nudges viewers toward the conclusion that Colborn did, in fact, plant evidence to frame Steven Avery. The same jury could also find the implicit conclusion false."

Page 26: "Colborn cites a trove of email chains that purportedly establish the actual malice of both the producers and Netflix. Most of these exchanges, however, support the Defendants' position that they did not intend to imply and were not aware that viewers might infer that Colborn actually planted evidence to frame Avery ... At most this collection of emails suggests the producers' sympathy for Avery's plight. But even sympathy for the devil is not clear and convincing proof of actual malice toward the Holy Trinity ... Furthermore, in interviews conducted contemporaneous to *Making a Murderer*'s release, Ricciardi and Demos said they were 'not trying to provide any answers,' and did not 'have a conclusion' and that 'there are a lot of questions here.' This undercuts any inference of defamatory intent or reckless disregard."

Page 27: "In sum, a reasonable jury might conclude that *Making a Murderer* implied that Colborn framed Avery, but because Colborn has no evidence that Ricciardi, Demos or Chrome intended that implication or recklessly disregarded its possible existence with malice, the producers are entitled to summary judgment."

Page 29: "In addition, as a matter of law, Netflix exhibited actual malice only if it intended to imply a defamatory, materially false, and unprivileged statement. But even if Netflix intended to imply that Colborn planted evidence, Colborn has no evidence that Netflix knew that statement to be false … No one on Netflix's creative team ever spoke to anyone depicted in *Making a Murderer*. They never even watched the raw trial footage, instead relying solely on the cuts the producers provided. Colborn himself admitted under oath that those who did not attend Avery's criminal trial could not have known what occurred there, including former District Attorney Michael Griesbach, who has written three books on the subject. By that logic, a handful of Netflix employees with no legal education and limited exposure to trial testimony cannot possibly have understood the intricacies of the case."

Finally, Judge Ludwig delivered his knockout punch for Colborn's lawsuit. On page 30, the Milwaukee judge delivered this zinger:

"In the end, Colborn's turn in *Making a Murderer* may not have been to his liking, but that does not make it defamatory. Few aspire to enter the cultural zeitgeist on such controversial terms. That possibility, though, is a necessary byproduct of the freedom of press that the First Amendment protects. If media could portray us only at our best, we would be a country of antiseptic caricatures and less intelligent for it. We have not sunken so low just yet."

'THE BOB DYLAN OF MAKING A MURDERER'

In the aftermath of *Making a Murderer*, several people across the globe became social media influencers because of their lively true-crime podcasts and spirited commentary. On the other hand, Stacy Seabrook found a different approach. The talented British Columbia resident used his musical talents to offer people a window into his mind and his interpretation of *Making a Murderer*.

"Looking back, most of the songs are a processing of my feelings of injustice," Seabrook wrote to me on October 13, 2023. "I had gone through a divorce shortly before watching *Making a Murderer*, and I think the injustice I felt over the series was charged by that which I felt from my breakup."

One of Seabrook's songs includes three different Steven Avery book titles weaved into the lyrics, which he called, "Illusion of Justice," naming it after Jerry Buting's 2017 book, *Illusion of Justice*. The other two books in his song are my book, *Wrecking Crew*, and *Indefensible*, by attorney Michael Griesbach.

In all, Seabrook has produced about two dozen songs for his *Making a Murderer* collection. You can find them all on YouTube. A couple of his songs such as "36 Million" and "Tick Tock Manitowoc" have a Jimmy Buffett-sound to them. His song "The Eternal Champion Erekose," a tribute to the late Steven Avery YouTube crusader, 44-year-old Richard McAdam of Scotland, AKA Erekose, sounds like a Johnny Cash tune.

Some of Seabrook's other songs include "Mama and Papa Avery," "As Justice Slowly Disappears," "The Steven Avery Case: It Really Matters," "Zellnami Comin," "Doubling Down," "Let's Brain Fingerprint Them All," and "They're Innocent."

Most of the songs were recorded with talented musician Marc Atkinson at the Barn Studio, Hornby Island, in British Columbia. Atkinson plays the bass guitar, piano, and the drums. "Justice Slowly Disappears" is reminiscent of a Bob Dylan tune, even carrying the harmonica.

"I'm not sure the style. Contemporary folk/advocacy," Seabrook answered. "I thought they would make a good series for Netflix, 20 songs with 20 backstories to match the 20 episodes, but it hasn't happened ... YET."

Were folk singers Bob Dylan and Gordon Lightfoot major influences on the songs he wrote about Steven Avery's case?

Lightfoot, not so much, Seabrook remarked.

"Obviously, Bob Dylan has probably influenced everybody and his 'Hurricane' song about Rubin Carter was about raising awareness too. So, ya, Dylan was more of a lyrical influence on me. I like the cryptic, multidimensional meanings his lyrics can have. One of my favorite comments on my YouTube videos was, 'The Bob Dylan of Making a Murderer.' Funny thing is, and which many people find odd, is that, so, I don't really listen to music," Seabrook revealed. "I did growing up and stuff, but that was the classic rock in the radio, etc., but mostly, I just learned guitar at about 23 and wrote my own stuff ever since."

If you only listen to two Stacy Seabrook songs on YouTube, one, without question, must be "Avery Road."

"Avery Road is a song trying to remind people that they should care," Seabrook told me. "Encouraging them to not turn blind to injustices that they see. Basically, it's a musical reiteration of Martin Luther King Jr.'s quote, 'Injustice anywhere is a threat to justice everywhere' with regards to this case."

Stacy Seabrook's other must-listen-to song for fanatics of *Making a Murderer* is about Manitowoc County Sheriff's Deputy Andy Colborn. The song, "Dear Andy," and YouTube video is 2 minutes 53 seconds. Additionally, Seabrook recorded a "Behind the Songs" video that offers great insight into the lyrics Seabrook wrote for "Dear Andy."

The commentary begins with Seabrook staring into his video camera and lamenting, "I think, he probably hasn't heard the song." From there, "Dear Andy" dissects the 2007 murder trial testimony, describing Colborn's role in discovering the spare ignition key for Halbach's Toyota RAV4 on Avery's bedroom floor. Without the key, Avery probably goes free and never gets charged with killing Halbach.

> *Dear Andy:*
> *You can avoid*
> *You can delay*
> *But you can't escape*
> *Your judgment day.*
> *Dear Andy,*
> *Said time's running out on you.*

"The idea that we get away with anything in life is, as I get older, I realize we carry everything with us," Seabrook reflected during his February 2022 behind the songs video. "Take Andy Colborn. If he lied or if he withheld evidence or planted evidence, he might think he's getting away with it, but, we carry that stuff and guilt, shame, all that stuff, is internalized in a human body. You will see that we don't get away with anything in life. I always wonder if Andy Colborn ever heard that song, because it was a message to him, for him to think. You can avoid, you can delay, but you can't escape your judgment day."

From there, Seabrook's lyrics focus on Colborn's preparation for his trial testimony.

> *I want to know*
> *Who convinced you to say*
> *That ridiculous story*
> *On the stand that day.*
> *Dear Andy,*
> *Said time's running out on you.*

I said Dear Andy,
Who was telling you what to do?

Seabrook's behind the song video shows Colborn's 2007 televised trial testimony where Colborn testifies, "I'll be the first to admit, I handled it rather roughly, twisting it, shaking it, pulling it."

"They needed to sell this story as the legitimate way that the key was produced," Seabrook tells his audience. "Because they had been into the bedroom, searched it, six or seven times beforehand. And they came up with this story, just bizarre story. There's three of them in this very small bedroom. (Calumet County Deputy Dan) Kucharski on the bed, apparently the crime scene, and he's sitting or lounging on the bed doing paperwork. Andy Colborn takes this bookcase, and he shakes it, and he twists it, and he says, 'I'll be the first to admit, I was quite rough with it.' It's just a weird thing to say. And so, my question goes, 'Why is this officer having to do this on the stand? Why is this story, hey, it must be embarrassing in a way, just personally for him, to have to come up and try to sell that. That's why in the song I say, 'That Ridiculous Story.' I say, 'Dear Andy, Dear Andy, Who was telling you what to do?' Who was telling him what to do? Who was guiding him? In the song, there's like a list of people that might have been helping him along."

Was it Bald Jimmy?
Or Sabbatical Tom?
Or Sweaty Kenny?
Or, Norm 'Them Bones Be' Gahn?
Dear Andy,
Said time's running out on you.
I said Dear Andy
Can't you see they were using you?

After the third verse, the music fades and Seabrook looks at the camera and asks his nagging question. "Who was telling him what to do? Was it Jimmy, which is Jim Lenk. Kind of guy that's been Andy's right-hand man, his boss for a long time, very influential on Andy. Or, sabbatical Tom. That was Tom Fallon, the assistant attorney general for Wisconsin. He magically went on sabbatical after things started to heat up in this case once they found out that the bones of Teresa Halbach had been given away, and so I coined him Sabbatical Tom.

"Sweaty Kenny, that's Ken Kratz," Seabrook tells viewers. "He's the one that told in the press conference, he emphasized sweat on Steven Avery and then emphasized sweat DNA, an attempt to continually try to whenever he mentioned that word, he tries to tie it back to peoples' vivid memory of the horrific account that he fabricated and told the press. And Norm "Them Bones Be" Gahn is Norm Gahn. He's a DNA specialist. He's higher up in the Wisconsin Attorney General's Office. Norm Gahn was in the decision-making process to give bones back to Teresa Halbach's family ... It's a Wisconsin statute. The state must keep the evidence until the inmate is released, or all appeals are ... complete. And you think, well, they might have made a mistake, Norm Gahn, Tom Fallon, they gather, they decide, well, we can give this evidence back, and they can plead ignorance or, no big deal. However, the statute which stipulates that the state has to hold onto evidence was actually written by Norm Gahn. So, once again, it's a very weird twist and turn."

> *And, yes we know how rough you were*
> *With that bookcase,*
> *But why were the coins on top*
> *In virtually the same place?*
> *Dear Andy,*
> *We're waiting for answers from you.*

"When stories are fairly elaborate, they often indicate someone's lying. They're embellishing. They're trying to sell it and that's what I read Andy Colborn's testimony like," Seabrook told listeners in February 2022. "He creates this sort of unreal situation to explain the key being produced.

When you look at the story at face value, most people would scratch their head, thinking why are you shaking, pulling and doing this all to the bookcase, and then he goes on to say he was putting these books back into the case, quite violently or aggressively, that this key popped out of the back. They dislodged the back of the cabinet and this key just popped out. You wonder why the key didn't pop out when he was twisting, pulling it and shaking it. I wonder why he was doing that in the first place? There's photographs of the case before he did all this. There's no evidence of a key tucked in. The idea that Steven Avery or anyone else would attempt to hide a key in such a bizarre manner, for me, it's all a lie. That's why Dear Andy. That's why I wrote the song.

> *I said Dear Andy,*
> *Said time's running out on you.*
> *Oh, but Dear Andy,*
> *There's still time to do*
> *The right thing to do*
> *Oh, but Dear Andy*
> *Said time's running out on you.*

"Time's running out on you," Seabrook reflected in his video. "It's more like with his own conscience. Sometimes, we can remedy, make amends for things we do in life. It's best to do that as soon as possible after you recognize there's been some sort of infraction, or you made a mistake. If you let that go, it becomes more difficult, and I think that's the situation Andrew Colborn finds himself in. He's unable to now. It's gone too long, and he's dug in too deep. It doesn't matter though because he's going to have to do it one or another."

With that, Seabrook played the full rendition of his YouTube song, "Dear Andy," featuring and produced by Marc Atkinson along with James Emerson providing background vocals:

> *You can avoid*
> *You can delay,*

But you can't escape your
Judgment day.
Dear Andy,
Said time's running out on you.
I want to know
Who convinced you to say
That ridiculous story
On the stand that day.
Dear Andy,
Said time's running out on you.
I said Dear Andy,
Who was telling you what to do?
Was it Bald Jimmy?
Or Sabbatical Tom?
Or Sweaty Kenny?
Or, Norm 'Them Bones Be' Gahn?
Dear Andy,
Said time's running out on you.
I said Dear Andy
Can't you see they were using you?
And, yes we know how rough you were
With that bookcase,
But why were the coins on top
In virtually the same place?
Dear Andy,
We're waiting for answers from you.
I said Dear Andy,
Said time's running out on you.
Oh, but Dear Andy,
There's still time to do
The right thing to do
Oh, but Dear Andy
Said time's running out on you.

Suburban Chicago wrongful conviction lawyer Kathleen Zellner has fought for Steven Avery's innocence since taking over his post-conviction case in 2016. "So we began to really look at the individuals on the property at the time of the murder, and everything led us back to Bobby Dassey," Zellner explained.

Bobby Dassey became the star witness for prosecutor Ken Kratz during Steven Avery's 2007 murder trial. "Steven has always felt that he was involved because he was very obsessed with Teresa Halbach," attorney Kathleen Zellner said.

According to world-famous wrongful conviction attorney Kathleen Zellner, "Steven Avery, the biggest blow to him was when his mother died."

Attorney Kathleen Zellner maintains the newly discovered evidence showing that Bobby Dassey was in possession of Teresa Halbach's vehicle means Bobby Dassey had the opportunity and access to plant evidence in the vehicle and from the vehicle.

During a November 2023 interview with his lawyer from Fox Lake Correctional Center in Wisconsin, Steven Avery was asked about his nephew, Brendan Dassey, who also remains incarcerated for the murder. "I don't know if he's guilty or innocent. I don't know if he helped Bobby or not. I don't know," Avery remarked.

In recent years, attorney Kathleen Zellner of suburban Chicago has uncovered multiple witnesses including Thomas Sowinski, the Manitowoc newspaper delivery carrier, who saw Bobby Dassey pushing Teresa Halbach's RAV4, just hours before the RAV4 turned up on the edge of the Avery Salvage Yard.

Attorney Kathleen Zellner was not surprised that Andy Colborn of the Manitowoc County Sheriff's Department and his lawyers lost their defamation lawsuit against Netflix and the film producers of Making a Murderer. "It was one of the most frivolous lawsuits I've seen in a long time," Zellner declared. "I think they probably should have been sanctioned for filing it, and I think it was maybe a publicity stunt."

"No one really knows when she was murdered," Steven Avery's lawyer Kathleen Zellner said of Teresa Halbach. "There's this huge window ... The truth was, Teresa Halbach was into pretty dangerous boudoir photography, and she had some very strange relationships."

EPILOGUE

STEVEN AVERY TALKS

On Nov. 10, 2023, Steven Avery spoke with Zellner for a half-hour during a tape-recorded phone call made from Avery's medium security prison in Fox Lake, Wisconsin. The call's purpose was to provide readers of WRECKING CREW with an update of Avery's plight, his prospects for a new murder trial and his reflections on his sister Barb Tadych's son, Bobby Dassey, as the alternative suspect in the 2005 death of Teresa Halbach.

"John Ferak is updating his book, and it's going to come out in a couple of weeks," Zellner told Avery. "And so I'm going to ask you a series of questions, OK?"

Zellner began by asking Avery for his reaction to the recent assignment of a new judge to handle his post-conviction appeals.

"Well, it was about time. Get rid of her," Avery said, referring to Sheboygan Judge Angela Sutkiewicz. "Well, because, I wrote to the (Wisconsin) Supreme Court. I wrote to her boss, to kind of get rid of her."

"Actually, the way this happened," Zellner explained to Avery, "she made a motion to the court to be removed from the case. So they didn't remove her. She removed herself. I don't know if you were aware of that. It didn't have anything to do with what we tried to do. Because, we filed formal motions a couple of years ago, but there wasn't any legal way to have her removed. I mean, people complain about judges all the time. But what she did was, she removed herself. So, she's off the case. What do you think about having a new judge?"

"Well, a lot better," Avery answered. "Terrific. Better than her. I don't think she should be on the bench. If she can't follow the law, then she don't need to be on there."

Zellner's next question pertained to the newly elected judge from Manitowoc, Anthony Lambrecht, who was just assigned to handle Avery's post-conviction appeals.

"Well, I know he's six months on the bench," Avery replied. "He worked for the public defender's office, and some on the police department, but that's all I know."

"Well, do you think he's going to be more balanced?" Zellner inquired. "He's been on both sides. He's been a police officer and also working for the public defender."

"Yeah, it's probably a little bit better. Because then he's coming into it a new set of eyes," Avery said, before pausing and finally blurting out, "Maybe," as he began laughing.

"I feel the same way," Zellner told him. "I feel optimistic about it. I think it's a good thing."

From there, the conversation steered toward Bobby Dassey.

Zellner reminded Avery how her law office identified multiple witnesses including Thomas Sowinski, the Manitowoc newspaper carrier, who saw Bobby Dassey pushing Halbach's RAV4 along Avery Road during the middle of the night, just hours before the RAV4 turned up on the edge of Avery Salvage Yard.

"(Kevin) Rahmlow having seen the car, (Thomas) Buresh having seen Bobby driving the car. What's your assessment of all of that?" What effect should that have on the case?" Zellner asked.

"Well," Avery answered, "that kind of proves that he's got her car. Saying that I'm right. That I got nothing to do with it. He does. It's all going back to him. And the computer. That he was sick on the computer. All of that is a factor."

"Do you think he was interested in Teresa Halbach?" Zellner followed up.

"Well, most of the time, he was watching her," Avery said of his nephew, Bobby Dassey. "Every time she came, he would always say something. He'd say, 'I see your girlfriend came.' Which is, he wanted her. He knew every time that she was going to come out."

"So, you noticed that he was very interested in Teresa Halbach," Zellner wondered.

"When she came, he was always there and looking out the window," Avery pointed out.

"So, he was watching her?"

"Yeah," Avery answered. "Because I talked about it when I got her coming, one day, with all the vehicles, and the boat and the trailer. He'd always say and comment on it."

Zellner wanted to know if Avery remembered how Bobby Dassey acted once the Manitowoc County Sheriff's deputies, notably Deputy Colborn, visited Avery Salvage Yard in the days after Halbach went missing. "How did Bobby act then?"

"Well, he was different," Avery replied. "He felt nervous and with Mike (Osmunson) and all of that."

"How did he act differently?" Zellner pressed.

"Well, he was mostly nervous," Avery said. "Then we wanted to go to Menards, and he had something to do. But then when I went down in the pit with the other ones, when Chucky seen the taillights, or headlights, he wanted to come with me. Now, all the other times, he didn't want to come. He was busy. But now he made sure he wanted to come. 'I'll come with you. I'll come with you.'"

"Did he know that your finger was bleeding?" Zellner inquired.

"Yeah."

Next, Avery was asked what happened when he and his brother, Chuck, left Avery Salvage Yard to drive to the

Menards store in Manitowoc. At that point, the criminal investigation into Halbach's disappearance was still in its infancy.

"And you pulled out onto the road, what did you notice in the rearview mirrors?" Zellner inquired.

"Well, I seen taillights back behind me," Avery remembered. "I said, oh, I've seen tail lights, I told Chucky. Then he asked me, do you want to turn around and look? And I said, I don't know. Then we just got up the road a little bit, I think, and I said, yeah, let's turn around, let's go back. So then he turned the flatbed around, and we went back, and I looked all over, and I didn't see nothing."

The lawyer asked if Avery suspected a vehicle just left his trailer.

"Yeah," he agreed. "We just left from there, I know there was nothing there. There were no cars moving, so the only one that I think was there, was Bobby."

"And so did you notice at any point that someone tried to get in your trailer?"

"No, not at that time, no," Avery answered.

Avery recalled it was not until after he was arrested and awaiting his trial for murder that he began reviewing various crime scene evidentiary photographs from the police. One photograph in particular caught his eye because it showed the door to his red trailer with pry bar marks on it.

"And that's when you realized that the door had probably been pried open?" Zellner wondered.

"Yeah," Avery agreed.

"What about with Bobby, though? What was your observation about his relationship with Mike Osmunson?"

"I know they were close," Avery told her. "They always hung out with each other. They were like two peas in a pod."

"What about that conversation where they were trying to testify against you about a conversation after Teresa had disappeared. What do you remember about that?"

"Well, they walked up to me and I don't know where I was, by Barbara's van or something, somewhere in that area," Avery recalled. "And then they just made a comment, 'You got her in the bedroom or in the closet or something?' And then I said some comment back."

"And then when they tried to testify, did you think they were lying about the conversation? The date?" Zellner followed up.

"Yeah," Avery answered.

"And when Bobby testified at trial, what did you think when you saw him testify?"

"When he got nerves, and I don't know, tried to pin everything on me," Avery responded.

"Was he lying?" Zellner followed up.

"Oh yeah, he lies about everything," Avery remarked. "Sometimes I let him use my Cadillac and my Blazer and take it to school, and then he lied about that because he'd do some donuts with it and squawk them tires, and then he said he never did it, and then I hear from everybody else he did. And back in the (salvage) yard, he'd take stereos out of cars and radios and sell it to the people in the school."

"Was he lying to you guys about that, about taking that, about taking that stuff?"

"Oh yeah," Avery replied.

"What about his computer? What did you know about that? Was he on the computer a lot?"

"Well, pretty much," Avery said. "But then Barbara tried to get somebody in because it was, I don't know, she was having problems with it. That's when it was in Bobby's room. She had a couple people come over and try to fix it. They tried to get shit off or something."

"She talked to Brad Dassey about trying to get items on it deleted, right?"

"Yeah, I think that after the second time, when she tried to do that," Avery responded.

"But she had computer people come and try and look at it?"

"I don't know, a friend or someone she knew or something," Avery explained.

Zellner asked Avery to describe what kind of relationship his co-defendant, Brendan Dassey, had with his brother, Bobby.

"Well, it was kind of rough," Avery said. "Brendan would do his schoolwork and Bobby would come and (hit) him on the side of the head and go out the door. He was a mean guy. He'd pick on him all the time."

"Did either Brendan or Blaine ever talk about Bobby looking at a lot of porn on the computer?"

"Yeah, I don't know. I don't really remember," Avery said.

Zellner reminded Avery that when Bobby Dassey testified at Avery's trial, he told everyone he last saw Halbach walking toward Avery's red trailer. "Did she come to your trailer door that day?" Zellner asked.

"No," Avery replied.

"So you knew that he was lying, right?"

"Oh yeah because I don't think you can see my front door from their house," Avery noted. "From Barbara's house."

"And he said he was watching out the window?"

"Yeah."

"So, in your mind, do you feel pretty confident that he's the one that murdered Teresa Halbach?"

"Oh yeah," Avery answered. "Might say 100 percent. And then other people are involved, maybe that Mike. Maybe Scott. I don't know. Scott was there that day. He was on Barbara's property, talking to Bobby."

"What time of day was he there?"

"Around noon, somewhere in there," Avery said. "And I knew Barbara wasn't home, so I was wondering why is he out here, when Barbara ain't here, and then I seen Bobby talking to him."

"And then, of course, Scott lied about that at trial, right? He never admitted being there," Zellner reminded Avery. "Do you remember the story they had, they drove by each other, exactly at 3 p.m.?"

"Yeah, yeah, I think that that was all a lie," Avery suggested. "If they were by Fisherville Road, Jambo Creek Road, their cell phones would come off of Mishicot, not the other way. So that's all a lie."

"What do you think about the timing of Scott and Barb's marriage?" Zellner inquired.

"Well, it's all strange," Avery responded. "Everything is strange. Tom (Janda) and Barbara would always go over there, by his trailer, almost every night."

"To Scott's trailer?"

"Yeah."

"Do you think the timing of their marriage before the trial had anything to do with the trial itself?" Zellner asked.

"Yeah, I would say. Because if they get married, then husband and wife don't have to testify against each other," Avery said.

"What about Brendan at this point? What are your thoughts about him?"

"I don't know," Avery replied. "That's all up to him. I don't know if he's guilty or innocent. I don't know if he helped Bobby or not. I don't know. I don't know if they put her in that blue trailer or what. He come up with a story for a reason. I don't know why."

"So you think that he lied, what he was talking about actually might have happened, but it was Bobby instead of you?" Zellner asked.

"Yeah," Avery agreed. "And that trailer was the blue trailer, and that's why they got rid of it."

Zellner asked where the blue trailer was kept.

"It was right aside the road, coming down to me," Avery recalled. "Right before Barbara's house."

"Okay, and at what point was that trailer disposed of? Was it before the trial?"

"I don't know," Avery answered. "All I know is that Earl moved it down in the pit, and they put up a fence and after that, I couldn't tell you. Whenever they put up the fence, they took it out of there."

"And then it was destroyed?"

"Yeah, then they destroyed it," Avery said. "And they destroyed Bobby's Blazer and all of that."

"Yeah, so tell me about that," Zellner inquired. "So Bobby, was it the Blazer that he was driving that day that Teresa disappeared?"

"Yeah, yeah, black Blazer," Avery pointed out.

"And who took the Blazer and destroyed it?"

"It must have been Earl and Chucky," Avery said of his two brothers. "Because he only had it for a month. He only had it for a month."

"Was it in good condition?"

"Yeah, it was in good condition. Ran good. Transmission was good. The tires were good. The brakes were good. Everything was good on it," Avery insisted.

"So they destroyed both the Blazer and the blue trailer, right?"

"Yeah, yeah, and they got rid of Barbara's vehicles too, and they crushed them all," Avery remarked. "The van and everything. Everything which she had sitting there."

"So the van that she was going to sell, they crushed it?"

"Yeah, yeah, they crushed all of that."

"And can you think of any reason to have done that?"

"Well, they wanted to make sure there was no evidence nowhere. That's all that I can think of," Avery surmised.

"Do you believe, and we put forth in the briefs, that it was Bobby. What do you think Barb thinks? Do you think Barb knows that he was involved?"

"Well, maybe not at first, but I figured after that, yeah, they all knew," Avery replied.

"Have any of them ever explained how Teresa's bones ended up in the Dassey burn barrel?" Zellner asked.

"No. Mmmm," Avery replied.

"And has Barb ever responded or said anything about Bobby pushing Teresa's car?"

"No. No. She never wanted to talk about it."

"And at some point did she put on Facebook that Bobby had told her that he never saw Teresa walk towards your trailer?"

"Yeah, I think there was a time that she put it on Facebook that Bobby said she left."

"So, tell me now at this point, the appeal is pending with the new evidence with Thomas Sowinski, what do you hope, like best case scenario, what do you hope will happen, when it gets to the appellate court?" Zellner inquired.

"Well, I think they should just give me a new trial and let the jury decide," Avery answered. "That's what I think they're going to do is just give me a new trial, and it will go back to circuit court."

"And probably would be in front of this judge, the new judge we've got," Zellner noted. "Don't you think?"

"Yeah," Avery responded.

"Because he won't have had any involvement in the decision on the appeal because Sutkiewicz did that, but it would come back to him for trial," Zellner explained. "Do you think you'd get a fair trial with him? Or would you want to try to move it?"

"I don't know. I don't know nothing about him or what. I just don't want a Manitowoc jury," Avery remarked.

"Right," Zellner agreed, laughing. "So you'd have to get a jury from elsewhere or try to move it from Manitowoc.

Is there any other message that you'd want for John Ferak to put in his book from you? I mean, you could actually just give the message right now to people that are following it, your prediction on what's going to happen."

"Well, I think I'm going to get a new trial, but then I want who's all involved, you know, to go to trial," Avery replied. "So this don't happen to another person again. You know, there's got to be consequences. If you set somebody up, you've got to make sure it don't happen again."

"So you would like to see if you had a new trial, and you're acquitted, then you would like to see that people that were involved in framing you, you would like to see those people go to prison?" Zellner asked.

"Yeah."

"And would you like to see Bobby Dassey charged with the murder?"

"Oh yeah. Yeah. That would be the first thing to do," Avery said. "Why don't they arrest him, and then they ought to let me go. We already got the judge saying that he's got the vehicle, so that should be enough evidence and everything."

"Right," Zellner quipped. "Nobody's really questioning that he had the car. OK, can you think of anything else that you would want to say in a book?"

"I'm sick of doing time for something I didn't do," Avery told his lawyer. "And I've got to put up with all this corruption in here. Oh, there's so much. H.S.U. (Health Services Unit), the medical department, the dentist is garbage. I've got to wait a year just to get a filling. They pulled my tooth, and they didn't have to. If they would have taken care of it right away, instead of wait. All they do is tell me, 'Oh, you're on the list, you're on the list.' And then with the phone and the video visits, the stuff is so old where you can't get through, and them phone lines are so old. They crackle and everything else. You know, they got no money for us, it's all for them. They get (John Deere) Gators and golf carts, and everything for them, but nothing for us.

"Then, the food is garbage. You can barely eat it. The water system is garbage," Avery opined.

"How do you feel that your health is now, just in the last year?" Zellner wondered.

"Oh, it's better than Waupun. You know, I get more fresh air."

Before ending the prison call, Zellner asked if Avery had anything else to say to his followers and fans across the globe.

"I don't know. Thanks for all of my supporters out there for me, for the truth. That's from the bottom of my heart. The truth has got to come out, sooner or later," Avery remarked.

***

In a concerted effort to chip away at the fame and fortune of Moira Demos and Laura Ricciardi, the filmmakers of *Making A Murderer*, right-wing, conservative TV narrator Candace Owens teamed up with film director Sean Rich to produce a rebuttal true-crime movie series. They launched their own 10-part documentary called *Convicting a Murderer* through DailyWire+ on Sept. 7, 2023.

The DailyWire promo for *Convicting A Murderer* proclaims that "In Making A Murderer, Steven Avery was portrayed as an innocent victim of corrupt law enforcement, but there's more to the story than what we were shown. Join Candace Owens as she sets the record straight by exposing hidden evidence in the murder of Teresa Halbach." The final part of the series aired Oct. 26, 2023, titled, "The Real Villain."

Meanwhile, one of Steven Avery's biggest supporters, Australian businessman Mark Hoddinott, hired a professional company to conduct a survey on *Convicting A Murderer* and the documentary's impact on public opinion. The survey was done during the six weeks *Convicting A Murderer* film was being broadcast.

The key findings of the survey, revealed by Hoddinott on Nov. 9, 2023, are as follows:

Less than 10 percent of responders to *Convicting A Murderer* had used the Netflix documentary, *Making a Murderer*, as their only source of case knowledge.

Convicting A Murderer did convince approximately 10 percent of the previous supporters of Steven Avery to believe in his guilt.

Approximately 83 percent of the survey respondents still believe Steven Avery is innocent.

A total of 73 percent of survey respondents felt *Convicting A Murderer* added little or nothing to their case knowledge.

A total of 74 percent of the respondents said *Convicting A Murderer* lacked information that a court would find admissible.

Another 69 percent of respondents said the documentary maker and presenter for *Convicting A Murderer* lacked a sound grasp of the case facts.

A total of 71 percent of survey respondents rated the quality of *Convicting A Murderer* as either average, below average, or poor when it came to an assessment of quality journalism.

And perhaps the most telling aspect of the professional survey came in the final question. A total of 88 percent of responders said they believe Steven Avery deserves a new murder trial, which, according to Australia's Hoddinott, includes respondents who believe Avery is guilty.

"Thank you to the over 320 people who participated," Hoddinott proclaimed on Twitter. By having a sample group totaling 320 people made the survey statistically significant in terms of reflecting public opinion around the world.

During a Nov. 17, 2023 interview with this author, Zellner said she found the survey "very accurate."

"So far, no one's been able to disprove Steven Avery's innocence," Zellner proclaimed. "And it's obvious to most people in the world, except for those that have a vested interest in profiting from and exploiting his conviction."

For More News About John Ferak,
Signup For Our Newsletter:
http://wbp.bz/newsletter

Word-of-mouth is critical to an author's long-term success. If you appreciated this book please leave a review on the Amazon sales page:
http://wbp.bz/wc2023

OTHER WILDBLUE PRESS
BOOKS BY JOHN FERAK

TERROR TOWN, USA: *The Untold Story
of Joliet's Notorious Serial Killer*
http://wbp.bz/terrortowna

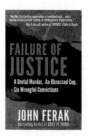

FAILURE OF JUSTICE: *A Brutal Murder, An
Obsessed Cop, Six Wrongful Convictions*
http://wbp.bz/foja

DIXIE'S LAST STAND: *Was It Murder Or Self-Defense?*
http://wbp.bz/dixiea

BODY OF PROOF: *Tainted Evidence In The Murder Of Jessica O'Grady*
http://wbp.bz/bopa

FROM JOHN FERAK AND WILDBLUE PRESS

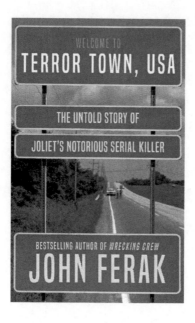

TERROR TOWN, USA by JOHN FERAK
http://wbp.bz/terrortowna

Read A Sample Chapter Next

CHAPTER 1

PILCHER PARK

In the Land of Lincoln, the main roads, waterways and communities leading toward Chicago are dominated by semi-trucks, shipping barges and freight train box cars. Urban sprawl created demand to build more homes, apartment buildings, factories and industrial business parks. The construction boom witnessed in many northern Illinois towns and cities on the outskirts of Chicago signaled the demise of family farms and tens of thousands of acres across the Prairie State.

Rolling hills, wetlands and open fields that stood the test of time for generations were gobbled up by tenacious developers and investment partners who had one thing on their mind: the almighty dollar.

During the early 1900s, Robert Pilcher made his fortune in the paper mill industry. But in his later years, Pilcher began to realize the sacredness of the many gifts bestowed by Mother Nature. Pilcher and his wife, Nora, owned several hundred acres of majestic beauty on the eastern edge of Joliet, Illinois, a tough-as-nails, blue-collar industrial city forty-five miles southwest of Chicago.

Pilcher's property was a sight to see. The hardwood forest consisted of thousands of giant maple trees affording the perfect shade for the squirrels, rabbits, raccoon, beaver, opossum and fox. The wetlands attracted red-winged blackbirds, mallards, Canada geese and colorful wood ducks. The great blue heron was a regular visitor to the area of Hickory Creek that flowed through Pilcher's land.

In 1920, Robert and Nora Pilcher donated 327 acres to the city of Joliet. The generous land donation was later shifted to the care and ownership of Joliet's Park District, a completely separate local government. The land once known as the Forest of Arden was renamed in honor of the donors.

It became Pilcher Park.

A century later, Pilcher Park remains a popular destination for outdoor enthusiasts. Every week, hundreds of people walk through the forest along its many hiking trails. Others prefer to stand along the banks of the Hickory Creek to try their luck at fishing. A bronze statue of a life-like Robert Pilcher in a sport coat, slacks and bow tie towers over the nature center. The engraved statue dedicated to Robert Pilcher reads: "Sturdy Pioneer, Loyal Citizen, Lover of Nature and His Fellowmen, A Dreamer Whose Dream Held."

The inscription along the bottom of the statue noted that the Pilcher Arboretum was dedicated on July 31, 1920.

One unusual attraction featured within Pilcher Park was called the Flowing Well. Tucked in the back of the forest, the Flowing Well featured pure artesian mineral water. Many Joliet area residents believed the mineral water was healthy and better tasting than their kitchen faucet tap water. On many days, several cars lined up along the secluded forest road as people filled their plastic jugs with mineral water from the Flowing Well to bring home for consumption.

If they were still alive today, Robert and Nora Pilcher would be pleased to know the Joliet Park District has done a fantastic job making sure that their generous donation of scenic woodlands remains off-limits to land developers, a century later.

On the other hand, the Pilcher's would be repulsed to discover that their well-intentioned land donation aimed at bringing good into the world also became a magnet for evil and wickedness.

Over the years, the Joliet Park District added amenities to Pilcher Park, including a greenhouse with hundreds of beautiful flowers and a nature education center for visitors to appreciate the local wildlife. Pilcher Park remained open year-round. During warmer weather, families and groups of friends picnicked and wandered the woods for a refreshing nature walk.

After sunset, Pilcher Park took on another persona, becoming known as a lover's lane. The forest's giant trees and meandering roads offered plenty of hiding spots for romantic couples to park. These roads were exceptionally narrow. There was barely room for one vehicle to pass.

On Feb. 15, 1970, Lee Chandler and his girlfriend drove to Pilcher Park even though temperatures remained in the teens. On this particular occasion, the dating couple parked on one of the back roads toward the Flowing Well. They chose this location figuring nobody would bother them. After all, during the frigid winter, Pilcher Park was hardly overrun with people.

A half-hour after their arrival, the young lovers noticed a car driving the wrong way through the forest.

"It stopped and it backed up and pulled in right behind us," Lee Chandler would later testify in court.

Moments later, the Joliet area teenagers heard tapping on their passenger window.

Chandler's girlfriend, Mary West, rolled down her window.

"Am I going the wrong way?" the stranger asked.

"Yes," she replied.

"Thank you," the voice responded.

The stranger walked back to his car, only to return a few minutes later.

He knocked on the teenage couple's passenger window a second time.

"How long are you going to be here?" the voice inquired.

"About ten minutes," the girl responded.

Suddenly, a shotgun barrel was pointed into their car.

"Bitch, open the door!" the stranger screamed.

As West complied, the intruder climbed into the backseat.

The shotgun-carrying creep asked the terrified teens how much money they had.

Lee had $20. Mary had $5.

"He told me to lay on the front seat and look down toward the brake pedal and stuff and not turn around," Chandler said.

The trapped teens tried to appease their captor. After all, he held a loaded shotgun and seemed not afraid to use it.

The gunman ordered the eighteen-year-old woman to disrobe.

"Broad, get in the back seat," he commanded.

After she took off some of her garments, the man's lustful eyes gazed upon her body.

"He turned around and looked at her and asked what that was. She said it was her slip," Chandler explained.

But because Mary West did not do exactly as her captor demanded, he punched her.

"I told you everything," the stranger hollered.

Next, the angry stranger wanted to know what brought the teenage couple to Pilcher Park on such a cold winter night.

"What were you doing here?" he inquired.

"Nothing," they both repeated.

Displeased by their response, he smacked the girl a second time.

"What were you doing here?" he demanded.

Mary West made up an answer, hoping to placate their captor.

"We were fucking," she claimed.

The man turned toward the scared young woman in the backseat with him.

"I'm going to fuck you," he told her.

The local teen was repulsed by the beast staring at her body.

"Shoot me first," she begged.

Angered by her response, the man smacked her hard as Lee Chandler crunched into a ball on the driver's side floorboard.

He sensed danger. Their car shook. His girlfriend cried.

Lee Chandler later recounted that the kidnapper announced, "Tell Lee exactly what we're doing and she says, we're making love."

But those weren't the right words, so the sadistic rapist punched her.

"We're screwing," she responded.

"No!" the rapist disagreed, hitting her again.

"OK, we're fucking," she admitted.

That was the right word choice.

"Okay," he agreed with satisfaction.

Deep inside the dark forest, Lee Chandler heard his girlfriend's attacker order her to "Kiss me and stick your tongue in my mouth."

"I heard her going, kind of mumble, moan-type thing," her boyfriend explained.

Then, the rapist announced, "Tell Lee what you're doing now."

"I'm sucking his dick," the helpless girlfriend responded.

The oral sex lasted a few minutes, but did not go well.

"Dumb broad," the rapist roared. "You don't know anything. Lay over on your stomach and spread the cheeks of your ass."

As Mary West was being humiliated and violated, her boyfriend feared that any slight movement on his part might provoke the foul-mouthed captor into killing them both.

Suddenly, he heard his girlfriend make a loud painful noise.

"They sat up and he says, 'Now, tell Lee what you're doing now.' She said, 'I'm jacking him off.'"

A few minutes later, the gunman asked his victims if they smoked cigarettes. Chandler answered no, but his girlfriend directed the rapist to her box of cigarettes on her dashboard.

"At that time, I felt like he was reaching over me and took the cigarettes. And he took the keys out of the ignition at the same time," Chandler observed. "I heard a sizzling noise, and I heard (her) screaming. It smelled like something burning."

The backseat rapist used the front seat cigarette lighter to torture his victim.

"He pushed it in to get it hot," the boyfriend recalled. "Then he took it out, and he told her to keep her hands still and not to move them, and he burned her a couple of times with the cigarette lighter. I could hear the sizzling more, and it was more like a hair burning, and she was screaming and crying."

The sadistic rapist began smacking the girl for no apparent reason.

"My jaw's broken. I heard it snap," she cried.

The Pilcher Park bogeyman turned his focus to the helpless boyfriend.

"At this time, I felt him reach over and pull a wallet out of my pocket," Chandler recalled.

The time had come for the shotgun-wielding rapist to decide whether to kill his prey or let them survive.

"Get out of the car," he snapped at Chandler. "Look down on the ground, and if you look at me I will kill you."

Wanting to live, the boyfriend complied.

"And he stayed far enough away from me where I couldn't grab the gun or anything, and he walked over to his car and shut the car door," Chandler remarked.

When the shotgun-toting rapist returned, Lee Chandler remained face down on the ground in the sprawling forest with no one around to help.

"OK, let's get back in the car," the stranger commanded. "Lay down on your stomach."

But before Chandler got back inside, the madman wanted to know whether Chandler had followed his orders.

"Yeah," he agreed.

What about his girlfriend?

"Yeah, I think she did," he answered.

"OK," the perpetrator relayed. "I want you to open the driver's side of the car now because I want the shotgun blast to go through when I kill both of you."

Lee Chandler was not ready to die a lonely and agonizing death at the hands of this cruel and tormenting madman.

As he opened the driver's door, Chandler made a daring dash into the dark forest.

"As soon as I got out of Pilcher Park, I stopped at a motel there, a pay phone there, and that's where I called them from," Chandler said.

Panicked, the rapist climbed behind the wheel of his victim's car. He drove her about a mile up the road to Silver Cross Hospital, a mammoth six-story, concrete building perched high on a hill along Route 6 and Draper Avenue. The towering 302-bed, Joliet medical center traced its origins to the early 1900s.

At the east-side hospital, doctors realized the Plainfield, Illinois, teenager suffered cigarette lighter burns to her vagina. Her rapist bit through one of her breasts and smashed her jaw.

"Plainfield Girl Critical After Attack In Park," read the next day's newspaper headline.

An 18-year-old Plainfield girl was reported in critical condition in the intensive care unit at Silver Cross Hospital after she was savagely beaten, tortured and raped late

Sunday night in Pilcher Park," read *The Joliet Herald-News article from February 1970.*

"The worst beating I've ever seen," Joliet Police Detective Sergeant Leroy Everson was quoted by the newspaper.

**

Joliet police evidence technician Reynold Rossi investigated the barbarous attack at the city's otherwise peaceful Pilcher Park.

Inside the Silver Cross Hospital trauma center, Rossi encountered Mary West as she lay dazed in bed recovering from the brutalizing attack.

Within a few hours, two of the Joliet Police Department's most-respected officers at the time, Dave Farmer and George Hernandez, made the arrest of nineteen-year-old Joliet resident, Milton Johnson. He was a high school dropout who lived with his mother and stepfather in Joliet's Forest Park area.

According to the 1970 newspaper accounts, the rapist "was so shaken by the girl's condition that he drove her to the hospital himself."

According to the local police, the Pilcher Park torture rapist was a sexual voyeur. Milton Johnson liked to troll desolate roads and out of the way parks in search of young lovers sharing affection. That way, he could watch and fantasize for a while as they remained oblivious to his presence hovering in the background under the cloak of darkness.

Indeed, he was no ordinary Peeping Tom.

"This is just an evil person who truly gets off on the joys of brutality," remarked now-retired Will County State's Attorney Ed Petka.

Sadly, Mary West never escaped the agony and emotional trauma that shattered her youthful innocence inside the wilderness of Pilcher Park. On the night of Feb. 15, 1970, she and her boyfriend had no inkling they were being watched by a methodical and deviant monster hiding in the woods, preparing to slaughter them.

Years later, the ex-boyfriend was asked in court to recall the sizzling sounds coming from his girlfriend's flesh.

"He told her to put her feet up on the roof of the car, and then he proceeded to take the cigarette lighter and burn her on her vagina," Chandler explained.

The atrocity inside Joliet's Pilcher Park transpired during a chaotic time in Richard Nixon's presidency as tensions escalated involving the Vietnam War. Fortunately for everyone, the sundown attack appeared to be an aberration. As the years passed, Joliet residents became less frightened of the wicked and ruthless monster that terrorized Pilcher Park on the bone-chilling night of Feb. 15, 1970.

Over time, people were no longer scared of a bogeyman lurking behind a tall tree or crouched beside a row of thick bushes, watching them as if they were unsuspecting animals of prey.

After a thirteen year absence, Milton Johnson returned to town. That year, 1983, happened to be the same year Joliet would be shaken after the supermarket tabloid, *The National Enquirer*, branded the city as "Terror Town U.S.A."

The shocker tabloid headline left city leaders outraged, but deep down, nobody could deny its accuracy.

http://wbp.bz/terrortowna

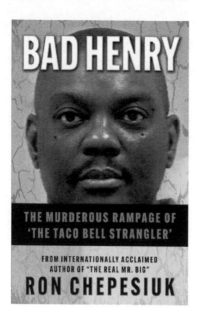

AVAILABLE FROM NIC EDWARDS, BRIAN WHITNEY, AND WILDBLUE PRESS!

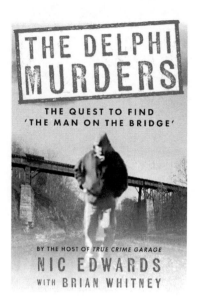

THE DELPHI MURDERS by NIC EDWARDS

In February 2017, teenagers Abigail Williams and Liberty German vanished near Monon High Bridge. Nic Edwards, host of True Crime Garage, delved into the case, culminating in Richard Allen's 2022 arrest. The book offers detailed insights into the investigation and the efforts to capture the killer.

http://wbp.bz/delphi

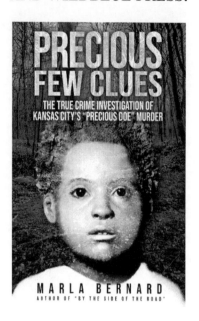

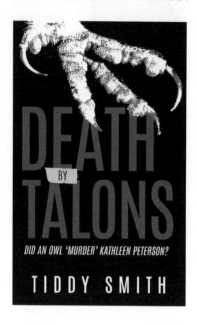

Printed in Great Britain
by Amazon

35000114R00249